The World of Evelyn Waugh

The World of
EVELYN WAUGH

Selected and Edited by

CHARLES J. ROLO

Little, Brown and Company
Boston   Toronto

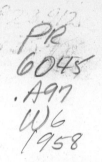

PRINTED IN THE UNITED STATES OF AMERICA

Introduction

When publishers are caroling the praises of some newly emerged maestro of sophisticated comedy, they can seldom resist the temptation of comparing him to "the early Evelyn Waugh." Despite the fact that *Brideshead Revisited,* a serious novel in the romantic key, has been read in the United States by more people than all of Waugh's other books put together, his name is still most apt to evoke a singular brand of comic genius. He is, *par excellence,* an example of the artist who has created a world peculiarly his own. The adjective "Waughsian" is too much of a tongue twister to have passed into our vocabulary, but a substitute phrase has — "It's pure Evelyn Waugh."

"Pure Evelyn Waugh." The expression evokes a riotously anarchic cosmos in which only the outrageous can happen, and when it does happen, is outrageously diverting; in which people reason and behave with awesome inconsequence and lunatic logic. The ruler of primitive Azania, eager to be modern, is induced by a wily contractor to purchase boots for his barefoot army: the savages joyfully heat up their cook-pots and devour the boots. An Oxford porter says to an undergraduate who has just been expelled: "I expect you'll be becoming a schoolmaster, sir. That's what most of the gentlemen does, sir, that gets sent down for indecent behaviour." A young man-about-Mayfair sells his fiancée to a rival to pay his hotel bill, and later buys her back for a week-end with a check which will bounce when presented on Monday. On the planet where Waugh's comic novels have their being, Oxford and Mayfair are as barbarous in their way as darkest Azania.

There are few contemporary writers of the first rank whose imagination runs to such appalling and macabre inventions as Waugh's does; and there is none who carries audacity to such lengths in using the atrocious as the material of farce. Consider a few of the ghastly episodes from which Waugh has succeeded in distilling the choicest entertainment. Agatha Runcible (one of the Bright Young People in *Vile*

Bodies) tipsily joins a motor race, has a crackup, and after a cocktail party in her sickroom, dies — "smiling deliriously, and bowing her bandaged head to imaginary visitors. *'Darling,'* she said. 'How *too* divine . . . how angelic of you all to come . . .'" The hero of *Black Mischief*, after feasting with savages on a delicious *pot-au-feu,* learns that he has just eaten his recent mistress, Prudence, daughter of the British Minister. *The Loved One* focuses with a bland and relentless fascination on every detail in the preparation of cadavers for burial by a de luxe establishment in Southern California.

Crazy accidents; cannibalism; cadavers. They are merely *outré* symbols of the theme which underlies all of Waugh's work (and is also to be found in that of T. S. Eliot) — that the life of our twentieth-century civilization resembles the irresponsibility of lunatics and the cannibalism of savages. In Waugh's view, the Modern Age has crazily destroyed and cannibalized what he finds supremely valuable — veneration for the past and for the hierarchical principle; the aristocratic way of life; the former greatness of England and the supremacy of the Catholic Church throughout Western society. At the conclusion of *Scott-King's Modern Europe,* the dim schoolmaster — warned that soon there won't be any place for a teacher of the classics — refuses to take on a more utilitarian subject. "I think it would be very wicked," he observes, "to do anything to fit a boy for the modern world."

There exists a myth about Waugh that calls for some correction. I refer to the not uncommon impression that in his early writings he was a "satirist of the English upper classes," and that in mid-career he "got religion" and emerged with a drastically changed outlook. For one thing, Waugh was received into the Church when he was twenty-seven and his literary career was just beginning. Secondly, he has at no time been a critic of what he considers the genuine upper class. The target of his early burlesques was the new "bogus" upper crust, which was well on its way to dominating London Society when Waugh's generation came of age — the world of frantic fashion-setters, money-makers, and party-givers; of the international set, press magnates, ambitious politicians, *parvenus* and careerists of all sorts; the world, too, of the rebellious Bright Young People. Toward the latter, Waugh's attitude was double-edged: while clearly he found their anarchic spirit exhilarating and was in sympathy with their disillusionment, he perceived that their revolt was negative, their design for living senselessly prodigal. Already the norms and ideals that stirred his loyalties were those of

INTRODUCTION

the Old Guard, of that "fine phalanx of the passing order" which he defined thus in *Vile Bodies:* "pious and honourable people (many of whom made the Anchorage House reception the one outing of the year), their women-folk gowned in rich and durable stuffs, their men-folk ablaze with orders; people who had represented their country in foreign places and sent their sons to die for her in battle, people of decent and temperate life, uncultured, unaffected, unembarrassed, unassuming, unambitious people, of independent judgment and marked eccentricities . . . brave and rather unreasonable people."

After rereading, as I have just done, all of Waugh's work in chronological sequence, it becomes unmistakably clear that his early comedies and his later novels — however different they may be in manner and in tone — are expressions of the same viewpoint. It dates back to his very first book, written when he was twenty-three, a capable and loving study of those nineteenth-century enemies of technology, the Pre-Raphaelites. It is glimpsed in his first novel, in a passage where "the dreaming ancestral beauty of the English country" becomes in the hero's mind a symbol of "something enduring and serene in a world which had lost its reason"; and the idyllic past — "the harmonious interdependence of rich and poor, of dignity, innocence, and tradition" — is sharply set in counterpoint against the garish and chaotic present. This past-versus-present theme is the mainspring of the plot in *A Handful of Dust,* whose hero's whole life is committed to preserving his Gothic house and is sustained by romantic daydreams of a "Gothic world." However, the prevalent impression that *Brideshead Revisited* marks a turning point in Waugh's work is true in one important respect: the novel ushers in a marked change in his artistic stance and temper — *a loss of detachment.* Hereafter Waugh's opinions, previously kept below the surface by the restraints of the ironic approach, are often projected into his fiction. From *Brideshead* on, Waugh's repudiation of the modern world becomes explicit and extreme — as it also has been, since the war, in the pattern of his personal life.

II

Evelyn Arthur St. John Waugh was born in a suburb of London in 1903, the younger son of a busy man-of-letters. He was educated at Lancing and at Oxford, where he was a contemporary of Harold Acton, who later drew (in *Memoirs of an Aesthete*) a striking portrait of

Waugh as an undergraduate: "I still see him as a prancing faun, thinly disguised by conventional apparel. His wide apart eyes, always ready to be startled under raised eyebrows, the curved sensual lips, the hyacinthine locks of hair, I had seen in marble and bronze at Naples. . . . [He was] so demure and yet so wild! A faun half-tamed by the Middle Ages, who would hide himself for months . . . and then burst upon the town with capricious caperings. His period of medieval tutelage drew him into a circle of Chestertonian friends. . . . [He] flirted with Conservative politics, spoke pithily at the Union, contributed cartoons like woodcuts to *The Isis* and *The Cherwell* . . . and was my chief support in *The Oxford Broom*. Whatever he did had a firm style of its own, a recognizable signature that set it apart from its surroundings. I have met other fauns, but none with such artistic integrity."

After eight terms, Waugh voluntarily left Oxford without a degree, and, like Paul Pennyfeather of *Decline and Fall*, took a job in a school for backward boys. Later, he worked for sixteen days on Lord Beaverbrook's *Daily Express*. His ambition was to be a painter, but a stint at art school left him dissatisfied with his talent. At this time, he has said, he was a pagan and "wanted to be a man of the world." He joined in the whirl of Michael Arlen's Mayfair. He "gadded among savages and people of fashion and politicians and crazy generals." But he was a worldling who could relish all this, and still find it wanting. In 1930, after instruction from the celebrated Father D'Arcy, Waugh entered the Catholic Church.

A few months earlier, his first marriage had ended in divorce. In 1937, he married again; his second wife, a Catholic, is a granddaughter of the Earl of Carnarvon. During the late nineteen-twenties and the nineteen-thirties, Waugh had traveled often and widely, by preference to wild places. The best parts of the four travel books written during this period were later reprinted in *When the Going Was Good*, and they are still lively reading. One is periodically reminded, however, that Waugh's touch is surer and more sparkling when he is using these same materials in his comic novels.

At the outbreak of the war, Waugh joined the Royal Marines, and later, as a Commando, saw action in the Middle East and in the Balkans.

After marriage, he settled in a secluded part of Gloucestershire, from which he occasionally makes sorties to his London clubs. "I live in a shabby stone house," he wrote in *Life*, "in which nothing is under a hundred years old except the plumbing, and that does not work. I collect old books in an inexpensive, desultory way. [His major avocation is the study of theology.] I have a fast-emptying cellar of wine and gardens fast reverting to jungle . . . I have numerous children [three girls and three boys] whom I see once a day for ten, I hope, awe-inspiring minutes." He has since removed to a rather similar house in an even more remote district.

A few years back Randolph Churchill said of Waugh: "He grows more old-fashioned every day. He seeks to live in an oasis." This is corroborated by Waugh in his arresting "Portrait of the Artist in Middle Age," which is the opening chapter of *The Ordeal of Gilbert Pinfold.* Waugh says of Pinfold, who by his own admission is "largely based on himself": "Since the end of the war his life had been strictly private. . . . He had never voted in a parliamentary election, maintaining an idiosyncratic toryism which was quite unrepresented in the political parties of his time. . . . He was sometimes referred to as a leading Catholic, but he preserved privacy in his religion, burrowed ever deeper into the rock. . . . His strongest tastes were negative. He abhorred plastics, Picasso, sunbathing and jazz — everything in fact that had happened in his own lifetime."

III

Complete rejection of the modern world is the source both of what is best in Waugh's work and of what is most vulnerable to criticism. Total repudiation, coupled with the almost total detachment which Waugh initially maintained in his fiction, makes for a peculiar purity of comic vision. The artist who dismisses, blandly and out of hand, the pretensions, ambitions and norms by which most members of his society live achieves something akin to the clear-eyed innocence of childhood. He sees writ large the element of the absurd in the life of his time, and becomes aware that human beings are of a startling singularity. In this lies Waugh's special genius: he isolates and magnifies aspects of reality — the cockeyed, the fantastic, the eccentric — which the ordinary eye glimpses only fuzzily through the haze of custom and cant.

However extravagant their façade, Waugh's comedies have solid roots in actuality. Manners and social types are observed with dazzling accuracy. The portraiture of the British Young People, though illumined with a glow which spotlights the fantastic, is profoundly *dans le vrai.*

So, too, are the parodies of the press in *Scoop*; of the Ministry of Information in *Put Out More Flags*; of the mortuary practices of California
in *The Loved One*. Indeed, it is astonishing how often contemporary
behavior and happenings resemble nothing so much as "pure Evelyn
Waugh."

In his youth, Waugh obviously relished the antics he burlesqued with
such enormous zest. But there has always been within his comic version
a core of tragic awareness, which gives his comedies the dimension of
serious art. Like Eliot, Waugh came to see the world around him as
a waste-land. His temperament and special gifts led him to transfigure
the waste-land into a circus, within whose tent we are treated to a
riotous harlequinade. But every so often the flap of the tent is blown
open; a vista of the wilderness intrudes; and the antics of the clowns
suddenly appear, as Agatha Runcible would say, "too spirit-crushing."
In countless scenes, a lapidary phrase or incident brings home the
tragic quality in the lives of Waugh's frivolous, madcap, or gaily un-
scrupulous characters. Waugh's cosmos is, in the literal sense, funny
as hell.

At his best — that is, when he remains detached — Waugh is certainly the finest comic artist to emerge since the nineteen-twenties;
Edmund Wilson has called him "the only first-rate comic genius that
has appeared in English since Bernard Shaw." His style is swift, exact,
almost unfailingly felicitous. His invention is entrancing, his timing
inspired; and his matter-of-fact approach to the incongruous produces
a perverse humor that is prodigiously effective. Even that ancient
comic device, the use of suggestive names, is boldly put to work by
Waugh with the happiest results. Mr. Outrage, the leader of His
Majesty's Opposition; Mrs. Melrose Ape, the phony evangelist; Lord
Copper, the press tycoon; Lady Circumference, Captain Grimes, Ambrose Silk, Aimée Thanatogenos — their names eloquently bespeak
their nature.

Waugh's rejection of the modern world is also, as I said earlier, the
source of the weaknesses which many critics have found in his later
works. The artist who repudiates the realities of his time must either
work in a detached, ironic key, which transmutes repudiation into
blandly destructive laughter; or, if he wishes to make a positive criticism,
he must offer possible alternatives to the status quo. But Waugh's
"idiosyncratic toryism," his nostalgia for the medieval world, his veneration for noble lineage, ritual, the hierarchical principle — all this

represents (as he himself appears to recognize in "Portrait of the Artist in Middle Age") simply a yearning for an irretrievably lost cause. Thus when Waugh abandons the ironic stance, he emerges as the champion of a romantic archaism which only a few of his readers can take seriously. Even Catholic and conservative critics have observed that when Waugh articulates his opinions and attitudes, his work tends to move, as Sean O'Faolain has put it, "within an enclosed and exclusive circle." In sum, the paradox is that when Waugh is being serious, he is apt to become parochial. When he is being comic and the moral criticism remains implied, he achieves a certain universality. In his finest pages, he makes luminous the failures of the age, confronts us tellingly with the zany realities.

I V

Waugh's first novel, *Decline and Fall* (1928), depicts a world in which villainy has the innocence of man's primeval state before The Fall. The story opens on the night of the annual orgy of Oxford's most aristocratic dining club: "A shriller note could now be heard rising from Sir Alastair's rooms; any who have heard that sound will shrink at the recollection of it; it is the sound of the English county families baying for broken glass."

Paul Pennyfeather, a colorless young man reading for Holy Orders, is debagged by the rowdies and then expelled by the authorities for indecent exposure. Presently he is taken up by an immensely rich young widow, whose fortune comes from a far-flung chain of bordellos. When the police get on her track, Paul goes to prison for White Slavery and the lady marries a Cabinet Minister. But Paul, equipped with a new identity, winds up exactly where he started — at Oxford, studying to become a clergyman. The fun is incessant and the comic portraiture is sheer delight, especially that of the hugely disreputable schoolmaster, Captain Grimes, and of the inventive butler-crook Philbrick — in his grander moments Sir Solomon Philbrick, tycoon. *Decline and Fall* is an unqualified success.

Vile Bodies (1930) is almost as good. Returning from Europe, young Adam Fenwick-Symes has the typescript of his "memoirs" — his only chance of solvency — confiscated by a customs officer outraged at finding Dante's *Purgatorio* in his luggage: " 'French, eh? . . . and pretty dirty, too, I shouldn't wonder. . . . Particularly against books the Home

Secretary is.' " There follows a telephone call to Adam's fiancée: " 'Oh, I say Nina, there's one thing — I don't think I shall be able to marry you after all.' — 'Oh, *Adam,* you are a bore.' " The combination of calamitous happenings and gay *insouciance* is marvelously sustained as the story follows the Bright Young People in their giddy dance through the condemned playground. But the farce, now, has grimmer overtones; and the climax finds Adam on history's greatest battlefield, clutching a bomb for the dissemination of leprosy.

Waugh's next book had its origin in the "crazy enchantment" of a visit to Addis Ababa for the coronation of Haile Selassie. The Abyssinia of the eary thirties — with its ancient Christianity and its enduring barbarism; its strivings to be modern, frustrated by picturesque ignorance and limitless inefficiency; its motley foreign colony; authentic savages; and wily promoters — provided Waugh with materials ideally suited to his talents. He worked them into a brilliantly realized and hugely funny novel, *Black Mischief* (1932), which introduces the cad-hero, Basil Seal, one of Waugh's most magistral creations.

Broadly speaking, the leading (male) characters in Waugh's comedies are of two types. There are the dim, decent ones who, in a stable, rigidly patterned society, would fruitfully live out their lives in their pre-destined niche, but who are doomed to be victims when circumstances project them into the jungle of the modern world. And then there are the resourceful pirates, who sponge off everyone, lie, swindle, and black-mail with complete aplomb and the lack of scruple of the early colonizers cast among savages. Of these, Basil Seal is the supreme exemplar.

Waugh's attitude toward both the types just mentioned is somewhat ambivalent. The punishment dished out to the dim, decent heroes suggests that Waugh, while he obviously has a deep affection for them, regards their kind as quite unfit to cope with the encroachments of barbarism. As for Basil Seal and the other gentlemen scoundrels, I take it that Waugh regards them as the disreputable products of an age that has killed the code of chivalry, and yet admires them for out-buccaneer-ing all comers in a buccaneering world.

A Handful of Dust (1934), the most somber of the prewar novels, originated as a short story, which now forms its ingeniously imagined and horrifying ending: the hero finds himself trapped in the recesses of the Amazonian jungle, condemned to spend the rest of his life reading Dickens to a cunning madman. "I wanted to discover," Waugh has said, "how the prisoner got there, and eventually the thing grew into a study of another sort of savage at home and the civilized man's helpless plight among them." Another aspect of the book deserves mention: the nursery world makes its first appearance in Waugh's work, and hereafter it frequently reappears as a symbol of the superiorities of the past. One of the finest things in *A Handful of Dust* is the moving portrait of the hero's small boy (who is tragically killed in a hunting accident). Indeed, English upper class childhood — with its unquestioning assumption of privilege, its ritualized routine, its all-powerful Nanny personifying authority and the wisdom of the ages — is, as might be expected, one of the most deeply felt experiences in Waugh's fictional universe.

In the next two books Waugh's polemical spirit showed its hand. His biography of the Catholic martyr Edmund Campion — in many respects a distinguished performance — is marred for non-Catholics by fierce partisanship. *Waugh in Abyssinia* (1936), the product of an assignment as a war correspondent, is an embarrassing celebration of the Italian conquest. Strangely enough, the Ethiopian setting is again fictionally handled in *Scoop* (1937) with the same detached zest as in *Black Mischief* and with hardly less entertaining results. The book has a delightfully clever plot involving a double-barreled confusion of identity; and it contains uproarious and acute burlesques of the press and of contemporary civil wars ("When you *say* Black you mean Red, and when you mean Red you say White. . . . [But] Lord Copper only wants Patriot victories and both sides call themselves Patriots").

Put Out More Flags (1942), a novel about the phony war period, reintroduces Basil Seal, more ingeniously iniquitous than ever. His use of three loathsome evacué children as a source of blackmail, and several other episodes in the book, are Waugh at his superlative best. At the conclusion Basil volunteers for the Commandos — there was "a new spirit abroad"; and the dedication to Randolph Churchill speaks of "the Churchillian Renaissance." The war apparently aroused in Waugh high hopes that victory would open the way to a return to Britain's former greatness. The hero of a later novel, *Men at Arms*, a man of Waugh's age and faith, is clearly speaking for his creator when he soliloquizes at the outbreak of the conflict: "Eight years of shame and loneliness were ended . . . now, splendidly, everything had become clear. The enemy at last was plain in view, huge and hateful, all disguise cast off. It was the Modern Age in Arms." But Waugh's romanticism had led him into a misreading of the situation, for the

Allied side represented the Modern Age as much as did the enemy, and victory had precisely the opposite effects on Britain to those desired by Waugh. His deep and bitter disillusionment at this outcome probably explains the marked difference in the temper of his prewar and postwar fiction.

Brideshead Revisited (1945) is a romantic evocation of vanished splendors, which bring into relief the bleakness of the present. In the first part, Charles Ryder, the narrator, reverts to his youth at Oxford. Ryder's discovery of a world of aristocratic glamour and intoxicating pleasures through his friendship with Sebastian, younger son of the Marquis of Marchmain; the comic portrait of a precociously worldly and degenerate undergraduate, Anthony Blanche, "the aesthete, *par excellence*"; the picture of Ryder's holidays at home with his grotesquely remote and cagily self-centered father — these passages are among the most memorable that Waugh has written.

The second part of the book describes Ryder's unhappy marriage and his adulterous love affair with Sebastian's sister; the return to his ancestral home of the dying Lord Marchmain, who has lived in scandalous exile in Venice and has turned against the Church; and his dramatic assent, an instant before death, to the last sacraments. In all of this, Waugh abandons the detached stance, with the sometimes unfortunate results which were discussed earlier. For two reasons, however, the second rather the first half of *Brideshead* had been included in this anthology. It forms a more or less self-contained story, which has seemed to me a prerequisite for every selection. More importantly, part two of *Brideshead*, with its development of the book's religious theme, occupies a unique place in Waugh's work; and no picture of his fictional world would be representative without it.

The Loved One (1948) — included in full in this volume — is of all Waugh's books the most startling in conception, the most audacious in the treatment of macabre detail, and the most cruelly funny. As a lampoon on the rites of West Coast morticians and the sickening hokum peddled by high-priced California burial grounds, *The Loved One* is a coruscating tour de force. When the satire reaches out to other aspects of American folkways, it is sometimes overly familiar or marred by overt revelations of prejudice and distaste. There is not the same devastating innocence of observation as in the prewar farces — not the hard objectivity which registered its effects on a plane where opinions were irrelevant. Even so, with its classic design, its (to quote Wolcott

Gibbs) "murderous daintiness of expression," and its stop-at-nothing parody of the portentous themes of love and death, *The Loved One* is an authentic and original work of art. It probably belongs among the half-dozen most arresting comic novellas which this century has produced.

The Loved One was followed by another satire, *Scott-King's Modern Europe*, and by a novel with a religious theme, *Helena*. Based on the life of Saint Helena, the mother of Constantine the Great, it is of all Waugh's books the one which stands highest in his affections, a sentiment not shared by American readers and critics.

Men at Arms (1952) and *Officers and Gentlemen* (1955) form a two-volume work (which must be in good measure autobiographical) about the Second World War. The story begins, as Waugh has put it, with the hero "inspired by an illusion," and it ends with his "deflation." Guy Crouchback — a lonely, frustrated man, who can find no outlets for his loyalties in an age he detests — experiences a vitalizing rebirth of hope at the outbreak of the war. He sees not the Nazis specifically but the Modern Age as the enemy that has finally been challenged, and he identifies his country's cause with the romantic outlook he cherishes. This illusion is sustained while he is training for a commission in the Halberdiers. With its proud traditions and ceremonious rituals; its *esprit de corps;* its stern discipline and taxing duties, the ancient regiment is a replica, in spirit, of the world he longs for; and it fills him with a sense of dignity and purpose. But his subsequent experiences — climaxed by participation, as a Commando, in the Cretan debacle — bring him the desolating recognition that he has been living in a dream. He finds himself right back in the bad, ambiguous world, where the "common man" is exalted, where gentlemen can turn out to be cowards, and where his country is led into dishonor (the alliance with Russia).

The central weakness of this wartime saga is that the reader knows from the start that Crouchback has wishfully misread the situation, and his eventual disillusionment is therefore totally anticlimactic. Where Waugh's talents shine brightly in both novels is in the rich vein of comic portraiture and in the marvelously felicitous observation of military life. Among the protagonists is one of Waugh's happiest creations, Brigadier Ritchie-Hook — the ferocious, one-eyed, one-handed exponent of "biffing" — a hugely comic yet thoroughly convincing incarnation of the warrior spirit.

The special interest of *The Ordeal of Gilbert Pinfold* (1957) is that here Waugh, a fierce guardian of his privacy, indulges for the first time in more or less direct self-revelation. The book is a fictionalized account of a "bout of hallucination" which Waugh experienced as a result of prolonged overconsumption of a toxic sleeping draught. Its most striking chapter, "Portrait of the Artist in Middle Age," forms the conclusion of this anthology.

V

Now in his middle fifties, Waugh has written more than twenty books. Considering the high quality of his artistry, this output is proof of a remarkable creative power. No less remarkable is the fact that Waugh, though his basic viewpoint has changed relatively little, has continued throughout his career to produce books which have surprised his faithful readers — among them, *A Handful of Dust, Brideshead Revisited, The Loved One, Helena,* and most recently, *The Ordeal of Gilbert Pinfold.* The works still to come from Waugh remain highly unpredictable — except in two respects. It is certain that they will be entertaining and admirably written. Among Waugh's distinctions is a virtual incapacity to be dull and a preoccupation with style which has made him one of the three or four finest living writers of English prose.

To those who do not know the world of Evelyn Waugh this anthology will serve, I hope, as an introductory tour which whets the appetite for further travel — easily gratified, in this case, since a majority of Waugh's books are still in print. Old Waugh hands should find the present collection a short cut to places well worth revisiting. As in all anthologies, there are omissions which were heartbreaking to the anthologist. But in this connection I propose to follow that precept of Jowett's which is so effectively exemplified in all of Waugh's work — "Never apologize. Never explain."

CHARLES J. ROLO

Contents

The World of Evelyn Waugh

The Curse of the Horse Race

(Written at the age of 7 years 1 month)

Betting

I bet you 500 pounds I'll win. The speeker was Rupert a man of about 25 he had a dark bushy mistarsh and flashing eyes.

I shouldnot trust to much on your horse said Tom for ineed he had not the sum to spear.

The race was to take pleace at ten the following morning.

The Race

The next morning Tom took his seat in the gront stand while Rupert mounted Sally (which was his horse) with the others to wate for the pistol shot which would anounse the start.

The race was soon over and Rupet had lost. What was he to do could he do the deed? Yes I'll *kill* him in the night, he though

CHAPTER III

The Fire

Rupert crept stedfustly along with out a sound but as he drew his sword it squeeked a little this awoke Tom seasing a candle he lit it just at that moment Rupert struck and sent the candle flying

The candle lit the curtain Rupert trying to get away tumbled over the bed Tom maid a dash for the door and cleided with a perlisman who had come to see what was the matter and a panic took place.

CHAPTER IV
Explaind

While Tom and the peliesman were escaping through the door Rupert was adopting quite a diffrat methard of escape he puld the matris of the bed and hurled the it out of the window then jumed out he landed safe and sound on the matris then began to run for all he was worth

Now let us leave Rupert and turn to Tom and the peliesman as soon as they got out Tom told the peliesman what had hapend.

CHAPTER V
Hot on the Trail

"See there he is" said Tom "We must folow him and take him to prizen" said the peliesman.

Theres no time to spere said Tom letts get horses said the peliesman so they bort horses and and galerpin in the direcion thet had seen him go.

On they went until they were face to face with each other. the peliesman lept from his horse only to be stabed to the hart by Rupert then Tom jumped down and got Rupert a smart blow on the cheak.

CHAPTER VI
A Deadly Fight

This enraged Rupert that that he shouted and made a plung but Tom was too quick for him artfully dogeing the sword he brout his sword round on Ruperts other cheak.

Just at that moment Ruper slashed killed the peliesmans horse then lept on Toms horse and golapt off.

CHAPTER VII
The Mysterious Man

Of course ther was no chance of catching him on foot so Tom walked to the nearest inn to stay the night but it was ful up he had to share with another man.

Thou Tom was yery tired he could not sleep, their was something about the man he was he did not like he reminded him of some one he didnot know who.

Sudnly he felt something moveing on the bed looking up he saw the man fully dressed just getting off the bed

CHAPTER VIII
Run to Erth

Now Tom could see that the mysteraous man was Rupert. Has he come to do a merder? Or has he only cometostay the night? thees were the thoughts that rushed throu Toms head.

he lay still to what Rupert would do first he opened a cuberd and took out a small letter bag from this he too some thing wich made Toms blud turn cold it was a bistol Tom lept forward and seesed Rupert by the throught and flung him to the ground

then snaching a bit of robe from the ground he bound Rupert hand and foot.

CHAPTER IX
Hung

then Tom drest hinself then Ton took Rupert to the puliese cort Rupert was hung for killing the puliesman. I hope the story will be a leson to you never to bet.

From Decline and Fall

*INDECENT BEHAVIOUR**

Mr. Sniggs, the Junior Dean, and Mr. Postlethwaite, the Domestic Bursar, sat alone in Mr. Sniggs's room overlooking the garden quad at Scone College. From the rooms of Sir Alastair Digby-Vaine-Trumping-ton, two staircases away, came a confused roaring and breaking of glass. They alone of the senior members of Scone were at home that evening, for it was the night of the annual dinner of the Bollinger Club. The others were all scattered over Boar's Hill and North Oxford at gay, contentious little parties, or at other senior common rooms, or at the meetings of learned societies, for the annual Bollinger dinner is a difficult time for those in authority.

It is not accurate to call this an annual event, because quite often the Club is suspended for some years after each meeting. There is tradition behind the Bollinger; it numbers reigning kings among its past members. At the last dinner, three years ago, a fox had been brought in in a cage and stoned to death with champagne bottles. What an evening that had been! This was the first meeting since then, and from all over Europe old members had rallied for the occasion. For two days they had been pouring into Oxford: epileptic royalty from their villas of exile; uncouth peers from crumbling country seats; smooth young men of uncertain tastes from embassies and legations; illiterate lairds from wet granite hovels in the Highlands; ambitious young barristers and Conservative candidates torn from the London season and the indelicate advances of debutantes; all that was most sonorous of name and title was there for the beano.

"The fines!" said Mr. Sniggs, gently rubbing his pipe along the side of his nose. "Oh, my! the fines there'll be after this evening!"

There is some highly prized port in the senior common-room cellars

*This is the opening chapter of the novel. — *Ed.*

that is only brought up when the College fines have reached fifty pounds.

"We shall have a week of it at least," said Mr. Postlethwaite, "a week of Founder's port."

A shriller note could now be heard rising from Sir Alastair's rooms; any who have heard that sound will shrink at the recollection of it; it is the sound of the English county families baying for broken glass. Soon they would all be tumbling out into the quad, crimson and roaring in their bottle-green evening coats, for the real romp of the evening.

"Don't you think it might be wiser if we turned out the light?" said Mr. Sniggs.

In darkness the two dons crept to the window. The quad below was a kaleidoscope of dimly discernible faces.

"There must be fifty of them at least," said Mr. Postlethwaite. "If only they were all members of the College! Fifty of them at ten pounds each. Oh, my!"

"It'll be more if they attack the Chapel," said Mr. Sniggs. "Oh, please God, make them attack the Chapel."

"I wonder who the unpopular undergraduates are this term. They always attack their rooms. I hope they have been wise enough to go out for the evening."

"I think Partridge will be one; he possesses a painting by Matisse or some such name."

"And I'm told he has black sheets in his bed."

"And Sanders went to dinner with Ramsay MacDonald once."

"And Rending can afford to hunt, but collects china instead."

"And smokes cigars in the garden after breakfast."

"Austen has a grand piano."

"They'll enjoy smashing that."

"There'll be a heavy bill for to-night; just you see! But I confess I should feel easier if the Dean or the Master were in. They can't see us from here, can they?"

It was a lovely evening. They broke up Mr. Austen's grand piano, and stamped Lord Rending's cigars into his carpet, and smashed his china, and tore up Mr. Partridge's sheets, and threw the Matisse into his water jug; Mr. Sanders had nothing to break except his windows, but they found the manuscript at which he had been working for the Newdigate Prize Poem, and had great fun with that. Sir Alastair Digby-Vaine-Trumpington felt quite ill with excitement, and was supported to bed by Lumsden of Strathdrummond. It was half-past eleven. Soon the evening would come to an end. But there was still a treat to come.

Paul Pennyfeather was reading for the Church. It was his third year of uneventful residence at Scone. He had come there after a creditable career at a small public school of ecclesiastical temper on the South Downs, where he had edited the magazine, been President of the Debating Society, and had, as his report said, "exercised a wholesome influence for good" in the House of which he was head boy. At home he lived in Onslow Square with his guardian, a prosperous solicitor who was proud of his progress and abysmally bored by his company. Both his parents had died in India at the time when he won the essay prize at his preparatory school. For two years he had lived within his allowance, aided by two valuable scholarships. He smoked three ounces of tobacco a week — John Cotton, Medium — and drank a pint and a half of beer a day, the half at luncheon and the pint at dinner, a meal he invariably ate in Hall. He had four friends, three of whom had been at school with him. None of the Bollinger Club had ever heard of Paul Pennyfeather, and he, oddly enough, had not heard of them.

Little suspecting the incalculable consequences that the evening was to have for him, he bicycled happily back from a meeting of the League of Nations Union. There had been a most interesting paper about plebiscites in Poland. He thought of smoking a pipe and reading another chapter of the *Forsyte Saga* before going to bed. He knocked at the gate, was admitted, put away his bicycle, and diffidently, as always, made his way across the quad towards his rooms. What a lot of people there seemed to be about! Paul had no particular objection to drunkenness — he had read rather a daring paper to the Thomas More Society on the subject — but he was consumedly shy of drunkards.

Out of the night Lumsden of Strathdrummond swayed across his path like a druidical rocking stone. Paul tried to pass.

Now it so happened that the tie of Paul's old school bore a marked resemblance to the pale blue and white of the Bollinger Club. The difference of a quarter of an inch in the width of the stripes was not one that Lumsden of Strathdrummond was likely to appreciate.

"Here's an awful man wearing the Boller tie," said the Laird. It is not for nothing that since pre-Christian times his family has exercised chieftainship over uncharted miles of barren moorland.

Mr. Sniggs was looking rather apprehensively at Mr. Postlethwaite.

"They appear to have caught somebody," he said. "I hope they don't do him any serious harm.

"Dear me, can it be Lord Rending? I think I ought to intervene."

"No, Sniggs," said Mr. Postlethwaite, laying a hand on his impetuous colleague's arm. "No, no, no. It would be unwise. We have the prestige of the senior common room to consider. In their present state they might not prove amenable to discipline. We must at all costs avoid an *outrage.*"

At length the crowd parted, and Mr. Sniggs gave a sigh of relief.

"But it's quite all right. It isn't Rending. It's Pennyfeather — someone of no importance."

"Well, that saves a great deal of trouble. I am glad, Sniggs! I am, really. What a lot of clothes the young man appears to have lost!"

Next morning there was a lovely College meeting.

"Two hundred and thirty pounds," murmured the Domestic Bursar ecstatically, "*not* counting the damage! That means five evenings, with what we have already collected. Five evenings of Founder's port!"

"The case of Pennyfeather," the Master was saying, "seems to be quite a different matter altogether. He ran the whole length of the quadrangle, you say, *without his trousers.* It is unseemly. It is more: it is indecent. In fact, I am almost prepared to say that it is flagrantly indecent. It is *not* the conduct we expect of a scholar."

"Perhaps if we fined him really heavily?" suggested the Junior Dean.

"I very much doubt whether he could pay. I understand he is not well off. *Without trousers,* indeed! And at that time of night! I think we should do far better to get rid of him altogether. That sort of young man does the College no good."

Two hours later, while Paul was packing his three suits in his little leather trunk, the Domestic Bursar sent a message that he wished to see him.

"Ah, Mr. Pennyfeather," he said, "I have examined your rooms and notice two slight burns, one on the window sill and the other on the chimney-piece, no doubt from cigarette ends. I am charging you five-and-sixpence for each of them on your battels. That is all, thank you."

As he crossed the quad Paul met Mr. Sniggs.

"Just off?" said the Junior Dean brightly.

"Yes, sir," said Paul.

And a little farther on he met the Chaplain.

"Oh, Pennyfeather, before you go, surely you have my copy of Dean Stanley's *Eastern Church?*"

"Yes. I left it on your table."

"Thank you. Well, good-bye, my dear boy. I suppose that after that reprehensible affair last night you will have to think of some other profession. Well, you may congratulate yourself that you discovered your unfitness for the priesthood before it was too late. If a parson does a thing of that sort, you know, all the world knows. And so many do, alas! What do you propose doing?"

"I don't really know yet."

"There is always commerce, of course. Perhaps you may be able to bring to the great world of business some of the ideals you have learned at Scone. But it won't be easy, you know. It is a thing to be lived down with courage. What did Dr. Johnson say about fortitude? . . . Dear, dear! *no trousers!*"

At the gates Paul tipped the porter.

"Well, good-bye, Blackall," he said. "I don't suppose I shall see you again for some time."

"No, sir, and very sorry I am to hear about it. I expect you'll be becoming a schoolmaster, sir. That's what most of the gentlemen does, sir, that gets sent down for indecent behaviour."

"God damn and blast them all to hell," said Paul meekly to himself as he drove to the station, and then he felt rather ashamed, because he rarely swore.

THE SPORTS

The following extract from DECLINE AND FALL *describes the annual sports at Llanabba Castle, the fantastic school in North Wales to which Paul Pennyfeather has gone as junior master after being expelled from Oxford (see "Indecent Behaviour"). The principal characters are:*

Dr. Augustus Fagan

Florence Fagan, known as Flossie
Diana Fagan, known as Dingy
Mr. Prendergast

Captain Grimes

Philbrick

Peter Beste-Chetwynde

The Honourable
   Mrs. Beste-Chetwynde

Little Lord Tangent

Headmaster of Llanabba Castle.

Dr. Fagan's elder daughter.
Dr. Fagan's younger daughter.
An ineffectual schoolmaster who is bullied by the boys.
A schoolmaster with a raffish past.
The butler, an imaginative con man with the grand manner.
One of the boys. Paul Pennyfeather, who knows no music, is giving him organ lessons.
Peter's mother, a widowed Society beauty w h o s e g r e a t wealth comes from a chain of bordellos in South America.
A schoolboy, son of Lord and Lady Circumference.

THAT morning just before luncheon the weather began to show signs of clearing, and by half-past one the sun was shining. The Doctor made one of his rare visits to the school dining hall. At his entry everybody stopped eating and laid down his knife and fork. "Boys," said the Doctor, regarding them benignly, "I have an announcement to make. Clutterbuck, will you kindly stop eating while I am addressing the school. The boys' manners need correcting, Mr. Prendergast. I look to the prefects to see to this. Boys, the chief sporting event of the year will take place in the playing fields to-morrow. I refer to the Annual School Sports, unfortunately postponed last year owing to the General Strike. Mr. Pennyfeather, who, as you know, is himself a distinguished athlete, will be in charge of all arrangements. The preliminary heats will be run off to-day. All boys must compete in all events. The Countess of Circumference has kindly consented to present the prizes. Mr. Prendergast will act as referee, and Captain Grimes as timekeeper. I shall myself be present to-morrow to watch the final competitions. That is all, thank you. Mr. Pennyfeather, per- haps you will favour me with an interview when you have finished your luncheon?"

"Good God!" murmured Paul.

"I won the long jump at the last sports," said Briggs, "but everyone said that it was because I had spiked shoes. Do you wear spiked shoes, sir?"

"Invariably," said Paul.

"Everyone said it was taking an unfair advantage. You see, we never know beforehand when there's going to be sports, so we don't have time to get ready."

"My mamma's coming down to see me to-morrow," said Beste- Chetwynde; "just my luck! Now I shall have to stay here all the after- noon."

After luncheon Paul went to the morning-room, where he found the Doctor pacing up and down in evident high excitement.

"Ah, come in, Pennyfeather! I am just making the arrangements for to-morrow's fête. Florence, will you get on to the Clutterbucks on the telephone and ask them to come over, and the Hope-Brownes. I think the Warringtons are too far away, but you might ask them, and of course the Vicar and old Major Sidebotham. The more guests the better, Florence!

"And, Diana, you must arrange the tea. Sandwiches, *foie gras* sand- wiches — last time, you remember, the liver sausage you bought made Lady Bunyan ill — and cakes, plenty of cakes, with coloured sugar! You had better take the car into Llandudno and get them there.

"Philbrick, there must be champagne cup, and will you help the men putting up the marquee? And flags, Diana! There should be flags left over from last time."

"I made them into dusters," said Dingy.

"Well, we must buy more. No expense must be spared. Penny- feather, I want you to get the results of the first heats out by four o'clock. Then you can telephone them to the printers, and we shall have the

programmes by to-morrow. Tell them fifty will be enough; they must
be decorated with the school colours and crest in gold. And there must
be flowers, Diana, banks of flowers," said the Doctor with an expansive
gesture. "The prizes shall stand among banks of flowers. Do you think
there ought to be a bouquet for Lady Circumference?"

"No," said Dingy.

"Nonsense!" said the Doctor. "Of course there must be a bouquet.
It is rarely that the scholarly calm of Llanabba gives place to festival,
but when it does taste and dignity shall go unhampered. It shall be
an enormous bouquet, redolent of hospitality. You are to procure the
most expensive bouquet that Wales can offer; do you understand?
Flowers, youth, wisdom, the glitter of jewels, music," said the Doctor,
his imagination soaring to dizzy heights under the stimulus of the words,
"music! There must be a band."

"I never heard of such a thing," said Dingy. "A band, indeed!
You'll be having fireworks next."

"*And fireworks*," said the Doctor, "and do you think it would be a
good thing to buy Mr. Prendergast a new tie? I noticed how shabby
he looked this morning."

"No," said Dingy with finality, "that is going too far. Flowers and
fireworks are one thing, but I insist on drawing the line somewhere.
It would be sinful to buy Mr. Prendergast a tie."

"Perhaps you are right," said the Doctor. "But there shall be music.
I understand that the Llanabba Silver Band was third at the North
Wales Eisteddfod last month. Will you get on to them, Florence? I
think Mr. Davies at the station is the bandmaster. Can the Clutterbucks come?"

"Yes," said Flossie, "six of them."

"Admirable! And then there is the Press. We must ring up the
Flint and Denbigh Herald and get them to send a photographer. That
means whisky. Will you see to that, Philbrick? I remember at one of
our sports I omitted to offer whisky to the Press, and the result was a
most unfortunate photograph. Boys do get into such indelicate positions
during the obstacle race, don't they?

"Then there are the prizes. I think you had better take Grimes into
Llandudno with you to help with the prizes. I don't think there is
any need for undue extravagance with the prizes. It gives boys a wrong
idea of sport. I wonder whether Lady Circumference would think it
odd if we asked her to present parsley crowns. Perhaps she would.

Utility, economy, and apparent durability are the qualities to be sought for, I think.

"And Pennyfeather, I hope you will see that they are distributed fairly evenly about the school. It doesn't do to let any boy win more than two events; I leave you to arrange that. I think it would be only right if little Lord Tangent won something, and Beste-Chetwynde — yes, his mother is coming down, too.

"I am afraid all this has been thrown upon your shoulders rather suddenly. I only learned this morning that Lady Circumference proposed to visit us, and as Mrs. Beste-Chetwynde was coming too, it seemed too good an opportunity to be missed. It is not often that the visits of two such important parents coincide. She is the Honourable Mrs. Beste-Chetwynde, you know — sister-in-law of Lord Pastmaster — a very wealthy woman, South American. They always say that she poisoned her husband, but of course little Beste-Chetwynde doesn't know that. It never came into court, but there was a great deal of talk about it at the time. Perhaps you remember the case?"

"No," said Paul.

"Powdered glass," said Flossie shrilly, "in his coffee."

"Turkish coffee," said Dingy.

"To work!" said the Doctor; "we have a lot to see to."

Happily enough, it did not rain next day, and after morning school everybody dressed up to the nines. Dr. Fagan appeared in a pale grey morning coat and sponge-bag trousers, looking more than ever *jeune premier*; there was a spring in his step and a pronounced sprightliness of bearing that Paul had not observed before. Flossie wore a violet frock of knitted wool made for her during the preceding autumn by her sister. It was the colour of indelible ink on blotting paper, and was ornamented at the waist with flowers of emerald green and pink. Her hat, also homemade, was the outcome of many winter evenings of ungrudged labour. All the trimmings of all previous hats had gone to its adornment. Dingy wore a little steel brooch made in the shape of a bull dog. Grimes wore a stiff evening collar of celluloid.

"Had to do something to celebrate the occasion," he said, "so I put on a 'choker.' Phew, though, it's tight. Have you seen my fiancée's latest creation? Ascot ain't in it. Let's get down to Mrs. Roberts for a quick one before the happy throng rolls up."

"I wish I could, but I've got to go round the ground with the Doctor."

"Righto, old boy! See you later. Here comes Prendy in his coat of many colours."

Mr. Prendergast wore a blazer of faded stripes, which smelt strongly of camphor.

"I think Dr. Fagan encourages a certain amount of display on these occasions," he said. "I used to keep wicket for my college, you know, but I was too short-sighted to be much good. Still, I am entitled to the blazer," he said with a note of defiance in his voice, "and it is more appropriate to a sporting occasion than a stiff collar."

"Good old Prendy!" said Grimes. "Nothing like a change of clothes to bring out latent pep. I felt like that my first week in khaki. Well, so long. Me for Mrs. Roberts. Why don't you come too, Prendy?"

"D'you know," said Mr. Prendergast, "I think I will."

Paul watched them disappear down the drive in amazement. Then he went off to find the Doctor.

"Frankly," said the Doctor, "I am at a loss to understand my own emotions. I can think of no entertainment that fills me with greater detestation than a display of competitive athletics, none — except possibly folk dancing. If there are two women in the world whose company I abominate — and there are very many more than two — they are Mrs. Beste-Chetwynde and Lady Circumference. I have, moreover, had an extremely difficult encounter with my butler, who — will you believe it? — waited at luncheon in a mustard-coloured suit of plus fours and a diamond tie pin, and when I reprimanded him, attempted to tell me some ridiculous story about his being the proprietor of a circus or swimming bath or some such concern. And yet," said the Doctor, "I am filled with a wholly delightful exhilaration. I can't understand it. It is not as though this was the first occasion of the kind. During the fourteen years that I have been at Llanabba there have been six sports days and two concerts, all of them, in one way or another, utterly disastrous. Once Lady Bunyan was taken ill; another time it was the matter of the press photographers and the obstacle race; another time some quite unimportant parents brought a dog with them which bit two of the boys very severely and one of the masters, who swore terribly in front of everyone. I could hardly blame him, but of course he had to go. Then there was the concert when the boys refused to sing 'God Save the King' because of the pudding they had had for luncheon. One way and another, I have been consistently unfortunate in my efforts at festivity. And yet I look forward to each new fiasco with the utmost relish. Perhaps, Pennyfeather, you will bring luck to Llanabba; in fact, I feel confident you have already done so. Look at the sun!"

Picking their way carefully among the dry patches in the water-logged drive, they reached the playing fields. Here the haphazard organization of the last twenty-four hours seemed to have been fairly successful. A large marquee was already in position, and Philbrick — still in plus fours — and three gardeners were at work putting up a smaller tent.

"That's for the Llanabba Silver Band," said the Doctor. "Philbrick, I required you to take off those loathsome garments."

"They were new when I bought them," said Philbrick, "and they cost eight pounds fifteen. Anyhow I can't do two things at once, can I? If I go back to change, who's going to manage all this, I'd like to know?"

"All right! Finish what you are doing first. Let us just review the arrangements. The marquee is for the visitors' tea. That is Diana's province. I expect we shall find her at work."

Sure enough, there was Dingy helping two servants to arrange plates of highly coloured cakes down a trestle table. Two other servants in the background were cutting sandwiches. Dingy, too, was obviously enjoying herself.

"Jane, Emily, remember that that butter has to do for three loaves. Spread it thoroughly, but don't waste it, and cut the crusts as thin as possible. Father, will you see to it that the boys who come in with their parents come in *alone?* You remember last time how Briggs brought in four boys with him, and they ate all the jam sandwiches before Colonel Loder had had any. Mr. Pennyfeather, the champagne cup is *not* for the masters. In fact, I expect you will find yourselves too much occupied helping the visitors to have any tea until they have left the tent. You had better tell Captain Grimes that, too. I am sure Mr. Prendergast would not think of pushing himself forward."

Outside the marquee were assembled several seats and tubs of palms and flowering shrubs. "All this must be set in order," said the Doctor; "our guests may arrive in less than an hour." He passed on. "The cars shall turn aside from the drive here and come right into the ground. It will give a pleasant background to the photographs, and, Pennyfeather, if you would with tact direct the photographer so that more prominence was given to Mrs. Beste-Chetwynde's Hispano Suiza than to Lady Circumference's little motor car, I think it would be all to the good. All these things count, you know."

"Nothing seems to have been done about marking out the ground," said Paul.

"No," said the Doctor, turning his attention to the field for the first time, "nothing. Well, you must do the best you can. They can't do everything."

"I wonder if any hurdles have come?"

"They were ordered," said the Doctor. "I am certain of it. Philbrick, have any hurdles come?"

"Yes," said Philbrick with a low chuckle.

"Why, pray, do you laugh at the mention of hurdles?"

"Just you look at them!" said Philbrick. "They're behind the tea house there."

Paul and the Doctor went to look and found a pile of spiked iron railings in sections heaped up at the back of the marquee. They were each about five feet high and were painted green with gilt spikes.

"It seems to me that they have sent the wrong sort," said the Doctor. "Yes."

"Well, we must do the best we can. What other things ought there to be?"

"Weight, hammer, javelin, long-jump pit, high-jump posts, low hurdles, eggs, spoon and greasy pole," said Philbrick.

"Previously competed for," said the Doctor imperturbably. "What else?"

"Somewhere to run," suggested Paul.

"Why, God bless my soul, they've got the whole park! How did you manage yesterday for the heats?"

"We judged the distance by eye."

"Then that is what we shall have to do to-day. Really, my dear Pennyfeather, it is quite unlike you to fabricate difficulties in this way. I am afraid you are getting unnerved. Let them go on racing until it is time for tea; and remember," he added sagely, "the longer the race the more time it takes. I leave the details to you. I am concerned with *style*. I wish, for instance, we had a starting pistol."

"Would this be any use?" said Philbrick, producing an enormous service revolver. "Only take care; it's loaded."

"The very thing," said the Doctor. "Only fire into the ground, mind.

We must do everything we can to avoid an accident. Do you always carry that about with you?"

"Only when I'm wearing my diamonds," said Philbrick.

"Well, I hope that is not often. Good gracious! Who are these extraordinary-looking people?"

Ten men of revolting appearance were approaching from the drive. They were low of brow, crafty of eye and crooked of limb. They advanced huddled together with the loping tread of wolves, peering about them furtively as they came, as though in constant terror of ambush; they slavered at their mouths, which hung loosely over their receding chins, while each clutched under his ape-like arm a burden of curious and unaccountable shape. On seeing the Doctor they halted and edged back, those behind squinting and mouthing over their companions' shoulders.

"Crikey!" said Philbrick. "Loonies! This is where I shoot."

"I refuse to believe the evidence of my eyes," said the Doctor. "These creatures simply do not exist."

After brief preliminary shuffling and nudging, an elderly man emerged from the back of the group. He had a rough black beard and wore on his uneven shoulders a druidical wreath of brass mistletoe berries.

"Why, it's my friend the station-master!" said Philbrick.

"We are the silver band the Lord bless and keep you," said the station-master in one breath, "the band that no one could beat whatever but two indeed in the Eisteddfod that for all North Wales was look you."

"I see," said the Doctor; "I see. That's splendid. Well, will you please go into your tent, the little tent over there."

"To march about you would not like us?" suggested the station-master; "we have a fine yellow flag look you that embroidered for us was in silks."

"No, no. Into the tent!"

The station-master went back to consult with his fellow musicians. There was a baying and growling and yapping as of the jungle at moonrise, and presently he came forward again with an obsequious, sidelong shuffle.

"Three pounds you pay us would you said indeed to at the sports play."

"Yes, yes, that's right, three pounds. Into the tent!"

"Nothing whatsoever we can play without the money first," said the station-master firmly.

"How would it be," said Philbrick, "if I gave him a clout on the ear?"

"No, no, I beg you to do nothing of the kind. You have not lived in Wales as I have." He took a note-case from his pocket, the sight of which seemed to galvanize the musicians into life; they crowded round, twitching and chattering. The Doctor took out three pound notes and gave them to the station-master. "There you are, Davies!" he said. "Now take your men into the tent. They are on no account to emerge until after tea; do you understand?"

The band slunk away, and Paul and the Doctor turned back towards the Castle.

"The Welsh character is an interesting study," said Dr. Fagan. "I have often considered writing a little monograph on the subject, but I was afraid it might make me unpopular in the village. The ignorant speak of them as Celts, which is of course wholly erroneous. They are of pure Iberian stock — the aboriginal inhabitants of Europe who survive only in Portugal and the Basque district. Celts readily inter-marry with their neighbours and absorb them. From the earliest times the Welsh have been looked upon as an unclean people. It it thus that they have preserved their racial integrity. Their sons and daughters rarely mate with humankind except their own blood relations. In Wales there was no need for legislation to prevent the conquering people intermarrying with the conquered. In Ireland that was necessary, for their intermarriage was a political matter. In Wales it was moral. I hope, by the way, you have no Welsh blood?"

"None whatsoever," said Paul.

"I was sure you had not, but one cannot be too careful. I once spoke of this subject to the sixth form and learned later that one of them had a Welsh grandmother. I am afraid it hurt his feelings terribly, poor little chap. She came from Pembrokeshire, too, which is of course quite a different matter. I often think," he continued, "that we can trace almost all the disasters of English history to the influence of Wales. Think of Edward of Carnarvon, the first Prince of Wales, a perverse life, Pennyfeather, and an unseemly death, then the Tudors and the dissolution of the Church, then Lloyd George, the temperance movement, Non-conformity and lust stalking hand in hand through the country, wasting and ravaging. But perhaps you think I exaggerate? I have a certain rhetorical tendency, I admit."

"No, no," said Paul.

"The Welsh," said the Doctor, "are the only nation in the world that has produced no graphic or plastic art, no architecture, no drama. They just sing," he said with disgust, "sing and blow down wind instruments of plated silver. They are deceitful because they cannot discern truth from falsehood, depraved because they cannot discern the consequences of their indulgence. Let us consider," he continued, "the etymological derivations of the Welsh langauge. . . ."

But here he was interrupted by a breathless little boy who panted down the drive to meet them. "Please, sir, Lord and Lady Circumference have arrived, sir. They're in the library with Miss Florence. She asked me to tell you."

"The sports will start in ten minutes," said the Doctor. "Run and tell the other boys to change and go at once to the playing fields. I will talk to you about the Welsh again. It is a matter to which I have given some thought, and I can see that you are sincerely interested. Come in with me and see the Circumferences."

Flossie was talking to them in the library.

"Yes, isn't it a sweet colour?" she was saying. "I do like something bright myself. Diana made it for me; she does knit a treat, does Diana, but of course I chose the colour, you know, because, you see, Diana's taste is all for wishy-washy greys and browns. Mournful, you know. Well, here's the dad. Lady Circumference was just saying how much she likes my frock what you said was vulgar, so there!"

A stout elderly woman dressed in a tweed coat and skirt and jaunty Tyrolean hat advanced to the Doctor. "Hullo!" she said in a deep bass voice, "how are you? Sorry if we're late. Circumference ran over a fool of a boy. I've just been chaffing your daughter here about her frock. Wish I was young enough to wear that kind of thing. Older I get the more I like colour. We're both pretty long in the tooth, eh?" She gave Dr. Fagan a hearty shake of the hand that obviously caused him acute pain. Then she turned to Paul.

"So you're the Doctor's hired assassin, eh? Well, I hope you keep a firm hand on my toad of a son. How's he doin'?"

"Quite well," said Paul.

"Nonsense!" said Lady Circumference. "The boy's a dunderhead. If he wasn't he wouldn't be here. He wants beatin' and hittin' and knockin' about generally, and then he'll be no good. That grass is shockin' bad on the terrace, Doctor; you ought to sand it down and resow it, but you'll have to take that cedar down if you ever want it to grow properly at the side. I hate cuttin' down a tree — like losin' a tooth — but you have to choose, tree or grass; you can't keep 'em both. What d'you pay your head man?"

As she was talking Lord Circumference emerged from the shadows and shook Paul's hand. He had a long fair moustache and large watery eyes which reminded Paul a little of Mr. Prendergast.

"How do you do?" he said.

"How do you do?" said Paul.

"Fond of sport, eh?" he said. "I mean these sort of sports?"

"Oh, yes," said Paul. "I think they're so good for the boys."

"Do you? Do you think that?" said Lord Circumference very earnestly; "do you think they're good for the boys?"

"Yes," said Paul; "don't you?"

"Me? Yes, oh, yes. I think so, too. Very good for the boys."

"So useful in case of a war or anything," said Paul.

"D'you think so? D'you really and truly think so? That there's going to be another war, I mean?"

"Yes, I'm sure of it; aren't you?"

"Yes, of course, I'm sure of it too. And that awful bread, and people coming on to one's own land and telling one what one's to do with one's own butter and milk, and commandeering one's horses! Oh, yes, all over again! My wife shot her hunters rather than let them go to the army. And girls in breeches on all the farms! All over again! Who do you think it will be this time?"

"The Americans," said Paul stoutly.

"No, indeed, I hope not. We had German prisoners on two of the farms. That wasn't so bad, but if they start putting Americans on my land, I'll just refuse to stand it. My daughter brought an American down to luncheon the other day, and, do you know . . . ?"

"Dig it and dung it," said Lady Circumference. "Only it's got to be dug deep, mind. Now how did your calceolarias do?"

"Lovely," said Flossie.

"I don't believe a word of it," said Lady Circumference. "Nobody's calceolarias did well last year."

"Shall we adjourn to the playing fields?" said the Doctor. "I expect they are all waiting for us."

Talking cheerfully, the party crossed the hall and went down the steps.

"Your drive's awful wet," said Lady Circumference. "I expect there's a blocked pipe somewhere. Sure it ain't sewage?"

"I was never any use at short distances," Lord Circumference was saying. "I was always a slow starter, but I was once eighteenth in the Crick at Rugby. We didn't take sports so seriously at the 'Varsity when I was up: everybody rode. What college were you at?"

"Scone."

"Scone, were you? Ever come across a young nephew of my wife's called Alastair Digby-Vaine-Trumpington?"*

"I just met him," said Paul.

"That's very interesting. Greta, Mr. Pennyfeather knows Alastair."

"Does he? Well, that boy's doing no good for himself. Got fined twenty pounds the other day, his mother told me. Seemed proud of it. If my brother had been alive he'd have licked all that out of the young cub. It takes a man to bring up a man."

"Yes," said Lord Circumference meekly.

"Who else do you know at Oxford? Do you know Freddy French-Wise?"

"No."

"Or Tom Obblethwaite or that youngest Castleton boy?"

"No, I'm afraid not. I had a great friend called Potts."

"*Potts!*" said Lady Circumference, and left it at that.

All the school and several local visitors were assembled in the field. Grimes stood by himself, looking depressed. Mr. Prendergast, flushed and unusually vivacious, was talking to the Vicar. As the headmaster's party came into sight the Llanabba Silver Band struck up "Men of Harlech."

"Shockin' noise," commented Lady Circumference graciously.

The head prefect came forward and presented her with a programme, beribboned and embossed in gold. Another prefect set a chair for her. She sat down with the Doctor next to her and Lord Circumference on the other side of him.

"Pennyfeather," cried the Doctor above the band, "start them racing."

Philbrick gave Paul a megaphone. "I found this in the pavilion," he said. "I thought it might be useful."

"Who's that extraordinary man?" asked Lady Circumference.

"He is the boxing coach and swimming professional," said the Doctor. "A finely developed figure, don't you think?"

---

*One of the rowdies responsible for Pennyfeather's expulsion from Oxford. — *Ed.*

"First race," said Paul through the megaphone, "under sixteen. Quarter Mile!" He read out Grimes's list of starters.

"What's Tangent doin' in this race?" said Lady Circumference. "The boy can't run an inch."

The silver band stopped playing.

"The course," said Paul, "starts from the pavilion, goes round that clump of elms . . ."

"Beeches," corrected Lady Circumference loudly.

". . . and ends in front of the band stand. Starter, Mr. Prendergast; timekeeper, Captain Grimes."

"I shall say, 'Are you ready? one, two, three!' and then fire," said Mr. Prendergast. "Are you ready? One" — there was a terrific report. "Oh, dear! I'm sorry" — but the race had begun. Clearly Tangent was not going to win; he was sitting on the grass crying because he had been wounded in the foot by Mr. Prendergast's bullet. Philbrick carried him, wailing dismally, into the refreshment tent, where Dingy helped him off with his shoe. His heel was slightly grazed. Dingy gave him a large slice of cake, and he hobbled out surrounded by a sympathetic crowd.

"That won't hurt him," said Lady Circumference, "but I think someone ought to remove the pistol from that old man before he does anything serious."

"I knew that was going to happen," said Lord Circumference.

"A most unfortunate beginning," said the Doctor.

"Am I going to die?" said Tangent, his mouth full of cake.

"For God's sake, look after Prendy," said Grimes in Paul's ear. "The man's as tight as a lord, and on one whisky, too."

"First blood to me!" said Mr. Prendergast gleefully.

"The last race will be run again," said Paul down the megaphone. "Starter, Mr. Philbrick; timekeeper, Mr. Prendergast."

"On your marks! Get set." Bang went the pistol, this time without disaster. The six little boys scampered off through the mud, disappeared behind the beeches and returned rather more slowly. Captain Grimes and Mr. Prendergast held up a piece of tape.

"Well run, sir!" shouted Colonel Sidebotham. "Jolly good race."

"Capital," said Mr. Prendergast, and dropping his end of the tape, he sauntered over to the Colonel. "I can see you are a fine judge of a race, sir. So was I once. So's Grimes. A capital fellow, Grimes; a bounder, you know, but a capital fellow. Bounders can be capital fellows;

don't you agree, Colonel Slidebottom? In fact, I'd go farther and say that capital fellows *are* bounders. What d'you say to that? I wish you'd stop pulling at my arm, Pennyfeather. Colonel Shybotham and I are just having a most interesting conversation about bounders."

The silver band struck up again, and Mr. Prendergast began a little jig, saying: "Capital fellow! capital fellow!" and snapping his fingers. Paul led him to the refreshment tent.

"Dingy wants you to help her in there," he said firmly, "and, for God's sake, don't come out until you feel better."

"I never felt better in my life," said Mr. Prendergast indignantly. "Capital fellow! capital fellow!"

"It is not my affair, of course," said Colonel Sidebotham, "but if you ask me I should say that man had been drinking."

"He was talking very excitedly to me," said the Vicar, "about some apparatus for warming a church in Worthing and about the Apostolic Claims of the Church of Abyssinia. I confess I could not follow him clearly. He seems deeply interested in Church matters. Are you quite sure he is right in the head? I have noticed again and again since I have been in the Church that lay interest in ecclesiastical matters is often a prelude to insanity."

"Drink, pure and simple," said the Colonel. "I wonder where he got it? I could do with a spot of whisky."

"Quarter Mile Open!" said Paul through his megaphone.

Presently the Clutterbucks arrived. Both the parents were stout. They brought with them two small children, a governess, and an elder son. They debouched from the car one by one, stretching their limbs in evident relief.

"This is Sam," said Mr. Clutterbuck, "just down from Cambridge. He's joined me in the business, and we've brought the nippers along for a treat. Don't mind, do you, Doc? And last, but not least, my wife."

Dr. Fagan greeted them with genial condescension and found them seats.

"I am afraid you have missed all the jumping events," he said. "But I have a list of the results here. You will see that Percy has done extremely well."

"Didn't know the little beggar had it in him. See that, Martha? Percy's won the high jump and the long jump and the hurdles. How's your young hopeful been doing, Lady Circumference?"

"My boy has been injured in the foot," said Lady Circumference coldly.

"Dear me! Not badly, I hope? Did he twist his ankle in the jumping?"

"No," said Lady Circumference, "he was shot at by one of the assistant masters. But it is kind of you to enquire."

"Three Miles Open!" announced Paul. "The course of six laps will be run as before."

"On your marks! Get set." Bang went Philbrick's revolver. Off trotted the boys on another race.

"Father," said Flossie, "don't you think it's time for the tea interval?"

"Nothing can be done before Mrs. Beste-Chetwynde arrives," said the Doctor.

Round and round the muddy track trotted the athletes while the silver band played sacred music unceasingly.

"Last lap!" announced Paul.

The school and the visitors crowded about the tape to cheer the winner. Amid loud applause Clutterbuck breasted the tape well ahead of the others.

"Well run! Oh, good, jolly good, sir!" cried Colonel Sidebotham.

"Good old Percy! That's the stuff," said Mr. Clutterbuck.

"Well run, Percy!" chorused the two little Clutterbucks, prompted by their governess.

"That boy cheated," said Lady Circumference. "He only went round five times. I counted."

"I think unpleasantness so mars the afternoon," said the Vicar.

"How dare you suggest such a thing?" asked Mr. Clutterbuck. "I appeal to the referee. Percy ran the full course, didn't he?"

"Clutterbuck wins," said Captain Grimes.

"Fiddlesticks!" said Lady Circumference. "He deliberately lagged behind and joined the others as they went behind the beeches. The little toad!"

"Really, Greta," said Lord Circumference, "I think we ought to abide by the referee's decision."

"Well, they can't expect me to give away the prizes, then. Nothing would induce me to give that boy a prize."

"Do you understand, madam, that you are bringing a serious accusation against my son's honour?"

"Serious accusation fiddlesticks! What he wants is a jolly good hidin'."

"No doubt you judge other people's sons by your own. Let me tell you, Lady Circumference . . ."

"Don't you attempt to browbeat me, sir. I know a cheat when I see one."

At this stage of the discussion the Doctor left Mrs. Hope-Browne's side, where he had been remarking upon her son's progress in geometry, and joined the group round the winning post.

"If there is a disputed decision," he said genially, "they shall race again."

"Percy has won already," said Mr. Clutterbuck. "He has been adjudged the winner."

"Splendid! splendid! A promising little athlete. I congratulate you, Clutterbuck."

"But he only ran five laps," said Lady Circumference.

"Then clearly he has won the Five-furlong Race, a very exacting length."

"But the other boys," said Lady Circumference, almost beside herself with rage, "have run six lengths."

"Then they," said the Doctor imperturbably, "are first, second, third, fourth and fifth respectively in the Three Miles. Clearly there has been some confusion. Diana, I think we might now serve tea."

Things were not easy, but there was fortunately a distraction, for as he spoke an enormous limousine of dove-grey and silver stole soundlessly on to the field.

"But what could be more opportune? Here is Mrs. Beste-Chetwynde."

Three light skips brought him to the side of the car, but the footman was there before him. The door opened, and from the cushions within emerged a tall young man in a clinging dove-grey overcoat. After him, like the first breath of spring in the Champs Elysées came Mrs. Beste-Chetwynde — two lizard-skin feet, silk legs, chinchilla body, a tight little black hat pinned with platinum and diamonds, and the high invariable voice that may be heard in any Ritz Hotel from New York to Buda-Pesth.

"I hope you don't mind my bringing Chokey, Dr. Fagan?" she said. "He's just crazy about sport."

"I sure am that," said Chokey.

"Dear Mrs. Beste-Chetwynde!" said Dr. Fagan. "Dear, dear, Mrs.

Beste-Chetwynde!" He pressed her glove, and for the moment was at a loss for words of welcome, for "Chokey," though graceful of bearing and irreproachably dressed, was a Negro.

The refreshment tent looked very nice. The long table across the centre was covered with a white cloth. Bowls of flowers were ranged down it at regular intervals, and between them plates of sandwiches and cakes and jugs of lemonade and champagne cup. Behind it against a background of palms stood the four Welsh housemaids in clean caps and aprons pouring out tea. Behind them again sat Mr. Prendergast, a glass of champagne cup in his hand, his wig slightly awry. He rose unsteadily to his feet at the approach of the guests, made a little bow, and then sat down again rather suddenly.

"Will you take round the *fois gras* sandwiches, Mr. Pennyfeather?" said Dingy. "They are not for the boys or Captain Grimes."

"One for little me!" said Flossie as he passed her.

Philbrick, evidently regarding himself as one of the guests, was engaged in a heated discussion on greyhound racing with Sam Clutterbuck.

"What price the coon?" he asked as Paul gave him a sandwich.

"It does my heart good to see old Prendy enjoying himself," said Grimes. "Pity he shot that kid, though."

"There's not much the matter with him to see the way he's eating his tea. I say, this is rather a poor afternoon, isn't it?"

"Circulate, old boy, circulate. Things aren't going too smoothly."

Nor indeed were they. The sudden ebullition of ill-feeling over the Three-mile Race, though checked by the arrival of Mrs. Beste-Chetwynde, was by no means forgotten. There were two distinctly hostile camps in the tea tent. On one side stood the Circumferences, Tangent, the Vicar, Colonel Sidebotham and the Hope-Brownes, on the other the seven Clutterbucks, Philbrick, Flossie and two or three parents who had been snubbed already that afternoon by Lady Circumference. No one spoke of the race, but outraged sportsmanship glinted perilously in every eye. Several parents, intent on their tea, crowded round Dingy and the table. Eminently aloof from all these stood Chokey and Mrs. Beste-Chetwynde. Clearly the social balance was delicately poised, and the issue depended upon them. With or without her Negro, Mrs. Beste-Chetwynde was a woman of vital importance.

"Why, Dr. Fagan," she was saying, "it is too disappointing that we've missed the sports. We had just the slowest journey, stopping all the time to see the churches. You can't move Chokey once he's seen an old church. He's just crazy about culture, aren't you, darling?"

"I sure am that," said Chokey.

"Are you interested in music?" said the Doctor tactfully.

"Well, just you hear that, Baby," said Chokey; "am *I* interested in music? I should say I am."

"He plays just too divinely," said Mrs. Beste-Chetwynde.

"Has he heard my new records, would you say?"

"No, darling, I don't expect he has."

"Well, just you hear *them*, sir, and then you'll know — am I interested in music."

"Now, darling, don't get discouraged. I'll take you over and introduce you to Lady Circumference. It's his inferiority complex, the angel. He's just crazy to meet the aristocracy, aren't you, my sweet?"

"I sure am that," said Chokey.

"I think it's an insult bringing a nigger here," said Mrs. Clutterbuck. "It's an insult to our own women."

"Niggers are all right," said Philbrick. "Where I draw a line is a Chink, nasty inhuman things. I had a pal bumped off by a Chink once. Throat cut horrible, it was, from ear to ear."

"Good gracious!" said the Clutterbuck governess; "was that in the Boxer rising?"

"No," said Philbrick cheerfully. "Saturday night in the Edgware Road. Might have happened to any of us."

"What did the gentleman say?" asked the children.

"Never you mind, my dears. Run and have some more of the green cake."

They ran off obediently, but the little boy was later heard whispering to his sister as she knelt at her prayers, "cut horrible from ear to ear," so that until quite late in her life Miss Clutterbuck would feel a little faint when she saw a bus that was going to the Edgware Road.

"I've got a friend lives in Savannah," said Sam, "and he's told me a thing or two about niggers. Of course it's hardly a thing to talk about before the ladies, but, to put it bluntly, *they have uncontrollable passions.* See what I mean?"

"What a terrible thing!" said Grimes.

"You can't blame 'em, mind: it's just their nature. Animal, you know. Still, what I do say is, since they're like that, the less we see of them the better."

"Quite," said Mr. Clutterbuck.

"I had such a curious conversation just now," Lord Circumference was saying to Paul, "with your bandmaster over there. He asked me whether I should like to meet his sister-in-law; and when I said, 'Yes, I should be delighted to,' he said that it would cost a pound normally, but that he'd let me have special terms. What *can* he have meant, Mr. Pennyfoot?"

" 'Pon my soul," Colonel Sidebotham was saying to the Vicar, "I don't like the look of that nigger. I saw enough of Fuzzy-Wuzzy in the Soudan — devilish good enemy and devilish bad friend. I'm going across to talk to Mrs. Clutterbuck. Between ourselves, I think Lady C. went a bit far. I didn't see the race myself, but there are limits. . . ."

"Rain ain't doin' the turnip crop any good," Lady Circumference was saying.

"No, indeed," said Mrs. Beste-Chetwynde. "Are you in England for long?"

"Why, I live in England, of course," said Lady Circumference.

"My dear, how divine! But don't you find it just too expensive?"

This was one of Lady Circumference's favourite topics, but somehow she did not feel disposed to enlarge on it to Mrs. Beste-Chetwynde with the same gusto as when she was talking to Mrs. Sidebotham and the Vicar's wife. She never felt quite at ease with people richer than herself.

"Well, we all feel the wind a bit since the war," she said briefly. "How's Bobby Pastmaster?"

"Dotty," said Mrs. Beste-Chetwynde, "terribly dotty, and he and Chokey don't get on. You'll like Chokey. He's just crazy about England, too. We've been round all the cathedrals, and now we're going to start on the country houses. We were thinking of running over to see you at Castle Tangent one afternoon."

"That would be delightful, but I'm afraid we are in London at present. Which did you like best of the cathedrals, Mr. Chokey?"

"Chokey's not really his name, you know. The angel's called 'Mr. Sebastien Cholmondley.' "

"Well," said Mr. Cholmondley, "they were all just fine, just fine. When I saw the cathedrals my heart just rose up and sang within me. I sure am crazy about culture. You folk think because we're coloured we don't care about nothing but jazz. Why, I'd give all the jazz in the world for just one little stone from one of your cathedrals."

"It's quite true. He would."

"Well, that's most interesting, Mr. Cholmondley. I used to live just outside Salisbury when I was a girl, but, little as I like jazz, I never felt quite as strongly as that about it."

"Salisbury is full of historical interest, Lady Circumference, but in my opinion York Minster is the more refined."

"Oh, you angel!" said Mrs. Beste-Chetwynde. "I could eat you up every bit."

"And is this your first visit to an English school?" asked the Doctor.

"I should say not. Will you tell the Doctor the schools I've seen?"

"He's been to them all, even the quite new ones. In fact, he liked the new ones best."

"They were more spacious. Have you ever seen Oxford?"

"Yes; in fact, I was educated there."

"Were you, now? I've seen Oxford and Cambridge and Eton and Harrow. That's me all over. That's what I like, see? I appreciate art. There's plenty coloured people come over here and don't see nothing but a few night clubs. I read Shakespeare," said Chokey, "Hamlet, Macbeth, King Lear. Ever read them?"

"Yes," said the Doctor; "as a matter of fact, I have."

"My race," said Chokey, "is essentially an artistic race. We have the child's love of song and colour and the child's natural good taste. All you white folks despise the poor coloured man. . . ."

"No, no," said the Doctor.

"Let him say his piece, the darling," said Mrs. Beste-Chetwynde. "Isn't he divine!"

"You folks all think the coloured man hasn't got a soul. Anything's good enough for the poor coloured man. Beat him; put him in chains; load him with burdens. . . ." Here Paul observed a responsive glitter in Lady Circumference's eye. "But all the time that poor coloured man has a soul same as you have. Don't he breathe the same as you? Don't he eat and drink? Don't he love Shakespeare and cathedrals and the paintings of the old masters same as you? Isn't he just asking for your love and help to raise him from the servitude into which your forefathers plunged him? Oh, say, white folks, why don't you stretch out a helping hand to the poor coloured man, that's as good as you are, if you'll only let him be?"

"My sweet," said Mrs. Beste-Chetwynde, "you mustn't get discouraged. They're all friends here."

"Is that so?" said Chokey. "Should I sing them a song?"

"No, don't do that, darling. Have some tea."

"I had a friend in Paris," said the Clutterbuck governess, "whose sister knew a girl who married one of the black soldiers during the war, and you wouldn't believe what he did to her. Joan and Peter, run and see if Daddy wants some more tea. He tied her up with a razor strop and left her on the stone floor for the night without food or covering. And then it was over a year before she could get a divorce."

"Used to cut the tent ropes," Colonel Sidebotham was saying, "and then knife the poor beggars through the canvas."

"You can see 'em in Shaftesbury Avenue and Charing Cross Road any night of the week," Sam Clutterbuck was saying. "The women just hanging on to 'em."

"The mistake was ever giving them their freedom," said the Vicar. "They were far happier and better looked after before."

"It's queer," said Flossie, "that a woman with as much money as Mrs. Beste-Chetwynde should wear such *dull* clothes."

"That ring didn't cost less than five hundred," said Philbrick.

"Let's go and talk to the Vicar about God," said Mrs. Beste-Chetwynde. "Chokey thinks religion is just divine."

"My race is a very spiritual one," said Chokey.

"The band has been playing 'Men of Harlech' for over half an hour," said the Doctor. "Diana, do go and tell them to try something else."

"I sometimes think I'm getting rather bored with coloured people," Mrs. Beste-Chetwynde said to Lady Circumference. "Are you?"

"I have never had the opportunity."

"I daresay you'd be good with them. They take a lot of living up to; they *are* so earnest. Who's that dear, dim, drunk little man?"

"That is the person who shot my son."

"My dear, how too shattering for you. Not dead, I hope? Chokey shot a man at a party the other night. He gets gay at times, you know. It's only when he's on his best behaviour that he's so class-conscious. I must go and rescue the Vicar."

The station-master came into the tent, crab-like and obsequious.

"Well, my good man?" said the Doctor.

"The young lady I have been telling that no other tunes can we play whatever with the lady smoking at her cigarette look you."

"God bless my soul! Why not?"

"The other tunes are all holy tunes look you. Blasphemy it would be to play the songs of Sion while the lady at a cigarette smokes whatever. 'Men of Harlech' is good music look you."

"This is most unfortunate. I can hardly ask Mrs. Beste-Chetwynde to stop smoking. Frankly I regard this as impertinence."

"But no man can you ask against his Maker to blaspheme whatever unless him to pay more you were. Three pounds for the music is good and one for the blasphemy look you."

Dr. Fagan gave him another pound. The stationmaster retired, and in a few minutes the silver band began a singularly emotional rendering of "In Thy courts no more are needed Sun by day and moon by night."

As the last car drove away, the Doctor and his daughters and Paul and Grimes walked up the drive together towards the Castle.

"Frankly the day has been rather a disappointment to me," said the Doctor. "Nothing seemed to go quite right in spite of all our preparations."

"And expense," said Dingy.

"I am sorry, too, that Mr. Prendergast should have had that unfortunate disagreement with Mrs. Beste-Chetwynde's coloured friend. In all the ten years during which we have worked together I have never known Mr. Prendergast so self-assertive. It was *not* becoming of him. Nor was it Philbrick's place to join in. I was seriously alarmed. They seemed so angry, and all about some minor point of ecclesiastical architecture."

"Mr. Cholmondley was very sensitive," said Flossie.

"Yes, he seemed to think that Mr. Prendergast's insistence on the late development of the rood screen was in some way connected with colour prejudice. I wonder why that was? To my mind it showed a very confused line of thought. Still, it would have been more seemly if Mr. Prendergast had let the matter drop, and what could Philbrick know of the matter?"

"Philbrick is not an ordinary butler," said Dingy.

"No, indeed not," said the Doctor. "I heartily deplore his jewellery."

"I didn't like Lady Circumference's speech," said Flossie. "Did you?"

"I did not," said the Doctor; "nor, I think, did Mrs. Clutterbuck. I thought her reference to the Five-furlong Race positively brutal. I was glad Clutterbuck had done so well in the jumping yesterday."

"She rather wanders from the point, doesn't she?" said Dingy. "All that about hunting, I mean."

"I don't think Lady Circumference is conscious of any definite divisions in the various branches of sport. I have often observed in women of her type a tendency to regard all athletics as inferior forms of fox-hunting. It is *not* logical. Besides, she was nettled at some remark of Mr. Cholmondley's about cruelty to animals. As you say, it was irrelevant and rather unfortunate. I also resented the references to the Liberal party. Mr. Clutterbuck has stood three times, you know. Taken as a whole, it was *not* a happy speech. I was quite glad when I saw her drive away."

"What a pretty car Mrs. Beste-Chetwynde has got!" said Flossie, "but how ostentatious of her to bring a footman."

"I can forgive the footman," said Dingy, "but I can't forgive Mr. Cholmondley. He asked me whether I had ever heard of a writer called Thomas Hardy."

"He asked *me* to go to Reigate with him for the week-end," said Flossie, ". . . in rather a sweet way, too."

"Florence, I trust you refused?"

"Oh, yes," said Flossie sadly, "I refused."

They went on up the drive in silence. Presently Dingy asked: "What are we going to do about those fireworks you insisted on buying? Everyone has gone away."

"I don't feel in a mood for fireworks," said the Doctor. "Perhaps another time, but not now."

From Vile Bodies

*TOO SHAMING**

It was clearly going to be a bad crossing.

With Asiatic resignation Father Rothschild, S.J., put down his suitcase in the corner of the bar and went on deck. (It was a small suitcase of imitation crocodile hide. The initials stamped on it in Gothic characters were not Father Rothschild's, for he had borrowed it that morning from the *valet-de-chambre* of his hotel. It contained some rudimentary underclothes, six important new books in six languages, a false beard and a school atlas and gazetteer heavily annotated.) Standing on the deck Father Rothschild leant his elbow on the rail, rested his chin in his hands and surveyed the procession of passengers coming up the gangway, each face eloquent of polite misgiving.

Very few of them were unknown to the Jesuit, for it was his happy knack to remember everything that could possibly be learned about everyone who could possibly be of any importance. His tongue protruded very slightly and, had they not all been so concerned with luggage and the weather, someone might have observed in him a peculiar resemblance to those plaster reproductions of the gargoyles of Notre Dame which may be seen in the shop windows of artists' colourmen tinted the colour of "Old Ivory," peering intently from among stencil outfits and plasticene and tubes of water-colour paint. High above his head swung Mrs. Melrose Ape's travel-worn Packard car, bearing the dust of three continents, against the darkening sky, and up the companion-way at the head of her angels strode Mrs. Melrose Ape, the woman evangelist.

"Faith."

"Here, Mrs. Ape."

"Charity."

This selection contains the three opening chapters of the novel. — Ed.

"Here, Mrs. Ape."

"Fortitude."

"Here, Mrs. Ape."

"Chastity. . . . Where is Chastity?"

"Chastity didn't feel well, Mrs. Ape. She went below."

"That girl's more trouble than she's worth. Whenever there's any packing to be done, Chastity doesn't feel well. Are all the rest here — Humility, Prudence, Divine Discontent, Mercy, Justice and Creative Endeavour?"

"Creative Endeavour lost her wings, Mrs. Ape. She got talking to a gentleman in the train. . . . Oh, there she is."

"Got 'em?" asked Mrs. Ape.

Too breathless to speak, Creative Endeavour nodded. (Each of the angels carried her wings in a little black box like a violin case.)

"Right," said Mrs. Ape, "and just you hold on to 'em tight and not so much talking to gentlemen in trains. You're angels, not a panto, see?"

The angels crowded together disconsolately. It was awful when Mrs. Ape was like this. My, how they would pinch Chastity and Creative Endeavour when they got them alone in their nightshirts. It was bad enough their going to be so sick without that they had Mrs. Ape pitching into them too.

Seeing their discomfort, Mrs. Ape softened and smiled. She was nothing if not "magnetic."

"Well, girls," she said, "I must be getting along. They say it's going to be rough, but don't you believe it. If you have peace in your hearts your stomach will look after itself, and remember if you *do* feel queer — sing. There's nothing like it."

"Good-bye, Mrs. Ape, and thank you," said the angels; they bobbed prettily, turned about and trooped aft to the second-class part of the ship. Mrs. Ape watched them benignly, then, squaring her shoulders and looking (except that she had really no beard to speak of) every inch a sailor, strode resolutely forrard to the first-class bar.

Other prominent people were embarking, all very unhappy about the weather; to avert the terrors of seasickness they had indulged in every kind of civilised witchcraft, but they were lacking in faith.

Miss Runcible was there, and Miles Malpractice, and all the Younger Set. They had spent a jolly morning strapping each other's tummies with sticking plaster (how Miss Runcible had wriggled).

The Right Honourable Walter Outrage, M.P., last week's Prime Minister, was there. Before breakfast that morning (which had suffered in consequence) Mr. Outrage had taken twice the maximum dose of a patent preparation of chloral, and losing heart later had finished the bottle in the train. He moved in an uneasy trance, closely escorted by the most public-looking detective sergeants. These men had been with Mr. Outrage in Paris, and what they did not know about his goings on was not worth knowing, at least from a novelist's point of view. (When they spoke about him to each other they called him "the Right Honourable Rape," but that was more by way of being a pun about his name than a criticism of the conduct of his love affairs, in which, if the truth were known, he displayed a notable diffidence and the liability to panic.)

Lady Throbbing and Mrs. Blackwater, those twin sisters whose portrait by Millais auctioned recently at Christie's made a record in rock-bottom prices, were sitting on one of the teak benches eating apples and drinking what Lady Throbbing, with late Victorian *chic*, called "a bottle of pop," and Mrs. Blackwater, more exotically, called *"champagne,"* pronouncing it as though it were French.

"Surely, Kitty, that is Mr. Outrage, last week's Prime Minister."

"Nonsense, Fanny, where?"

"Just in front of the two men with bowler hats, next to the clergyman."

"It is certainly like his photographs. How strange he looks."

"Just like poor Throbbing . . . all that last year."

". . . And none of us even suspected . . . until they found the bottles under the board in his dressing-room . . . and we all used to think it was drink . . ."

"I don't think one finds *quite* the same class as Prime Minister nowadays, do you think?"

"They say that only *one* person has any influence with Mr. Outrage . . ."

"At the Japanese Embassy . . ."

"Of course, dear, not so loud. But tell me, Fanny, seriously, do you think really and truly Mr. Outrage has IT?"

"He has a very nice figure for a man of his age."

"Yes, but *his* age, and the bull-like type is so often disappointing. Another glass? You will be grateful for it when the ship begins to move."

"I quite thought we *were* moving."

"How absurd you are, Fanny, and yet I can't help laughing."

So arm in arm and shaken by little giggles the two tipsy old ladies went down to their cabin.

Of the other passengers, some had filled their ears with cotton wool, others wore smoked glasses, while several ate dry captain's biscuits from paper bags, as Red Indians are said to eat snake's flesh to make them cunning. Mrs. Hoop repeated feverishly over and over again a formula she had learned from a yogi in New York City. A few "good sailors," whose luggage bore the labels of many voyages, strode aggressively about smoking small, foul pipes and trying to get up a four of bridge.

Two minutes before the advertised time of departure, while the first admonitory whistling and shouting was going on, a young man came on board carrying his bag. There was nothing particularly remarkable about his appearance. He looked exactly as young men like him do look; he was carrying his own bag, which was disagreeably heavy, because he had no money left in francs and very little left in anything else. He had been two months in Paris writing a book and was coming home because, in the course of his correspondence, he had got engaged to be married. His name was Adam Fenwick-Symes.

Father Rothschild smiled at him in a kindly manner.

"I doubt whether you remember me," he said. "We met at Oxford five years ago at luncheon with the Dean of Balliol. I shall be interested to read your book when it appears — an autobiography, I understand. And may I be one of the first to congratulate you on your engagement? I am afraid you will find your father-in-law a little eccentric — and forgetful. He had a nasty attack of bronchitis this winter. It is a draughty house— far too big for these days. Well, I must go below now. It is going to be rough and I am a bad sailor. We meet at Lady Metroland's on the twelfth, if not, as I hope, before."

Before Adam had time to reply the Jesuit disappeared. Suddenly the head popped back.

"There is an extremely dangerous and disagreeable woman on board — a Mrs. Ape."

Then he was gone again, and almost at once the boat began to slip away from the quay towards the mouth of the harbour.

Sometimes the ship pitched and sometimes she rolled and sometimes she stood quite still and shivered all over, poised above an abyss of dark water; then she would go swooping down like a scenic railway train into a windless hollow and up again with a rush into the gale; sometimes she would burrow her path, with convulsive nosings and scramblings like a terrier in a rabbit hole; and sometimes she would drop dead like a lift. It was this last movement that caused the most havoc among the passengers.

"Oh," said the Bright Young People. "Oh, oh, oh."

"It's just exactly like being inside a cocktail shaker," said Miles Malpractice. "Darling, your face — eau de Nil."

"Too, too sick-making," said Miss Runcible, with one of her rare flashes of accuracy.

Kitty Blackwater and Fanny Throbbing lay one above the other in their bunks rigid from wig to toe.

"I wonder, do you think the *champagne* . . . ?"

"Kitty."

"Yes, Fanny, dear."

"Kitty, I think, in fact, I am sure I have some sal volatile. . . . Kitty, I thought that perhaps as you are nearer . . . it would really hardly be safe for me to try and descend . . . I might break a leg."

"Not after *champagne*, Fanny, do you think?"

"But I need it. Of course, dear, *if it's too much trouble?*"

"Nothing is too much trouble, darling, you know that. But now I come to think of it, I remember, quite clearly, for a fact, that you did *not* pack the sal volatile."

"Oh, Kitty, oh, Kitty, please . . . you would be sorry for this if I died . . . oh."

"But I saw the sal volatile on your dressing-table after your luggage had gone down, dear. I remember thinking, I must take that down to Fanny, and then, dear, I got confused over the tips, so you see . . ."

"I . . . put . . . it . . . in . . . myself . . . Next to my brushes . . . you . . . beast."

"Oh, Fanny . . ."

"Oh . . . Oh . . . Oh."

To Father Rothschild no passage was worse than any other. He thought of the sufferings of the saints, the mutability of human nature, the Four Last Things, and between whiles repeated snatches of the penitential psalms.

The Leader of His Majesty's Opposition lay sunk in a rather glorious coma, made splendid by dreams of Oriental imagery — of painted paper houses; of golden dragons and gardens of almond blossom; of golden limbs and almond eyes, humble and caressing; of very small golden feet among almond blossoms; of little painted cups full of golden tea; of a golden voice singing behind a painted paper screen; of humble, caressing little golden hands and eyes shaped like almonds and the colour of night.

Outside his door two very limp detective sergeants had deserted their posts.

"The bloke as could make trouble on a ship like this 'ere deserves to get away with it," they said.

The ship creaked in every plate, doors slammed, trunks fell about, the wind howled; the screw, now out of the water, now in, raced and churned, shaking down hat-boxes like ripe apples; but above all the roar and clatter there rose from the second-class ladies' saloon the despairing voices of Mrs. Ape's angels, in frequently broken unison, singing, singing, wildly, desperately, as though their hearts would break in the effort and their minds lose their reason, Mrs. Ape's famous hymn, "There ain't no flies on the Lamb of God."

The Captain and the Chief Officer sat on the bridge engrossed in a crossword puzzle.

"Looks like we may get some heavy weather if the wind gets up," he said. "Shouldn't wonder if there wasn't a bit of a sea running tonight."

"Well, we can't always have it quiet like this," said the Chief Officer. "Word of eighteen letters meaning carnivorous mammal. Search me if I know how they do think of these things."

Adam Fenwick-Symes sat among the good sailors in the smoking-room drinking his third Irish whisky and wondering how soon he would feel definitely ill. Already there was a vague depression gathering at the top of his head. There were thirty-five minutes more, probably longer with the head wind keeping them back.

Opposite him sat a much-travelled and chatty journalist telling him smutty stories. From time to time Adam interposed some more or less appropriate comment. "No, I say that's a good one," or, "I must remember that," or just, "Ha, ha, ha," but his mind was not really in a receptive condition.

Up went the ship, up, up, up, paused and then plunged down with a sidelong slither. Adam caught at his glass and saved it. Then shut his eyes.

When things were at their lowest, Mrs. Ape reappeared in the smoking-room. She stood for a second or two in the entrance balanced between swinging door and swinging door-post; then as the ship momentarily righted herself, she strode to the bar, her feet well apart, her hands in the pockets of her tweed coat.

"Double rum," she said and smiled magnetically at the miserable little collection of men seated about the room. "Why, boys," she said, "but you're looking terrible put out over something. What's it all about? Is it your souls that's wrong or is it that the ship won't keep still? Rough? 'Course it's rough. But let me ask you this. If you're put out this way over just an hour's seasickness" ("Not seasick, ventilation," said Mr. Henderson mechanically) "what are you going to be like when you make the mighty big journey that's waiting for us all? Are you right with God?" said Mrs. Ape. "Are you prepared for death?"

"Oh, am I not?" said Arthur. "I 'aven't thought of nothing else for the last half-hour."

"Now, boys, I'll tell you what we're going to do. We're going to sing a song together, you and me." ("Oh, God," said Adam.) "You may not know it, but you are. You'll feel better for it body *and* soul. It's a song of Hope. You don't hear much about Hope these days, do you? Plenty about Faith, plenty about Charity. They've forgotten all about Hope. There's only one great evil in the world to-day. Despair. I know all about England, and I tell you straight, boys, I've got the goods for you. Hope's what you want and Hope's what I got. Here, steward, hand round these leaflets. There's the song on the back. Now all together . . . sing. Five bob for you, steward, if you can shout me down. Splendid, all together, boys."

In a rich, very audible voice Mrs. Ape led the singing. Her arms rose, fell and fluttered with the rhythm of the song. The bar steward was hers already — inaccurate sometimes in his reading of the words, but with a sustained power in the low notes that defied competition. The journalist joined in next and Arthur set up a little hum. Soon they were all at it, singing like blazes, and it is undoubtedly true that they felt the better for it.

Father Rothschild heard it and turned his face to the wall.

Kitty Blackwater heard it.
"Fanny."
"Well."
"Fanny, dear, do you hear singing?"
"Yes, dear, thank you."
"Fanny, dear, I hope they aren't holding a *service*. I mean, dear, it sounds so like a hymn. Do you think, possibly, we are *in danger?* Fanny, are we going to be wrecked?"
"I should be neither surprised nor sorry."
"Darling, how can you? . . . We should have heard it, shouldn't we, if we had actually *hit* anything? . . . Fanny, dear, if you like I will have a look for your sal volatile."
"I hardly think that would be any help, dear, since you *saw* it on my dressing-table."
"I may have been mistaken."
"You *said* you *saw* it."

The Captain heard it. "All the time I been at sea," he said, "I never could stand for missionaries."
"Word of six letters beginning with ZB," said the Chief Officer, "meaning 'used in astronomic calculations.'"
"Z can't be right," said the Captain after a few minutes' thought.

The Bright Young People heard it. "So like one's first parties," said Miss Runcible, "being sick with other people singing."

Mrs. Hoop heard it. "Well," she thought, "I'm through with theosophy after this journey. Reckon I'll give the Catholics the once over."

Aft, in the second-class saloon, where the screw was doing its worst, the angels heard it. It was some time since they had given up singing.
"Her again," said Divine Discontent.

Mr. Outrage alone lay happily undisturbed, his mind absorbed in lovely dream sequences of a world of little cooing voices, so caressing, so humble; and dark eyes, night-coloured, the shape of almonds over painted paper screens; little golden bodies, so flexible, so firm, so surprising in the positions they assumed.

They were still singing in the smoking-room when, in very little more than her usual time, the ship came into the harbour at Dover. Then Mrs. Ape, as was her invariable rule, took round the hat and collected nearly two pounds, not counting her own five shillings which she got back from the bar steward. "Salvation doesn't do them the same good if they think it's free," was her favourite axiom.

I I

"HAVE you anything to declare?"

"Wings."

"Have you wore them?"

"Sure."

"That's all right, then."

"Divine Discontent gets all the smiles all the time," complained Fortitude to Prudence. "Golly, but it's good to be on dry land."

Unsteadily, but with renewed hope, the passengers had disembarked.

Father Rothschild fluttered a diplomatic *laissez-passer* and disappeared in the large car that had been sent to meet him. The others were jostling one another with their luggage, trying to attract the Customs officers and longing for a cup of tea.

"I got half a dozen of the best stowed away," confided the journalist. "They're generally pretty easy after a bad crossing." And sure enough he was soon settled in the corner of a first-class carriage (for the paper was, of course, paying his expenses) with his luggage safely chalked in the van.

It was some time before Adam could get attended to.

"I've nothing but some very old clothes and some books," he said.

But here he showed himself deficient in tact, for the man's casual air disappeared in a flash.

"Books, eh?" he said. "And what sort of books, may I ask?"

"Look for yourself."

"Thank *you*, that's what I mean to do. *Books*, indeed."

Adam wearily unstrapped and unlocked his suitcase.

"Yes," said the Customs officer menacingly, as though his worst suspicions had been confirmed, "I should just about say you had got some books."

One by one he took the books out and piled them on the counter. A copy of Dante's *Purgatorio* excited his especial disgust.

"French, eh?" he said. "I guessed as much, and pretty dirty, too, I shouldn't wonder. Now just you wait while I look up these here *books*" — how he said it! — "in my list. Particularly against books the Home Secretary is. If we can't stamp out literature in the country, we can at least stop its being brought in from outside. That's what he said the other day in Parliament, and I says 'Hear, hear. . . .' Hullo, hullo, what's this, may I ask?"

Gingerly, as though it might at any moment explode, he produced and laid on the counter a large pile of typescript.

"That's a book, too," said Adam. "One I've just written. It is my memoirs."

"Ho, it is, is it? Well, I'll take that along, too, to the chief. You better come too."

"But I've got to catch the train."

"You come along. There's worse things than missing trains," he hinted darkly.

They went together into an inner office, the walls of which were lined with contraband pornography and strange instruments, whose purpose Adam could not guess. From the next room came the shrieks and yells of poor Miss Runcible, who had been mistaken for a well-known jewel smuggler, and was being stripped to the skin by two terrific wardresses.

"Now then, what's this about books?" said the chief.

With the help of a printed list, which began "Aristotle, Works of (Illustrated)," they went through Adam's books, laboriously, one at a time, spelling out the titles.

Miss Runcible came through the office, working hard with lipstick and compact.

"Adam, darling, I never saw you on the boat," she said. "My dear, I can't *tell* you the *things* that have been happening to me in there. The way they looked . . . too, too shaming. Positively surgical, my dear, and *such* wicked old women, just like *Dowagers*, my dear. As soon as I get to London I shall just ring up every Cabinet Minister and *all* the newspapers and give them all the most shy-making details."

The chief was at this time engrossed in Adam's memoirs, giving vent at intervals to a sinister chuckling sound that was partly triumphant and partly derisive, but in the main genuinely appreciative.

"Coo, Bert," he said. "Look at this; that's rich, ain't it?"

Presently he collected the sheets, tied them together and put them on one side.

"Well, see here," he said. "You can take these books on architecture and the dictionary, and I don't mind stretching a point for once and letting you have the history books too. But this book on economics comes under Subversive Propaganda. That you leaves behind. And this here *Purgatorio* doesn't look right to me, so that stays behind, pending enquiries. But as for this autobiography, that's just downright dirt, and we burns that straight away, see."

"But good heavens, there isn't a word in the book — you must be misinterpreting it."

"Not so much of it. I know dirt when I sees it or I shouldn't be where I am to-day."

"But do you realise my whole livelihood depends on this book?"

"And *my* livelihood depends on stopping works like this coming into the country. Now 'ook it quick if you don't want a police-court case."

"Adam, angel, don't fuss or we shall miss the train."

Miss Runcible took his arm and led him back to the station and told him all about a lovely party that was going to happen that night.

"Fanny, surely that is Agatha Runcible, poor Viola Chasm's daughter?"

"I wonder Viola allows her to go about like that. If she were my daughter . . ."

"*Your* daughter, Fanny . . ."

"Kitty, that was not kind."

"My dear, I only meant . . . have you, by the way, heard of her lately?"

"The last we heard was worse than anything, Kitty. She has left Buenos Aires. I am afraid she has severed her connection with Lady Metroland altogether. They think that she is in some kind of touring company."

"Darling, I'm sorry. I should never have mentioned it, but whenever I see Agatha Runcible I can't help thinking . . . girls seem to know so much nowadays. We had to learn everything for ourselves, didn't we, Fanny, and it took so long. If I'd had Agatha Runcible's chances . . . Who is the young man with her?"

"I don't know, and, frankly, I don't think, do you? . . . He has that self-contained look."

"He has very nice eyes. And he moves well."

"I daresay when it came to the point . . . Still, as I say, if I had had Agatha Runcible's advantages . . ."

"What are you looking for, darling?"

"Why, darling, such an extraordinary thing. Here *is* the sal volatile next to my brushes all the time."

"Fanny, how awful of me, if I'd only known . . ."

"I daresay there must have been another bottle you saw on the dressing-table, sweetest. Perhaps the maid put it there. You never know at the Lotti, do you?"

"Fanny, forgive me . . ."

"But, dearest, what is there to forgive? After all, you *did see* another bottle, didn't you, Kitty darling?"

"Why, look, there's Miles."

"Miles?"

"Your son, darling. My nephew, you know."

"*Miles.* Do you know, Kitty, I believe it is. He never comes to see me now, the naughty boy."

"My dear, he looks terribly *tapette*."

"Darling, I know. It is a great grief to me. Only I try not to think about it too much — he had so little chance with poor Throbbing what he was."

"The sins of the fathers, Fanny . . ."

Somewhere not far from Maidstone Mr. Outrage became fully conscious. Opposite him in the carriage the two detectives slept, their bowler hats jammed forwards on their foreheads, their mouths open, their huge red hands lying limply in their laps. Rain beat on the windows; the carriage was intensely cold and smelt of stale tobacco. Inside there were advertisements of horrible picturesque ruins; outside in the rain were hoardings advertising patent medicines and dog biscuits. "Every Molassine dog cake wags a tale." Mr. Outrage read, and the train repeated over and over again, "Right Honourable gent, Right Honourable gent, Right Honourable gentleman, Right Honourable gent . . ."

Adam got into the carriage with the Younger Set. They still looked a bit queer, but they cheered up wonderfully when they heard about Miss Runcible's outrageous treatment at the hands of the Customs officers.

"*Well,*" they said. "*Well!* how too, too shaming, Agatha, darling," they said. "How devastating, how unpoliceman-like, how goat-like, how sick-making, how too, too awful." And then they began talking about Archie Schwert's party that night.

"Who's Archie Schwert?" asked Adam.

"Oh, he's someone new since you went away. The *most* bogus man. Miles discovered him, and since then he's been climbing and climbing and *climbing,* my dear, till he hardly knows us. He's rather sweet really, only too terribly common, poor darling. He lives at the Ritz, and I think that's rather grand, don't you?"

"Is he giving his party there?"

"My dear, of course not. In Edward Throbbing's house. He's Miles's brother, you know, only he's frightfully dim and political, and doesn't know anybody. He got ill and went to Kenya or somewhere and left his perfectly sheepish house in Hertford Street, so we've all gone to live there. You'd better come, too. The caretakers didn't like it a bit at first, but we gave them drinks and things, and now they're simply thrilled to the marrow about it and spend all their time cutting out 'bits,' my dear, from the papers about our goings on.

"One awful thing is we haven't got a car. Miles broke it, Edward's I mean, and we simply can't afford to get it mended, so I think we shall have to move soon. Everything's getting rather broken up, too, and dirty, if you know what I mean. Because, you see there aren't any servants only the butler and his wife and they are always tight now. So demoralising. Mary Mouse has been a perfect angel, and sent us great hampers of caviare and things. . . . She's paying for Archie's party tonight, of course."

"Do you know, I rather think I'm going to be sick again?"

"Oh, Miles!"

(Oh, Bright Young People!)

Packed all together in a second-class carriage the angels were late in recovering their good humour.

"She's taken Prudence off in her car again," said Divine Discontent, who once, for one delirious fortnight, had been Mrs. Ape's favourite girl. "Can't see what she sees in her. What's London like, Fortitude? I never been there but once."

"Just exactly heaven. Shops and all."

"What are the men like, Fortitude?"

"Say, don't you never think of nothing but *men*, Chastity?"

"I should say I do. I was only asking."

"Well, they ain't much to look at, not after the shops. But they has their uses."

"Say, did you hear that? You're a cute one, Fortitude. Did you hear what Fortitude said, she said 'they have their uses.' "

"What, shops?"

"No, silly, men."

"*Men.* That's a good one, I should say."

Presently the train arrived at Victoria, and all these passengers were scattered all over London.

Adam left his bag at Shepheard's Hotel, and drove straight to Henrietta Street to see his publishers. It was nearly closing time, so that most of the staff had packed up and gone home, but by good fortune Mr. Sam Benfleet, the junior director with whom Adam always did his business, was still in his room correcting proofs for one of his women novelists. He was a competent young man, with a restrained elegance of appearance (the stenographer always trembled slightly when she brought him his cup of tea).

"No, she can't print that," he kept saying, endorsing one after another of the printer's protests. "No, damn it, she can't print *that*. She'll have us all in prison." For it was one of his most exacting duties to "ginger up" the more reticent of the manuscripts submitted and "tone down" the more "outspoken" until he had reduced them all to the acceptable moral standard of his day.

He greeted Adam with the utmost cordiality.

"Well, well, Adam, how are you? This is nice. Sit down. Have a cigarette. What a day to arrive in London. Did you have a good crossing?"

"Not too good."

"I say, I *am* sorry. Nothing so beastly as a beastly crossing, is there? Why don't you come round to dinner at Wimpole Street tonight? I've got some rather nice Americans coming. Where are you staying?"

"At Shepheard's — Lottie Crump's."

"Well, that's always fun. I've been trying to get an autobiography out of Lottie for ten years. And that reminds me. You're bringing us your manuscript, aren't you? Old Rampole was asking about it only the other day. It's a week overdue, you know. I hope you've liked the preliminary notices we've sent out. We've fixed the day of publication for the second week in December, so as to give it a fortnight's run before Johnnie Hoop's autobiography. That's going to be a seller. Sails a bit near the wind in places. We had to cut out some things — you know what old Rampole is. Johnnie didn't like it a bit. But I'm looking forward terribly to reading yours."

"Well, Sam, rather an awful thing happened about that . . ."

"I say, I hope you're not going to say it's not finished. The date on the contract, you know . . ."

"Oh, it's finished all right. Burnt."

"Burnt?"

"Burnt."

"What an awful thing. I hope you are insured."

Adam explained the circumstances of the destruction of his autobiography. There was a longish pause while Sam Benfleet thought.

"What worries me is how are we going to make that sound convincing to old Rampole."

"I should think it sounded convincing enough."

"You don't know old Rampole. It's sometimes very difficult for me, Adam, working under him. Now if I had my own way I'd say, 'Take your own time. Start again. Don't worry . . .' But there's old Rampole. He's a devil for contracts, you know, and you did *say*, didn't you . . . ? It's all very difficult. You know, I wish it hadn't happened."

"So do I, oddly enough," said Adam.

"There's another difficulty. You've had an advance already, haven't you? Fifty pounds, wasn't it? Well, you know, *that* makes things very difficult. Old Rampole never likes big advances like that to young authors. You know I hate to say it, but I can't help feeling that the best thing would be for you to repay the advance — plus interest, of course, old Rampole would insist on that — and cancel the contract. Then if you ever thought of rewriting the book, well, of course, we should be delighted to consider it. I suppose that, well, I mean it *would* be quite *convenient*, and all that, to repay the advance?"

"Not only inconvenient, but impossible," said Adam in no particular manner.

There was another pause.

"Deuced awkward," said Sam Benfleet. "It's a shame the way the Customs House officers are allowed to take the law into their own hands. Quite ignorant men, too. Liberty of the subject, I mean, and all that. I tell you what we'll do. We'll start a correspondence about it in the *New Statesman*. . . . It is all so deuced awkward. But I think I can see a way out. I suppose you could get the book rewritten in time for the Spring List? Well, we'll cancel the contract and forget all about the advance. No, no, my dear fellow, don't thank me. If only I was alone here I'd be doing that kind of thing all day. Now instead we'll have a new contract. It won't be quite so good as the last, I'm afraid. Old Rampole wouldn't stand for that. I'll tell you what, we'll give you our standard first-novel contract. I've got a printed form here. It won't take a minute to fill up. Just sign here."

"May I just see the terms?"

"Of course, my dear fellow. They look a bit hard at first, I know, but it's our usual form. We made a very special case for you, you know. It's very simple. No royalty on the first two thousand, then a royalty of two and a half per cent, rising to five per cent on the tenth thousand. We retain serial, cinema, dramatic, American, colonial and translation rights, of course. And, of course, an option on your next twelve books on the same terms. It's a very straightforward arrangement really. Doesn't leave room for any of the disputes which embitter the relations of author and publisher. Most of our authors are working on a contract like that. . . . Splendid. Now don't you bother any more about that advance. I understand *perfectly*, and I'll square old Rampole somehow, even if it comes out of my director's fees."

"Square old Rampole," repeated Mr. Benfleet thoughtfully as Adam went downstairs. It was fortunate, he reflected, that none of the authors ever came across the senior partner, that benign old gentleman, who once a week drove up to board meetings from the country, whose chief interest in the business was confined to the progress of a little book of his own about bee-keeping, which they had published twenty years ago and, though he did not know it, allowed long ago to drop out of print. He often wondered in his uneasy moments what he would find to say when Rampole died.

It was about now that Adam remembered that he was engaged to be married. The name of his young lady was Nina Blount. So he went into a tube station to a telephone-box, which smelt rather nasty, and rang her up.

"Hullo."

"Hullo."

"May I speak to Miss Blount, please?"

"I'll just see if she's in," said Miss Blount's voice. "Who's speaking, please?" She was always rather snobbish about this fiction of having someone to answer the telephone.

"Mr. Fenwick-Symes."

"Oh."

"Adam, you know. How are you, Nina?"

"Well, I've got rather a pain just at present."

"Poor Nina. Shall I come round and see you?"

"No, don't do that, darling, because I'm just going to have a bath. Why don't we dine together?"

"Well, I asked Agatha Runcible to dinner."

"Why?"

"She'd just had all her clothes taken off by some sailors."

"Yes, I know, it's all in the evening paper to-night. . . . Well, I'll tell you what. Let's meet at Archie Schwert's party. Are you going?"

"I rather said I would."

"That's all right, then. Don't dress up. No one will, except Archie."

"Oh, I say. Nina, there's one thing — I don't think I shall be able to marry you after all."

"Oh, *Adam,* you are a bore. Why not?"

"They burnt my book."

"Beasts. Who did?"

"I'll tell you about it to-night."

"Yes, *do.* Good-bye, darling."

"Good-bye, my sweet."

He hung up the receiver and left the telephone-box. People had crowded into the Underground station for shelter from the rain, and were shaking their umbrellas and reading their evening papers. Adam could see the headlines over their shoulders.

PEER'S DAUGHTER'S DOVER ORDEAL
SERIOUS ALLEGATIONS BY SOCIETY
BEAUTY
HON. A. RUNCIBLE SAYS "TOO
SHAMING"

"Poor pretty," said an indignant old woman at his elbow. "Disgraceful, I calls it. And such a good sweet face. I see her picture in the papers only yesterday. Nasty prying minds. That's what they got. And her poor father and all. Look, Jane, there's a piece about him, too.

'Interviewed at the Carlton Club this evening, Lord Chasm,' that's her dad, 'refused to make a definite statement. "The matter shall not be allowed to rest here," he said.' *And* quite right, too, I says. You know I feels about that girl just as though it was me own daughter. Seeing her picture so often and our Sarah having done the back stairs, Tuesdays, at them flats where her aunt used to live — the one as had that 'orrible divorce last year."

Adam bought a paper. He had just ten shillings left in the world. It was too wet to walk, so he took a very crowded tube train to Dover Street and hurried across in the rain to Shepheard's Hotel (which, for the purposes of the narrative, may be assumed to stand at the corner of Hay Hill).

III

LOTTIE CRUMP, proprietress of Shepheard's Hotel, Dover Street, attended invariably by two Cairn terriers, is a happy reminder to us that the splendours of the Edwardian era were not entirely confined to Lady Anchorage or Mrs. Blackwater. She is a fine figure of a woman, singularly unscathed by any sort of misfortune and superbly oblivious of those changes in the social order which agitate the more observant *grandes dames* of her period. When the war broke out she took down the signed photograph of the Kaiser and, with some solemnity, hung it in the men-servants' lavatory; it was her one combative action; since then she has had her worries — income-tax forms and drink restrictions and young men whose fathers she used to know, who give her bad cheques, but these have been soon forgotten; one can go to Shepheard's parched with modernity any day, if Lottie likes one's face, and still draw up, cool and uncontaminated, great, healing draughts from the well of Edwardian certainty.

Shepheard's has a plain, neatly pointed brick front and large, plain doorway. Inside it is like a country house. Lottie is a great one for sales, and likes, whenever one of the great houses of her day is being sold up, to take away something for old times' sake. There is a good deal too much furniture at Shepheard's, some of it rare, some of it hideous beyond description; there is plenty of red plush and red morocco and innumerable wedding presents of the 'eighties; in particular many of those massive, mechanical devices covered with crests and monograms, and associated in some way with cigars. It is the sort of house in which one expects to find croquet mallets and polo sticks in the bathroom, and children's toys at the bottom of one's chest of drawers, and an estate map and an archery target — exuding straw — and a bicycle and one of those walking-sticks which turn into saws, somewhere in passages, between baize doors, smelling of damp. (As a matter of fact, all you are likely to find in your room at Lottie's is an empty champagne bottle or two and a crumpled camisole.)

The servants, like the furniture, are old and have seen aristocratic service. Doge, the head waiter, who is hard of hearing, partially blind, and tortured with gout, was once a Rothschild's butler. He has, in fact, on more than one occasion in Father Rothschild's youth, *dandled* him on his knee, when he came with his father (at one time the fifteenth richest man in the world) to visit his still richer cousins, but it would be unlike him to pretend that he ever really liked the embryo Jesuit who was "too clever by half," given to asking extraordinary questions, and endowed with a penetrating acumen in the detection of falsehood and exaggeration.

Besides Doge, there are innumerable old housemaids always trotting about with cans of hot water and clean towels. There is also a young Italian who does most of the work and gets horribly insulted by Lottie, who once caught him powdering his nose, and will not let him forget it. Indeed, it is one of the few facts in Lottie's recent experience that seems always accessible.

Lottie's parlour, in which most of the life of Shepheard's centres, contains a comprehensive collection of signed photographs. Most of the male members of the royal families of Europe are represented (except the ex-Emperor of Germany, who has not been reinstated, although there was a distinct return of sentiment towards him on the occasion of his second marriage). There are photographs of young men on horses riding in steeple-chases, of elderly men leading in the winners of "classic" races, of horses alone and of young men alone, dressed in tight white collars or in the uniform of the Brigade of Guards. There are caricatures by "Spy," and photographs cut from illustrated papers, many of them with brief obituary notices, "killed in action." There are photographs of yachts in full sail and of elderly men in yachting caps; there are some terribly funny pictures of the earliest kind of motor car. There are very few writers or painters and no actors, for Lottie is true to the sound old snobbery of pounds sterling and strawberry leaves.

Lottie was standing in the hall abusing the Italian waiter when Adam arrived.

"Well," she said, "you are a stranger. Come along in. We were just thinking about having a little drink. You'll find a lot of your friends here."

She led Adam into the parlour, where they found several men, none of whom Adam had ever seen before.

"You all know Lord Thingummy, don't you?" said Lottie.

"Mr. Symes," said Adam.

"Yes, dear, that's what I said. Bless you, I knew you before you were born. How's your father? Not dead, is he?"

"Yes, I'm afraid he is."

"Well, I never. I could tell you some things about him. Now let me introduce you — that's Mr. What's-his-name, you remember him, don't you? And over there in the corner, that's the Major, and there's Mr. What-d'you-call-him, and that's an American, and there's the King of Ruritania."

"Alas, no longer," said a sad, bearded man.

"Poor chap," said Lottie Crump, who always had a weak spot for royalty even when deposed. "It's a shame. They gave him the boot after the war. Hasn't got a penny. Not that he ever did have much. His wife's locked up in a looney house, too."

"Poor Maria Cristina. It is true how Mrs. Crump says. Her brains, they are quite gone out. All the time she thinks everyone is a bomb."

"It's perfectly true, poor old girl," said Lottie with relish. "I drove the King down Saturday to see her . . . (I won't have him travelling third class.) It fair brought tears to my eyes. Kept skipping about all the time, she did, dodging. Thought they were throwing things at her."

"It is one strange thing, too," said the King. "All my family they have bombs thrown at them, but the Queen, never. My poor Uncle Joseph he blow all to bits one night at the opera, and my sister she find three bombs in her bed. But my wife, never. But one day her maid is brushing her hair before dinner, and she said, 'Madam,' she said, 'the cook has had lesson from the cook at the French Legation' — the food at my home was not what you call *chic*. One day it was mutton hot, then mutton cold, then the same mutton hot again, but less nicer, not *chic*, you understand me — 'he has had lessons from the French cook,' the maid say, 'and he has made one big bomb as a surprise for your dinner-party to-night for the Swedish Minister.' Then the poor

Queen say 'Oh,' like so, and since then always her poor brains has was all no-how."

The ex-King of Ruritania sighed heavily and lit a cigar.

"Well," said Lottie, brushing aside a tear, "what about a little drink? Here, you over there, your Honour Judge What's-your-name, how about a drink for the gentlemen?"

The American, who, like all the listeners, had been profoundly moved by the ex-King's recitation, roused himself to bow and say, "I shall esteem it a great honour if His Majesty and yourself, Mrs. Crump, and these other good gentlemen . . ."

"That's the way," said Lottie. "Hi, there, where's my Fairy Prince? Powdering hisself again, I suppose. Come here, Nancy, and put away the beauty cream."

In came the waiter.

"Bottle of wine," said Lottie, "with Judge Thingummy there." (Unless specified in detail, all drinks are champagne in Lottie's parlour. There is also a mysterious game played with dice which always ends with someone giving a bottle of wine to everyone in the room, but Lottie has an equitable soul and she generally sees to it, in making up the bills, that the richest people pay for everything.)

After the third or fourth bottle of wine Lottie said, "Who d'you think we've got dining upstairs to-night? *Prime Minister.*"

"Me, I have never liked Prime Ministers. They talk and talk and then they talk more. 'Sir, you must sign that.' 'Sir, you must go here and there.' 'Sir, you must do up that button before you give audience to the black plenipotentiary from Liberia.' Pah! After the war my people give me the bird, yes, but they throw my Prime Minister out of the window, bump right bang on the floor. Ha, ha."

"He ain't alone either," said Lottie with a terrific wink.

"What, Sir James Brown?" said the Major, shocked in spite of himself. "I don't believe it."

"No, name of Outrage."

"He's not Prime Minister."

"Yes, he is. I saw it in the paper."

"No, he's not. He went out of office last week."

"Well I never. How they keep changing. I've no patience with it. Doge. Doge. What's the Prime Minister's name?"

"Beg pardon, mum."

"What's the name of the Prime Minister?"

"Not to-night, I don't think, mum, not as I've been informed anyway."

"What's the name of the Prime Minister, you stupid old man?"

"Oh, I beg your pardon, mum. I didn't quite hear you. Sir James Brown, mum, Bart. A very nice gentleman, so I've been told. Conservative, I've heard said. Gloucestershire they come from, I think."

"There, what did I say?" said Lottie triumphantly.

"It is one very extraordinary thing, your British Constitution," said the ex-King of Ruritania. "All the time when I was young they taught me nothing but British Constitution. My tutor had been a master at your Eton school. And now when I come to England always there is a different Prime Minister and no one knows which is which."

"Oh, sir," said the Major, "that's because of the Liberal party."

"Liberals? Yes. We, too, had Liberals. I tell you something now, I had a gold fountain-pen. My godfather, the good Archduke of Austria, give me one gold fountain-pen with eagles on him. I loved my gold fountain-pen." Tears stood in the King's eyes. Champagne was a rare luxury to him now. "I loved very well my pen with the little eagles. And one day there was a Liberal minister. A Count Tampen, one man, Mrs. Crump, of exceedingly evilness. He come to talk to me and he stood at my little escritoire and he thump and talk too much about somethings I not understand, and when he go — where was my gold fountain-pen with the eagles — gone too."

"Poor old King," said Lottie. "I tell you what. You have another drink."

". . . Esteem it a great honour," said the American, "if your Majesty and these gentlemen and Mrs. Crump . . ."

"Doge, tell my little love-bird to come hopping in . . . you there, Judge wants another bottle of wine."

". . . Should honour it a great esteem . . . esteem it a great honour if Mrs. Majesty, and these gentlemen and His Crump . . ."

"That's all right, Judge. Another bottle coming."

". . . Should esteem it a great Crump if his honour and these Majesties and Mrs. Gentlemen . . ."

"Yes, yes, that's all right, Judge. Don't let him fall down, boys. Bless me, how these Americans do drink."

". . . I should Crump it a great Majesty if Mrs. Esteem . . ."

And his Honour Judge Skimp of the Federal High Court began to laugh rather a lot. (It must be remembered in all these people's favour that none of them had yet dined.)

Now there was a very bland, natty, moustachioed young man sitting there who had been drinking away quietly in the corner without talking to anyone except for an occasional "Cheerioh" to Judge Skimp. Suddenly he got up and said:

"Bet-you-can't-do-this."

He put three halfpennies on the table, moved them about very deliberately for a bit, and then looked up with an expression of pride. "Only touched each halfpenny five times, and changed their positions twice," he said. "Do-it-again if you like."

"Well, isn't he a clever boy?" said Lottie. "Wherever did they teach you that?"

"Chap-in-a-train showed me," he said.

"It didn't look very hard," said Adam.

"Just-you-try. Bet-you-anything-you-like you can't do it."

"How much will you bet?" Lottie loved this kind of thing.

"Anything-you-like. Five hundred pounds."

"Go on," said Lottie. "You do it. He's got lots of money."

"All right," said Adam.

He took the halfpennies and moved them about just as the young man had done. When he finished he said, "How's that?"

"Well, I'm jiggered," said the young man. "Never saw anyone do it like that before. I've won a lot of money this week with that trick. Here you are." And he took out a note-case and gave Adam a five-hundred-pound note. Then he sat down in his corner again.

"Well," said Lottie with approval, "that's sporting. Give the boys a drink for that."

So they all had another drink.

Presently the young man stood up again.

"Toss you double-or-quits," he said. "Best-out-of-three."

"All right," said Adam.

They tossed twice and Adam won both times.

"Well, I'm jiggered," said the young man, handing over another note. "You are a lucky chap."

"He's got pots of money," said Lottie. "A thousand pounds is nothing to him."

She liked to feel like that about all her guests. Actually in this young man's case she was wrong. He happened to have all that money in his pocket because he had just sold out his few remaining securities to buy a new motor car. So next day he bought a second-hand motor bicycle instead.

Adam felt a little dizzy, so he had another drink.

"D'you mind if I telephone?" he said.

He rang up Nina Blount.

"Is that Nina?"

"Adam dear, you're tight already."

"How d'you know?"

"I can hear it. What is it? I'm just going out to dinner."

"I just rang up to say that it's all right about our getting married. I've got a thousand pounds."

"Oh, good. How?"

"I'll tell you when we meet. Where are we dining?"

"Ritz. Archie. Darling, I *am* glad about our getting married."

"So am I. But don't let's get intense about it."

"I wasn't, and anyway you're tight."

He went back to the parlour. Miss Runcible had arrived and was standing in the hall very much dressed up.

"Who's that tart?" asked Lottie.

"That's not a tart, Lottie, that's Agatha Runcible."

"Looks like a tart. How do you do, my dear, come in. We're just thinking of having a little drink. You know everyone here, of course, don't you? That's the King with the beard. . . . No, deary, the King of Ruritania. You didn't mind my taking you for a tart, did you, dear? You look so like one, got up like that. Of course, I can see you aren't now."

"*My dear*," said Miss Runcible, "if you'd seen me this afternoon . . ." and she began to tell Lottie Crump about the Customs House.

"What would you do if you suddenly got a thousand pounds?" Adam asked.

"A thousand *pound*," said the King, his eyes growing dreamy at this absurd vision. "Well, first I should buy a house and a motor car and a yacht and a new pair of gloves, and then I would start one little newspaper in my country to say that I must come back and be the King, and then I don't know what I do, but I have such fun and grandness again."

"But you can't do all that with a thousand pounds, you know, sir."

"No . . . can't I not? . . . not with thousand pound. . . . Oh, well, then I think I buy a gold pen with eagles on him like the Liberals stole."

"I know what I'd do," said the Major. "I'd put it on a horse."

"What horse?"

"I can tell you a likely outsider for the November Handicap. Horse named Indian Runner. It's at twenty to one at present, and the odds are likely to lengthen. Now if you were to put a thousand on him to win and he won, why you'd be rich, wouldn't you?"

"Yes, so I would. How marvellous. D'you know, I think I'll do that. It's a *very* good idea. How can I do it?"

"Just you give me the thousand and I'll arrange it."

"I say, that's awfully nice of you."

"Not at all."

"No, really, I think that's frightfully nice of you. Look, here's the money. Have a drink, won't you?"

"No, you have one with me."

"I said it first."

"Let's both have one, then."

"Wait a minute though, I must go and telephone about this."

He rang up the Ritz and got on to Nina.

"Darling, you do telephone a lot, don't you?"

"Nina, I've something very important to say."

"Yes, darling."

"Nina, have you heard of a horse called Indian Runner?"

"Yes, I think so. Why?"

"What sort of a horse is it?"

"My dear, quite the worst sort of horse. Mary Mouse's mother owns it."

"Not a good horse?"

"No."

"Not likely to win the November Handicap, I mean."

"Quite sure not to. I don't suppose it'll run even. Why?"

"I say, Nina, d'you know I don't think we shall be able to get married after all."

"Why not, my sweet?"

"You see, I've put my thousand pounds on Indian Runner."

"That was silly. Can't you get it back?"

"I gave it to a major."

"What sort of a major?"

"Rather a drunk one. I don't know his name."

"Well I should try and catch him. I must go back and eat now. Good-bye."

But when he got back to Lottie's parlour the Major was gone.

"What major?" said Lottie, when he asked about him. "I never saw a major."

"The one you introduced me to in the corner."

"How d'you know he's a major?"

"You said he was."

"My dear boy, I've never seen him before. Now I come to think of it, he did look like a major, didn't he? But this sweet little girlie here is telling me a story. Go on, my dear. I can hardly bear to hear it, it's so wicked."

While Miss Runcible finished her story (which began to sound each time she told it more and more like the most lubricious kind of anti-Turkish propaganda) the ex-King of Ruritania told Adam about a major *he* had known, who had come from Prussia to reorganize the Ruritanian Army. He had disappeared south, taking with him all the mess plate of the Royal Guard, and the Lord Chamberlain's wife, and a valuable pair of candle-sticks from the Chapel Royal.

By the time Miss Runcible had finished, Lottie was in a high state of indignation.

"The very idea of it," she said. "The dirty hounds. And I used to know your poor father, too, before you were born *or* thought of. I'll talk to the Prime Minister about this," she said, taking up the telephone. "Give me Outrage," she said to the exchange boy. "He's up in No. 12 with a Japanese."

"Outrage isn't Prime Minister, Lottie."

"Of course he is. Didn't Doge say so? . . . Hullo, is that Outrage? This is Lottie. A fine chap you are, I don't think. Tearing the clothes off the back of a poor innocent girl."

Lottie prattled on.

Mr. Outrage had finished dinner, and, as a matter of fact, the phrasing of this accusation was not wholly inappropriate to his mood. It was some minutes before he began to realise that all this talk was only about Miss Runcible. By that time Lottie's flow of invective had come to an end, but she finished finely.

"Outrage your name, and Outrage your nature," she said, banging down the receiver. "And that's what I think of *him*. Now how about a little drink?"

But her party was breaking up. The Major was gone. Judge Skimp was sleeping, his fine white hair in an ash-tray. Adam and Miss Runcible were talking about where they would dine. Soon only the King remained. He gave her his arm with a grace he had acquired many years ago; far away in his sunny little palace, under a great chandelier which scattered with stars of light, like stones from a broken necklace, a crimson carpet woven with a pattern of crowned ciphers.

So Lottie and the King went in to dinner together.

Upstairs in No. 12, which is a suite of notable grandeur, Mr. Outrage was sliding back down the path of self-confidence he had so laboriously climbed. He really would have brought matters to a crisis if it had not been for that telephone, he told himself, but now the Baroness was saying she was sure he was busy, must be wanting her to go: would he order her car.

It was so difficult. For a European the implications of an invitation to dinner *tête-à-tête* in a private room at Shepheard's were definitively clear. Her acceptance on the first night of his return to England had thrown him into a flutter of expectation. But all through dinner she had been so self-possessed, so supremely social. Yet, surely, just before the telephone rang, surely then, when they left the table and moved to the fire, there had been *something* in the atmosphere. But you never knew with Orientals. He clutched his knees and said in a voice which sounded very extraordinary to him, must she go, it was lovely after a fortnight, and then, desperately, he had thought of her in Paris such a lot. (Oh, for words, words! That massed treasury of speech that was his to squander at will, to send bowling and spinning in golden pieces over the floor of the House of Commons; that glorious largesse of vocables he cast far and wide, in ringing handfuls about his constituency!)

The little Baroness Yoshiwara, her golden hands clasped in the lap of her golden Paquin frock, sat where she had been sent, more puzzled than Mr. Outrage, waiting for orders. What did the clever Englishman want? If he was busy with his telephone, why did he not send her away; tell her another time to come: if he wanted to be loved, why did he not tell her to come over to him? Why did he not pick her out of her red plush chair and sit her on his knee? Was she, perhaps, looking ugly to-night? She had thought not. It was so hard to know what these Occidentals wanted.

Then the telephone rang again.

"Will you hold on a minute? Father Rothschild wants to speak to you," said a voice. ". . . Is that you, Outrage? Will you be good enough to come round and see me as soon as you can? There are several things which I must discuss with you."

"Really, Rothschild . . . I don't see why I should. I have a guest."

"The Baroness had better return immediately. The waiter who brought you your coffee has a brother at the Japanese Embassy."

"Good God, has he? But why don't you go and worry Brown? He's P.M., you know, not me."

"You will be in office to-morrow. . . . As soon as possible, please, at my usual address."

"Oh, all right."

"Why, of course."

FASTER, FASTER

The second extract from Vile Bodies *is drawn from the conclud-ing section of the novel. Most of the protagonists have been introduced to the reader in the preceding extract. The others are:*

Miles Malpractice	*One of the Bright Young People. He has just become Mr. Chatterbox, the gossip columnist of the Daily Excess.*
"Ginger"	*Captain "Ginger" Littlejohn, a rich young man who is competing with Adam Fenwick-Symes for Nina Blount.*
Colonel Blount	*Nina's father, a wildly absent-minded eccen-tric. His passion is the cinema, and he has taken part in the making of a preposterous film on his estate in Buckinghamshire.*

Adam Fenwick-Symes, the Honorable Agatha Runcible, Miles Malpractice and Archie Schwert have gone to the motor races. Miles's latest boy friend is one of the drivers.

MILES's friend, even had it been possible in the uproar, seemed in-disposed to talk. He waved abstractedly and went on with his listen-ing. Presently he came across and shouted:

"Sorry I can't spare a moment, I'll see you in the pits. I've got you some brassards."

"My dear, what *can* that be?"

He handed them each a strip of white linen, terminating in tape.

"For your arms," he shouted. "You can't get into the pits without them."

"My dear, what bliss! Fancy them having pits."

Then they tied on their brassards. Miss Runcible's said, "SPARE DRIVER"; Adam's, "DEPOT STAFF"; Miles's, "SPARE MECHANIC"; and Archie's, "OWNER'S REPRESENTATIVE."

Up till now the little boys round the rope had been sceptical of the importance of Miss Runcible and her friends, but as soon as they saw these badges of rank they pressed forward with their autograph books. Archie signed them all with the utmost complaisance, and even drew a slightly unsuitable picture in one of them. Then they drove away in Archie's car.

The race was not due to start until noon, but any indecision which they may have felt about the employment of the next few hours was settled for them by the local police, who were engaged in directing all traffic, irrespective of its particular inclinations, on the road to the course. No pains had been spared about this point of organisation; several days before, the Chief Constable had issued a little route map which was to be memorised by all constables on point duty, and so well had they learned their lesson that from early that morning until late in the afternoon no vehicle approaching the town from any direction escaped being drawn into that broad circuit marked by the arrows and dotted line A–B which led to the temporary car park behind the Grand Stand. (Many doctors, thus diverted, spent an enjoyable day without apparent prejudice to their patients.)

The advance of the spectators had already assumed the form of a slow and unbroken stream. Some came on foot from the railway station, carrying sandwiches and camp stools; some on tandem bicycles; some in "runabouts" or motor cycle side-car combinations, but most were in modestly priced motor cars. Their clothes and demeanour proclaimed them as belonging to the middle rank; a few brought portable wireless sets with them and other evidence of gaiety, but the general air of the procession was one of sobriety and purpose. This was no Derby day holiday-making; they had not snatched a day from office to squander it among gipsies and roundabouts and thimble-and-pea men. They were there for the race. As they crawled along on bottom gear in a fog of exhaust gas, they discussed the technicalities of motor-car design and the possibilities of bloodshed, and studied their maps of the course to pick out the most dangerous corners.

The detour planned by the Chief Constable was a long one, lined with bungalows and converted railway carriages. Banners floated over it between the telegraph posts, mostly advertising the *London Despatch*, which was organising the race and paying for the victor's trophy — a silver gilt figure of odious design, symbolizing Fame embracing Speed. (This at the moment was under careful guard in the stewards' room, for the year before it had been stolen on the eve of the race by the official timekeeper, who pawned it for a ridiculously small sum in

Manchester, and was subsequently deprived of his position and sent to jail.) Other advertisements proclaimed the superiorities of various sorts of petrol and sparking plugs, while some said "£100 FOR LOSS OF LIMB. INSURE TODAY." There was an elderly man walking among the motor cars with a blue and white banner inscribed, "WITHOUT SHEDDING OF BLOOD IS NO REMISSION OF SIN," while a smartly dressed young man was doing a brisk trade in bogus tickets for the Grand Stand.

Adam sat in the back of the car with Miles, who was clearly put out about his friend's lack of cordiality. "What I can't make out," he said, "is why we came to this beastly place at all. I suppose I ought to be thinking of something to write for the *Excess*. I *know* this is just going to be the most dreary day we've ever spent."

Adam felt inclined to agree. Suddenly he became aware that someone was trying to attract his attention.

"There's an awful man shouting 'Hi' at you," said Miles. "My dear, *your friends.*"

Adam turned and saw not three yards away, separated from him by a young woman riding a push-bicycle in khaki shorts, her companion, who bore a knapsack on his shoulders, and a small boy selling programmes, the long-sought figure of the drunk Major. He looked sober enough this morning, dressed in a bowler hat and Burberry, and he was waving frantically to Adam from the dicky of a coupé car.

"Hi!" cried the drunk Major. "Hi! I've been looking for you everywhere."

"I've been looking for you," shouted Adam. "I want some money."*

"Can't hear — what do you want?"

"Money."

"It's no good — these infernal things make too much noise. What's your name? Lottie had forgotten."

"Adam Symes."

"Can't hear."

The line of traffic, creeping forward yard by yard, had at last reached the point B on the Chief Constable's map, where the dotted lines diverged. A policeman stood at the crossing directing the cars right and left, some to the parking place behind the Grand Stand, others to the mound above the pits. Archie turned off to the left. The drunk Major's car accelerated and swept away to the right.

---

*The horse on which the drunk Major promised to bet Adam's thousand pounds has won the November Handicap at odds of thirty-five to one. — Ed.

"I must know your name," he cried. All the drivers seemed to choose this moment to sound their horns; the woman cyclist at Adam's elbow rang her bell; the male cylist tooted a little horn like a Paris taxi, and the programme boy yelled in his ear, "Official programme — map of the course — all the drivers."

"Adam Symes," he shouted desperately, but the Major threw up his hands in despair and he disappeared in the crowd.

"The way you pick people up . . ." said Miles, startled into admiration.

"The pits" turned out to be a line of booths, built of wood and corrugated iron immediately opposite the Grand Stand. Many of the cars had already arrived and stood at their "pits," surrounded by a knot of mechanics and spectators; they seemed to be already under repair. Busy officials hurried up and down, making entries in their lists. Over their heads a vast loud-speaker was relaying the music of a military band.

The Grand Stand was still fairly empty, but the rest of the course was already lined with people. It stretched up and down hill for a circle of thirteen or fourteen miles, and those who were fortunate enough to own cottages or public houses at the more dangerous corners had covered their roofs with unstable wooden forms, and were selling tickets like very expensive hot cakes. A grass-covered hill rose up sharply behind the pits. On this had been erected a hoarding where a troop of Boy Scouts were preparing to score the laps, passing the time contentedly with ginger beer, toffee, and rough-and-tumble fights. Behind the hoarding was a barbed-wire fence, and behind that again a crowd of spectators and several refreshment tents. A wooden bridge, advertising the *London Despatch,* had been built on the road. At various points officials might be seen attempting to understand each other over a field telephone. Sometimes the band would stop and a voice would announce, "Will Mr. So-and-So kindly report at once to the timekeeper's office"; then the band would go on.

Miss Runcible and her party found their way to the pit numbered 13 and sat on the match-board counter smoking and signing autograph books. An official bore down on them.

"No smoking in the pits, please."

"My dear, I'm terribly sorry. I didn't know."

There were six open churns behind Miss Runcible, four containing petrol and two water. She threw her cigarette over her shoulder, and by a beneficent attention of Providence, which was quite rare in her career, it fell into the water. Had it fallen into the petrol it would probably have been all up with Miss Runcible.

Presently No. 13 appeared. Miles's friend and his mechanic, wearing overalls, crash helmets, and goggles, jumped out, opened the bonnet and began to reconstruct it again.

"They didn't ought to have a No. 13 at all," said the mechanic. "It isn't fair."

Miss Runcible lit another cigarette.

"No smoking in the pits, *please*," said the official.

"My dear, how *awful* of me. I quite forgot."

(This time it fell in the mechanic's luncheon basket and lay smouldering quietly on a leg of chicken until it had burnt itself out.)

Miles's friend began filling up his petrol tank with the help of a very large funnel.

"Listen," he said. "You're not allowed to hand me anything direct, but if Edwards holds up his left hand as we come past the pits, that means we shall be stopping next lap for petrol. So what you've got to do is to fill up a couple of cans and put them on the shelf with the funnel for Edwards to take. If Edwards holds up his right hand . . ." elaborate instructions followed. "You're in charge of the depot," he said to Archie. "D'you think you've got all the signals clear? The race may depend on them, remember."

"What does it mean if I wave the blue flag?"

"That you want me to stop."

"Why should I want you to stop?"

"Well, you might see something wrong — leaking tank or anything like that, or the officials might want the number plate cleaned."

"I think perhaps I won't do anything much about the blue flag. It seems rather too bogus for me."

Miss Runcible lit another cigarette.

"Will you kindly leave the pits if you wish to smoke?" said the official.

"What a damned rude man," said Miss Runcible. "Let's go up to that divine tent and get a drink."

They climbed the hill past the Boy Scouts, found a gate in the wire fence, and eventually reached the refreshment tent. Here an atmosphere of greater geniality prevailed. A profusion of men in plus fours were having "quick ones" before the start. There was no nonsense about not smoking. There was a middle-aged woman sitting on the grass with a bottle of stout and a baby.

"Home from home," said Miss Runcible.

Suddenly the military band stopped and a voice said, "Five minutes to twelve. All drivers and mechanics on the other side of the track, please."

There was a hush all over the course, and the refreshment tent began to empty quickly.

"Darling, we shall miss the start."

"Still, a drink *would* be nice."

So they went into the tent.

"Four whiskies, please," said Archie Schwert.

"You'll miss the start," said the barmaid.

"What a pig that man was," said Miss Runcible. "Even if we weren't suppose to smoke, he might at least have asked us politely."

"My dear, it was only you."

"Well, I think that made it worse."

"Lor', Miss," said the barmaid. "You surely ain't going to miss the start?"

"It's the one thing I want to see more than anything . . . my dear, I believe they're off already."

The sudden roar of sixty high-power engines rose from below. "They *have* started . . . how too shaming." They went to the door of the tent. Part of the road was visible over the heads of the spectators, and they caught a glimpse of the cars running all jammed together like pigs being driven through a gate; one by one they shook themselves free and disappeared round the bend with a high shriek of acceleration.

"They'll be round again in quarter of an hour," said Archie. "Let's have another drink."

"Who was ahead?" asked the barmaid anxiously.

"I couldn't see for certain," said Miss Runcible, "but I'm fairly sure it was No. 13."

"*My!*"

The refreshment tent soon began to fill up again. The general opinion seemed to be that it was going to be a close race between No. 13 and No. 28, a red Omega car, driven by Marino, the Italian "ace."

"Dirtiest driver I ever seen," said one man with relish. "Why, over at Belfast 'e was just tipping 'em all into the ditches, just like winking."

"There's one thing you *can* be sure of. They won't *both* finish."

"It's sheer murder the way that Marino drives — a fair treat to see 'im."

"He's a one all right — a real artist and no mistake about it."

Adam and Miss Runcible and Archie and Miles went back to their pit.

"After all," said Miss Runcible, "the poor sweet may be wanting all sorts of things and signalling away like mad, and no one there to pay any attention to him — so discouraging."

By this time the cars were fairly evenly spread out over the course. They flashed by intermittently with dazzling speed and a shriek; one or two drew into their pits and the drivers leapt out, trembling like leaves, to tinker with the works. One had already come to grief — a large German whose tyre had burst — punctured, some said, by a hireling of Marino's. It had left the road and shot up a tree like a cat chased by a dog. Two little American cars had failed to start; their team worked desperately at them amid derisive comments from the crowd. Suddenly two cars appeared coming down the straight, running abreast within two feet of each other.

"It's No. 13," cried Miss Runcible, really excited at last. "And there's that Italian devil just beside it. Come on, thirteen! Come on!" she cried, dancing in the pit and waving a flag she found at hand. "Come on. Oh! Well done, thirteen."

The cars were gone in a flash and succeeded by others.

"Agatha, darling, you shouldn't have waved the blue flag."

"My dear, how awful. Why not?"

"Well, that means that he's to stop next lap."

"Good God. Did I wave a blue flag?"

"My dear, you know you did."

"*How* shaming. What *am* I to say to him?"

"Let's all go away before he comes back."

"D'you know, I think we'd better. He might be furious, mightn't he? Let's go to the tent and have another drink — don't you think, or don't you?"

So No. 13 pit was again deserted.

"What did I say?" said the mechanic. "The moment I heard we'd drawn this blinkin' number I knew we was in for trouble."

The first person they saw when they reached the refreshment tent was the drunk Major.

"Your boy friend again," said Miles.

"Well, there you are," said the Major. "D'you know I've been chasing you all over London. What have you been doing with yourself all this time?"

"I've been staying at Lottie's."

"Well, she said she'd never heard of you. You see, I don't mind admitting I'd had a few too many that night, and to tell you the truth I woke up with things all rather a blur. Well then I found a thousand pounds in my pocket, and it all came back to me. There'd been a cove at Lottie's who gave me a thousand pounds to put on Indian Runner. Well, as far as I knew, Indian Runner was no good. I didn't want to lose your money for you, but the devil of it was I didn't know you from Adam." ("I think that's a perfect joke," said Miss Runcible.) "And apparently Lottie didn't either. You'd have thought it was easy enough to trace the sort of chap who deals out thousands of pounds to total strangers, but I couldn't find one finger-print."

"Do you mean," said Adam, a sudden delirious hope rising in his heart, "that you've still got my thousand?"

"Not so fast," said the Major. "I'm spinning this yarn. Well, on the day of the race I didn't know what to do. One half of me said, keep the thousand. The chap's bound to turn up some time, and it's his business to do his own punting — the other half said, put it on the favourite for him and give him a run for his money."

"So you put it on the favourite?" Adam's heart felt like lead again.

"No, I didn't. In the end I said, well, the young chap must be frightfully rich. If he likes to throw away his money, it's none of my business, so I planked it all on Indian Runner for you."

"You mean . . ."

"I mean I've got the nice little packet of thirty-five thou. waiting until you condescend to call for it."

"Good heavens . . . look here, have a drink, won't you?"

"That's a thing I never refuse."

"Archie, lend me some money until I get this fortune."

"How much?"

"Enough to buy five bottles of champagne."

"Yes, if you can get them."

The barmaid had a case of champagne at the back of the tent.

("People often feel queer through watching the cars go by so fast — ladies especially," she explained.) So they took a bottle each and sat on the side of the hill and drank to Adam's prosperity.

"Hullo, everybody," said the loud-speaker. "Car No. 28, the Italian Omega, driven by Captain Marino, has just completed the course in twelve minutes one second, lapping at an average speed of 78.3 miles per hour. This is the fastest time yet recorded."

A burst of applause greeted this announcement, but Adam said, "I've rather lost interest in this race."

"Look here, old boy," the Major said when they were well settled down, "I'm in rather a hole. Makes me feel an awful ass, saying so, but the truth is I got my note-case pinched in the crowd. Of course, I've got plenty of small change to see me back to the hotel and they'll take a cheque of mine there, naturally, but the fact is I was keen to make a few bets with some chaps I hardly know. I wonder, old boy, could you possibly lend me a fiver? I can give it to you at the same time as I hand over the thirty-five thousand."

"Why, of course," said Adam. "Archie, led me a fiver, can you?"

"Awfully good of you," said the Major, tucking the notes into his hip pocket. "Would it be all the same if you made it a tenner while we're about it?"

"I'm sorry," said Archie, with a touch of coldness. "I've only just got enough to get home with."

"That's all right, old boy, I understand. Not another word. . . . Well, here's to us all."

"I was on the course at the November Handicap," said Adam. "I thought I saw you."

"It would have saved a lot of fuss if we'd met, wouldn't it? Still, all's well that ends well."

"What an *angelic* man your Major is," said Miss Runcible.

When they had finished their champagne, the Major — now indisputably drink — rose to go.

"Look here, old boy," he said. "I must be toddling along now. Got to see some chaps. Thanks no end for the binge. So jolly having met you all again. Bye-bye, little lady."

"When shall we meet again?" said Adam.

"Any time, old boy. Tickled to death to see you at any time you care to drop in. Always a pew and a drink for old friends. So long, everybody."

"But couldn't I come and see you soon? About the money, you know."

"Sooner the better, old boy. Though I don't know what you mean about money."

"My thirty-five thousand."

"Why, yes, to be sure. Fancy my forgetting that. I tell you what. You roll along to-night to the Central and I'll give it to you then. Jolly glad to get it off my chest. Seven o'clock at the American bar — or a little before."

"Let's go back and look at the motor cars," said Archie.

They went down the hill feeling buoyant and detached (as one should if one drinks a great deal before luncheon). When they reached the pits they decided they were hungry. It seemed too far to climb up to the dining tent, so they ate as much of the mechanic's lunch as Miss Runcible's cigarette had spared.

Then a mishap happened to No. 13. It drew into the side uncertainly, with the mechanic holding the steering wheel. A spanner, he told them, thrown from Marino's car as they were passing him under the railway bridge, had hit Miles's friend on the shoulder. The mechanic helped him get out, and supported him to the Red Cross tent. "May as well scratch," he said. "He won't be good for anything more this afternoon. It's asking for trouble having a No. 13." Miles went to help his friend, leaving Miss Runcible and Adam and Archie staring rather stupidly at their motor car. Archie hiccoughed slightly as he ate the mechanic's apple.

Soon an official appeared.

"What happened here?" he said.

"Driver's just been murdered," said Archie. "Spanner under the railway bridge. Marino."

"Well, are you going to scratch? Who's spare driver?"

"I don't know. Do you, Adam? I shouldn't be a bit surprised if they hadn't murdered the spare driver, too."

"I'm spare driver," said Miss Runcible. "It's on my arm."

"She's spare driver. Look, it's on her arm."

"Well, do you want to scratch?"

"Don't you scratch, Agatha."

"No, I don't want to scratch."

"All right. What's your name?"

"Agatha. I'm the spare driver. It's on my arm."

"I can see it is — all right, start off as soon as you like."

"Agatha," repeated Miss Runcible firmly as she climbed into the car. "It's on my arm."

"I say, Agatha," said Adam. "Are you sure you're all right?"

"It's on my arm," said Miss Runcible severely.

"I mean, are you quite certain it's absolutely safe?"

"Not *absolutely* safe, Adam. Not if they throw spanners. But I'll go quite slowly at first until I'm used to it. Just you see. Coming too?"

"I'll stay and wave the flag," said Adam.

"That's right. Good-bye . . . goodness, how too stiff-scaring. . . ."

The car shot out into the middle of the road, missed a collision by a foot, swung round and disappeared with a roar up the road.

"I say, Archie, is it all right being tight in a car, if it's on a race course? They won't run her in or anything?"

"No, no, that's all right. All tight on the race course."

"Sure?"

"Sure."

"All of them?"

"Absolutely everyone — tight as houses."

"That's all right then. Let's go and have a drink."

So they went up the hill again, through the Boy Scouts, to the refreshment tent.

It was not long before Miss Runcible was in the news.

"Hullo, everybody," said the loud-speaker. "No. 13, the English Plunket-Bowse, driven by Miss Agatha, came into collision at Headlong Corner with No. 28, the Italian Omega car, driven by Captain Marino. No. 13 righted itself and continued on the course. No. 28 overturned and has retired from the race."

"Well done, Agatha," said Archie.

A few minutes later:

"Hullo, everybody. No. 13, the English Plunket-Bowse, driven by Miss Agatha, has just completed the course in nine minutes forty-one seconds. This constitutes a record for the course."

Patriotic cheers broke out on all sides, and Miss Runcible's health was widely drunk in the refreshment tent.

A few minutes later:

"Hullo, everybody; I have to contradict the announcement recently made that No. 13, the English Plunket-Bowse, driven by Miss Agatha, had established a record for the course. The stewards have now reported that No. 13 left the road just after the level crossing and cut across country for five miles, rejoining the track at the Red Lion corner. The lap has therefore been disallowed by the judges."

A few minutes later:

"Hullo, everybody; No. 13, the English Plunket-Bowse car, driven by Miss Agatha, has retired from the race. It disappeared from the course some time ago, turning left instead of right at Church Corner, and was last seen proceeding south on the bye-road, apparently out of control."

"My dear, that's lucky for me," said Miles. "A really good story my second day on the paper. This ought to do me good with the *Excess* — *very* rich-making," and he hurried off to the post-office tent — which was one of the amenities of the course — to despatch a long account of Miss Runcible's disaster.

Adam accompanied him and sent a wire to Nina: *"Drunk Major in refreshment tent not bogus thirty-five thousand married tomorrow everything perfect Agatha lost love Adam."*

"That seems quite clear," he said.

They went to the hospital tent after this — another amenity of the course — to see how Miles's friend was getting on. He seemed in some pain and showed anxiety about his car.

"I think it's very heartless of him," said Adam. "He ought to be worried about Agatha. It only shows . . ."

"Motor men *are* heartless," said Miles, with a sigh.

Presently Captain Marino was borne in on a stretcher. He turned on his side with a deep groan and spat at Miles's friend as he went past him. He also spat at the doctor who came to bandage him and bit one of the V.A.D.'s.

They said Captain Marino was no gentleman in the hospital tent.

There was no chance of leaving the course before the end of the race, Archie was told, and the race would not be over for at least two hours. Round and round went the stream of cars. At intervals the Boy Scouts posted a large red R against one or other of the numbers, as engine trouble or collision or Headlong Corner took its toll. A long queue stretched along the top of the hill from the door of the luncheon tent. Then it began to rain.

There was nothing for it but to go back to the bar.

At dusk the last car completed its course. The silver gilt trophy was presented to the winner. The loudspeaker broadcast "God Save the King," and a cheerful "Good-bye, everybody." The tail of the queue outside the dining tent were respectfully informed that no more luncheons could be served. The barmaids in the refreshment tent said, "All glasses, ladies and gentlemen, please." The motor ambulances began a final round of the track to pick up survivors. Then Adam and Miles and Archie Schwert went to look for their car.

Darkness fell during the drive back. It took an hour to reach the town. Adam and Miles and Archie Schwert did not talk much. The effect of their drinks had now entered on that secondary stage, vividly described in temperance hand-books, when the momentary illusion of well-being and exhilaration gives place to melancholy, indigestion and moral decay. Adam tried to concentrate his thoughts upon his sudden wealth, but they seemed unable to adhere to this high pinnacle, and as often as he impelled them up, slithered back helplessly to his present physical discomfort.

The sluggish procession in which they were moving led them eventually to the centre of the town and the soberly illuminated front of the Imperial Hotel. A torrential flow of wet and hungry motor enthusiasts swept and eddied about the revolving doors.

"I shall die if I don't eat something soon," said Miles. "Let's leave Agatha until we've had a meal."

But the manager of the Imperial was unimpressed by numbers or necessity and manfully upheld the integrity of British hotel-keeping. Tea, he explained, was served daily in the Palm Court with orchestra on Thursdays and Sundays between the hours of four and six. A *table d'hôte* dinner was served in the dining-room from seven-thirty until nine o'clock. An *à la carte* dinner was also served in the grill-room at the same time. It was now twenty minutes past six. If the gentlemen cared to return in an hour and ten minutes he would do his best to accommodate them, but he could not promise to reserve a table. Things were busy that day. There had been motor races in the neighbourhood, he explained.

The commissionaire was more helpful, and told them that there was a tea-shop restaurant called the Café Royal a little way down the High Street, next to the Cinema. He seemed, however, to have given the same advice to all comers, for the Café Royal was crowded and overflowing. Everyone was being thoroughly cross, but only the most sarcastic and overbearing were given tables, and only the gross and outrageous were given food. Adam and Miles and Archie Schwert then tried two more tea-shops, one kept by "ladies" and called The

Honest Injun, a workmen's dining-room and a fried-fish shop. Eventually they bought a bag of mixed biscuits at a co-operative store, which they ate in the Palm Court of the Imperial, maintaining a moody silence.

It was now after seven, and Adam remembered his appointment in the American bar. There, too, inevitably, was a dense crowd. Some of the "Speed Kings" themselves had appeared, pink from their baths, wearing dinner-jackets and stiff white shirts, each in his circle of admirers. Adam struggled to the bar.

"Have you seen a drunk major in here anywhere?" he asked.

The barmaid sniffed. "I should think not, indeed," she said. "And I shouldn't serve him if he *did* come in. I don't have people of that description in *my* bar. *The very idea.*"

"Well, perhaps he's not drunk now. But have you seen a stout, red-faced man, with a single eyeglass and a turned-up moustache?"

"Well, there *was* someone like that not so long ago. Are you a friend of his?"

"I want to see him badly."

"Well, all I can say is I wish you'd try and look after him and don't bring him in here again. Going on something awful he was. Broke two glasses and got very quarrelsome with the other gentlemen. He had three or four pound notes in his hand. Kept waving them about and saying. 'D'you know what? I met a mutt today. I owe him thirty-five thousand pounds and he lent me a fiver.' Well, that's not the way to talk before strangers, is it? He went out ten minutes ago. I was glad to see the back of him, I can tell you."

"Did he say that — about having met a mutt?"

"Didn't stop saying it the whole time he was in here — most monotonous."

But as Adam left the bar he saw the Major coming out of the gentlemen's lavatory. He was walking very deliberately, and stared at Adam with a glazed and vacant eye.

"Hi!" cried Adam. "Hi!"

"Cheerio," said the drunk Major distantly.

"I say," said Adam. "What about my thirty-five thousand pounds?"

The drunk Major stopped and adjusted his monocle.

"Thirty-five thousand and five pounds," he said. "What about them?"

"Well, where are they?"

"They're safe enough. National and Provincial Union Bank of England, Limited. A perfectly sound and upright company. I'd trust them with more than that if I had it. I'd trust them with a million, old boy, honest I would. One of those fine old companies, you know. They don't make companies like that now. I'd trust that bank with my wife and kiddies. . . . You mustn't think I'd put your money into anything that wasn't straight, old boy. You ought to know me well enough for that. . . ."

"No, of course not. It's terribly kind of you to have looked after it — you said you'd give me a cheque this evening. Don't you remember?"

The drunk Major looked at him craftily. "Ah," he said. "That's another matter. I told *someone* I'd give him a cheque. But how am I to know it was you? . . . I've got to be careful, you know. Suppose you were just a crook dressed up. I don't say you are, mind, but supposing. Where'd I be then? You have to look at both sides of a case like this."

"Oh, God. . . . I've got two friends here who'll swear to you I'm Adam Symes. Will that do?"

"Might be a gang. Besides *I* don't know that the name of the chap who gave me the thousand *was* Adam what-d'you-call-it at all. Only your word for it. I'll tell you what," said the Major, sitting down in a deep armchair, "I'll sleep on it. Just forty winks. I'll let you know my decision when I wake up. Don't think me suspicious, old boy, but I've got to be careful . . . other chap's money, you know . . ." And he fell asleep.

Adam struggled through the crowd to the Palm Court, where he had left Miles and Archie. News of No. 13 had just come through. The car had been found piled up on the market cross of a large village about fifteen miles away (doing irreparable damage to a monument already scheduled for preservation by the Office of Works). But there was no sign of Miss Runcible.

"I suppose we ought to do something about it," said Miles. "This is the most miserable day I ever spent. Did you get your fortune?"

"The Major was too drunk to recognise me. He's just gone to sleep."

"*Well.*"

"We must go to this beastly village and look for Agatha."

"I can't leave my Major. He'll probably wake up soon and give the fortune to the first person he sees."

"Let's just go and shake him until he gives us the fortune now," said Miles.

But this was impracticable, for when they reached the chair where Adam had left him, the drunk Major was gone.

The hall porter remembered him going out quite clearly. He had pressed a pound into his hand, saying, "Met-a-mutt-today," and taken a taxi to the station.

"D'you know," said Adam, "I don't believe that I'm ever going to get that fortune."

"Well, I don't see that you've very much to complain of," said Archie. "You're no worse off than you were. *I've* lost a fiver and five bottles of champagne."

"That's true," said Adam, a little consoled.

They got into the car and drove through the rain to the village where the Plunket-Bowse had been found. There it stood, still smoking and partially recognisable, surrounded by admiring villagers. A constable in a waterproof cape was doing his best to preserve it intact from the raids of souvenir hunters who were collecting the smaller fragments.

No one seemed to have witnessed the disaster. The younger members of the community were all at the races, while the elders were engaged in their afternoon naps. One thought he had heard a crash.

Enquiries at the railway station, however, disclosed that a young lady, much dishevelled in appearance, and wearing some kind of band on her arm, had appeared in the booking office early that afternoon and asked where she was. On being told, she said, well, she wished she wasn't, because someone had left an enormous stone spanner in the middle of the road. She admitted feeling rather odd. The station-master had asked her if she would like to come in and sit down and offered to get her some brandy. She said, "No, no more brandy," and bought a first-class ticket to London. She had left on the 3.25 train.

"So that's all right," said Archie.

Then they left the village and presently found an hotel on the Great North Road, where they dined and spent the night. They reached London by luncheon time next day, and learned that Miss Runcible had been found early that morning staring fixedly at a model engine in the central hall at Euston Station. In answer to some gentle questions, she replied that to the best of her knowledge she had no name, pointing to the brassard on her arm, as if in confirmation of this fact. She had come in a motor car, she explained, which would not stop. It was full of bugs which she had tried to kill with drops of face lotion. One of them threw a spanner. There had been a stone thing in the way. They shouldn't put up symbols like that in the middle of the road, should they, or should they?

So they conveyed her to a nursing home in Wimpole Street and kept her for some time in a darkened room.

II

ADAM rang up Nina.

"Darling, I've been so happy about your telegram. Is it really true?"

"No, I'm afraid not."

"The Major *is* bogus?"

"Yes."

"You haven't got any money?"

"No."

"We aren't going to be married to-day?"

"No."

"I see."

"Well?"

"I said, I see."

"Is that all?"

"Yes, that's all, Adam."

"I'm sorry."

"I'm sorry, too. Good-bye."

"Good-bye, Nina."

Later Nina rang up Adam.

"Darling, is that you? I've got something rather awful to tell you."

"Yes?"

"You'll be furious."

"Well?"

"I'm engaged to be married."

"Who to?"

"I hardly think I can tell you."

"Who?"

"Adam, you won't be beastly about it, will you?"

"Who is it?"

"Ginger."

"I don't believe it."

"Well, I am. That's all there is to it."

"You're going to marry Ginger?"

"Yes."

"I see."

"Well?"

"I said, I see."

"Is that all?"

"Yes, that's all, Nina."

"When shall I see you?"

"I don't want ever to see you again."

"I see."

"Well?"

"I said, I see."

"Well, good-bye."

"Good-bye. . . . I'm sorry, Adam."

I I I

TEN days later Adam bought some flowers at the corner of Wigmore Street and went to call on Miss Runcible at her nursing home. He was shown first into the matron's room. She had numerous photographs in silver frames and a very nasty fox terrier. She smoked a cigarette in a greedy way, making slight sucking noises.

"Just taking a moment off in my den," she explained. "Down, Spot, down. But I can see you're fond of dogs," she added, as Adam gave Spot a half-hearted pat on the head. "So you want to see Miss Runcible? Well, I ought to warn you first that she must have no kind of excitement whatever. She's had a severe shock. Are you a relation, may I ask?"

"No, only a friend."

"A very *special* friend, perhaps, eh?" said the Matron archly. "Never mind, I'll spare your blushes. Just you run up and see her. But not more than five minutes, mind, or you'll have me on your tracks."

There was a reek of ether on the stairs which reminded Adam of the times when, waiting to take her to luncheon, he had sat on Nina's bed while she did her face. (She invariably made him turn his back until it was over, having a keen sense of modesty about this one part of her toilet, in curious contrast to some girls, who would die rather than be seen in their underclothes, and yet openly flaunt unpainted faces in front of anyone.)

It hurt Adam deeply to think much about Nina.

Outside Miss Runcible's door hung a very interesting chart which showed the fluctuations of her temperature and pulse and many other curious details of her progress. He studied this with pleasure until a nurse, carrying a tray of highly polished surgical instruments, gave him such a look that he felt obliged to turn away.

Miss Runcible lay in a high, narrow bed in a darkened room.

A nurse was crocheting at her side when Adam entered. She rose, dropping a few odds and ends from her lap, and said, "There's some-one come to see you, dear. Now remember you aren't to talk much." She took the flowers from Adam's hand, said, "Look what lovelies. Aren't you a lucky girl?" and left the room with them. She returned a moment later carrying them in a jug of water. "There, the thirsties," she said. "Don't they love to get back to the nice cool water?"

Then she went out again.

"Darling," said a faint voice from the bed, "I can't really see who it is. Would it be awful to draw the curtains?"

Adam crossed the room and let in the light of the grey December afternoon.

"My dear, how blind-making. There are some cocktail things in the wardrobe. Do make a big one. The nurses love them so. It's such a nice nursing home this, Adam, only all the nurses are starved, and there's a breath-taking young man next door who keeps putting his head in and asking how I am. He fell out of an *aeroplane*, which is rather grand, don't you think?"

"How are you feeling, Agatha?"

"Well, rather odd, to tell you the truth. . . . How's Nina?"

"She's got engaged to be married — haven't you heard?"

"My dear, the nurses are interested in no one but Princess Elizabeth. Do tell me."

"A young man called Ginger."

"*Well?*"

"Don't you remember him? He came on with us after the airship party."

"Not the one who was sick?"

"No, the other."

"I don't remember . . . does Nina call him Ginger?"

"Yes."

"Why?"

"He asked her to."

"*Well?*"

"She used to play with him when they were children. So she's going to marry him."

"My dear, isn't that rather sad-making for you?"

"I'm desperate about it. I'm thinking of committing suicide, like Simon."*

"Don't do that, darling . . . did Simon commit suicide?"

"My dear, you know he did. The night all those libel actions started."

"Oh, *that* Simon. I thought you meant *Simon.*"

"Who's Simon?"

"The young man who fell out of the aeroplane. The nurses call him Simple Simon because it's affected his brains . . . but, Adam, I *am* sorry about Nina. I'll tell you what we'll do. As soon as I am well again we'll make Mary Mouse give a lovely party to cheer you up."

"Haven't you heard about Mary?"

"No, what?"

"She went off to Monte Carlo with the Maharajah of Pukkapore."

"*My dear,* aren't the Mice furious?"

"She's just receiving religious instruction before her official reception as a royal concubine. Then they're going to India."

"How people are *disappearing*, Adam. Did you get that money from the drunk Major?"

"No, he disappeared too."

"D'you know, all that time when I was dotty I had the most awful dreams. I thought we were all driving round and round in a motor race and none of us could stop, and there was an enormous audience composed entirely of gossip writers and gate crashers and Archie Schwert and people like that, all shouting at us at once to go faster, and car after car kept crashing until I was left all alone driving and driving — and then I used to crash and wake up."

Then the door opened, and Miles came popping in.

"Agatha, Adam, my dears. The *time* I've had trying to get in. I can't tell you how bogus they were downstairs. First I said I was Lord Chasm, and that wasn't any good; and I said I was one of the doctors, and that wasn't any good; and I said I was your young man, and *that* wasn't any good; and I said I was a gossip writer, and they

---

*The previous Mr. Chatterbox. — Ed.

let me up at once and said I wasn't to excite you, but would I put a piece in my paper about their nursing home. *How* are you, Aggie darling? I brought up some new records."

"You are angelic. Do let's try them. There's a gramophone under the bed."

"There's a whole lot more people coming to see you to-day. I saw them all at luncheon at Margot's. Johnnie Hoop and Van and Archie Schwert. I wonder if they'll all manage to get in."

They got in.

So soon there was quite a party, and Simon appeared from next door in a very gay dressing-gown, and they played the new records and Miss Runcible moved her bandaged limbs under the bed-clothes in Negro rhythm.

Last of all, Nina came in looking quite lovely and very ill.

"Nina, I hear you're engaged."

"Yes, it's very lucky. My papa has just put all his money into a cinema film and lost it all."

"My dear, it doesn't matter at all. My papa lost all his twice. It doesn't make a bit of difference. That's just one of the things one has to learn about losing all one's money. . . . Is it true that you really call him Ginger?"

"Well, yes, only, Agatha, please don't be unkind about it."

And the gramophone was playing the song which the black man sang at the Café de la Paix.

Then the nurse came in.

"Well, you are noisy ones, and no mistake," she said. "I don't know what the Matron would say if she were here."

"Have a chocolate, sister?"

"*Ooh, chocs!*"

Adam made another cocktail.

Miles sat on Miss Runcible's bed and took up the telephone and began dictating some paragraphs about the nursing home.

"What it is to have a friend in the Press," said the nurse.

Adam brought her a cocktail. "Shall I?" she said. "I hope you haven't made it too strong. Suppose it goes to my head. What would the patients think if their sister came in tiddly? Well, if you're *sure* it won't hurt me, thanks."

"*. . . Yesterday I visited the Hon. Agatha Runcible comma Lord Chasm's lovely daughter comma at the Wimpole Street nursing home*

where she is recovering from the effects of the motor accident recently
described in this column stop. Miss Runcible was entertaining quite
a large party which included . . ."

Adam, handing round cocktails, came to Nina.

"I thought we were never going to meet each other again."

"We were obviously bound to, weren't we?"

"Agatha's looking better than I expected, isn't she? What an amusing nursing home."

"Nina, I must see you again. Come back to Lottie's this evening and have dinner with me."

"No."

"*Please.*"

"No. Ginger wouldn't like it."

"Nina, you aren't in love with him?"

"No, I don't think so."

"Are you in love with me?"

"I don't know . . . I was once."

"Nina, I'm absolutely miserable not seeing you. Do come and dine with me tonight. What can be the harm in that?"

"My dear, I know exactly what it will mean."

"Well, why not?"

"You see, Ginger's not like us really about that sort of thing. He'd be furious."

"Well, what about me? Surely I have first claim?"

"Darling, don't *bully*. Besides, I used to play with Ginger as a child. His hair was a very pretty colour then."

"*. . . Mr. 'Johnnie' Hoop, whose memoirs are to be published next month, told me that he intends to devote his time to painting in future, and is going to Paris to study in the spring. He is to be taken into the studio of . . ."*

"For the last time, Nina . . ."

"Well, I suppose I must."

"*Angel!*"

"I believe you knew I was going to."

"*. . . Miss Nina Blount, whose engagement to Mr. 'Ginger' Little-john, the well-known polo player. . . . Mr. Schwert . . ."*

"If only you were as rich as Ginger, Adam, or only half as rich. Or if only you had any money at all."

"Well," said the Matron, appearing suddenly. "Whoever heard of cocktails and a gramophone in a concussion case? Sister Briggs, pull down those curtains at once. Out you go, the whole lot of you. Why, I've known cases die with less."

Indeed, Miss Runcible was already showing signs of strain. She was sitting bolt upright in bed, smiling deliriously, and bowing her bandaged head to imaginary visitors.

"*Darling*," she said. "How *too* divine . . . *how* are you? . . . and how are *you*? . . . how angelic of you all to come . . . only you must be careful not to fall out at the corners . . . ooh, just missed it. There goes that nasty Italian car . . . I wish I knew which thing was which in this car . . . darling, do try and drive more straight, my sweet, you were nearly into me then. . . . Faster . . ."

"That's all right, Miss Runcible, that's all right. You mustn't get excited," said the Matron. "Sister Briggs, run for the ice-pack quickly."

"All friends here," said Miss Runcible, smiling radiantly. "Faster. . . . Faster . . . it'll stop all right when the times comes . . ."

That evening Miss Runcible's temperature went rocketing up the chart in a way which aroused great interest throughout the nursing home. Sister Briggs over her evening cup of cocoa said she would be sorry to lose that case. Such a nice bright girl — but terribly excitable.

At Shepheard's Hotel Lottie said to Adam: "That chap's been in here again after you."

"What chap, Lottie?"

"How do I know what chap? Same chap as before."

"You never told me about a chap."

"Didn't I, dear? Well, I meant to."

"What did he want?"

"I don't know — something about money. Dun, I expect. Says he is coming back to-morrow."

"Well, tell him I've gone to Manchester."

"That's right, dear. . . . What about a glass of wine?"

Later that evening Nina said: "You don't seem to be enjoying yourself very much to-night."

"Sorry, am I being a bore?"

"I think I shall go home."

"Yes."

"Adam, darling, what's the matter?"

"I don't know. . . . Nina, do you ever feel that things simply can't go on much longer?"

"What d'you mean by things — us or everything?"

"Everything."

"No — I wish I did."

"I daresay you're right . . . what are you looking for?"

"Clothes."

"Why?"

"Oh, Adam, what *do* you want . . . you're too impossible this evening."

"Don't let's talk any more, Nina, d'you mind?"

Later he said: "I'd give anything in the world for something different."

"Different from me or different from everything?"

"Different from everything . . . only I've got nothing . . . what's the good of talking?"

"Oh, Adam, my dearest . . ."

"Yes?"

"Nothing."

When Adam came down next morning Lottie was having her morning glass of champagne in the parlour.

"So your little bird's flown, has she? Sit down and have a glass of wine. That dun's been in again. I told him you was in Manchester."

"Splendid."

"Seemed rather shirty about it. Said he'd go and look for you."

"Better still."

Then something happened which Adam had been dreading for days. Lottie suddenly said:

"And that reminds me. What about *my* little bill?"

"Oh, yes," said Adam, "I've been meaning to ask for it. Have it made out and sent up to me sometime, will you?"

"I've got it here. Bless you, what a lot you seem to have drunk."

"Yes, I do, don't I? Are you sure some of this champagne wasn't the Judge's?"

"Well, it may have been," admitted Lottie. "We get a bit muddled with the books now and then."

"Well, thank you so much, I'll send you down a cheque for this."

"No, dear," said Lottie. "Suppose you write it down here. Here's the pen, here's the ink, and here's a blank cheque book."

(Bills are delivered infrequently and irregularly at Lottie's, but when they come, there is no getting away from them.) Adam wrote out a cheque for seventy-eight pounds sixteen shillings.

"And twopence for the cheque," said Lottie.

And twopence, Adam added.

"There's a dear," said Lottie, blotting the cheque and locking it away in a drawer. "Why look who's turned up. If it isn't Mr. Thingummy."

It was Ginger.

"Good morning, Mrs. Crump," he said rather stiffly.

"Come and sit down and have a glass of wine, dear. Why I knew you before you were born."

"Hullo, Ginger," said Adam.

"Look here, Symes," said Ginger, looking in an embarrassed manner at the glass of champagne which had been put into his hand, "I want to speak to you. Perhaps we can go somewhere where we shan't be disturbed."

"Bless you, boys, I won't disturb you," said Lottie. "Just you have a nice talk. I've got lots to see to."

She left the parlour, and soon her voice could be heard raised in anger against the Italian waiter.

"Well?" said Adam.

"Look here, Symes," said Ginger, "what I mean to say is, what I'm going to say may sound damned unpleasant, you know, and all that, but look here, you know, damn it, I mean *the better man won* — not that I mean I'm the *better* man. Wouldn't say that for a minute. And anyway, Nina's a damn sight too good for either of us. It's just that I've been lucky. Awful rough luck on you, I mean, and all that, but still, when you come to think of it, after all, well, look here, damn it, I mean, d'you see what I mean?"

"Not quite," said Adam gently. "Now tell me again. Is it something about Nina?"

"Yes, it is," said Ginger in a rush. "Nina and I are engaged, and

I'm not going to have you butting in or there'll be hell to pay." He paused, rather taken aback at his own eloquence.

"What makes you think I'm butting in?"

"Well, hang it all, she dined with you last night, didn't she, and stayed out jolly late, too."

"How do you know how late she stayed out?"

"Well, as a matter of fact, you see I wanted to speak to her about something rather important, so I rang her up once or twice and didn't get an answer until three o'clock."

"I suppose you rang her up about every ten minutes?"

"Oh, no, damn it, not as often as that," said Ginger. "No, no, not as often as that. I know it sounds rather unsporting and all that, but you see I wanted to speak to her, and, anyway, when I did get through, she just said she had a pain and didn't want to talk; *well, I mean to say.* After all, I mean, one is a gentleman. It isn't as though you were just a sort of friend of the family, is it? I mean, you were more or less engaged to her yourself, weren't you, at one time? Well, what would you have thought if I'd come butting in? You must look at it like that, from my point of view, too, mustn't you, I mean?"

"Well, I think that's rather what did happen."

"Oh, no, look here, Symes, I mean, damn it; you mustn't say things like that. D'you know all the time I was out East I had Nina's photograph over my bed, honest I did. I expect you think that's sentimental and all that, but what I mean is I didn't stop thinking of that girl once all the time I was away. Mind you, there were lots of other frightfully jolly girls out there, and I don't say I didn't sometimes get jolly pally with them, you know, tennis and gymkhana and all that sort of thing, I mean, and dancing in the evenings, but never anything serious, you know. Nina was the only girl I really thought of, and I'd sort of made up my mind when I came home to look her up, and if she'd have me . . . see what I mean? So you see it's awfully rough luck on me when someone comes butting in. You must see that, don't you?"

"Yes," said Adam.

"And there's another thing, you know, sentiment and all that apart. I mean Nina's a girl who likes nice clothes and things, you know, comfort and all that. Well, I mean to say, of course, her father's a topping old boy, absolutely one of the best, but he's rather an ass about money, if you know what I mean. What I mean, Nina's going to be frightfully hard up, and all that, and I mean you haven't got an awful lot of money, have you?"

"I haven't any at all."

"No, I mean, that's what I mean. *Awfully rough on you*. No one thinks the worse of you, respects you for it, I mean earning a living and all that. Heaps of fellows haven't any money nowadays. I could give you the names of dozens of stout fellows, absolute toppers, who simply haven't a bean. No, all I mean is, when it comes to marrying, then that does make a difference, doesn't it?"

"What you've been trying to say all this time is that you're not sure of Nina?"

"Oh, rot, my dear fellow, absolute bilge. Damn it, I'd trust Nina anywhere, of course I would. After all, damn it, what does being in love mean if you can't trust a person?"

("What, indeed?" thought Adam), and he said, "Now, Ginger, tell the truth. What's Nina worth to you?"

"Good Lord, why what an extraordinary thing to ask; everything in the world, of course. I'd go through fire and water for that girl."

"Well, I'll sell her to you."

"No, why, look here, good God, damn it, I mean . . ."

"I'll sell you my share in her for a hundred pounds."

"You pretend to be fond of Nina and you talk about her like that! Why, hang it, it's not decent. Besides, a hundred pounds is the deuce of a lot. I mean, getting married is a damned expensive business, don't you know. And I'm just getting a couple of polo ponies over from Ireland. That's going to cost a hell of a lot, what with one thing and another."

"A hundred down, and I leave Nina to you. I think it's cheap."

"Fifty."

"A hundred."

"Seventy-five."

"A hundred."

"I'm damned if I'll pay more than seventy-five."

"I'll take seventy-eight pounds sixteen and twopence. I can't go lower than that."

"All right, I'll pay that. *You really will go away?*"

"I'll try, Ginger. Have a drink."

"No, thank you . . . this only shows what an escape Nina's had —
poor girl."

"Good-bye, Ginger."

"Good-bye, Symes."

"Young Thingummy going?" said Lottie, appearing in the door. "I
was just thinking about a little drink."

Adam went to the telephone-box. . . . "Hullo, is that Nina?"

"Who's speaking, please? I don't think Miss Blount is in."

"Mr. Fenwick-Symes."

"Oh, Adam. I was afraid it was Ginger. I woke up feeling I just
couldn't bear him. He rang up last night just as I got in."

"I know. Nina, darling, something awful's happened."

"What?"

"Lottie presented me with her bill."

"Darling, what *did* you do?"

"Well, I did something rather extraordinary. . . . My dear, I sold
you."

"Darling . . . *who to?*"

"Ginger. You fetched seventy-eight pounds sixteen and twopence."

"*Well?*"

"And now I never am going to see you again."

"Oh, but Adam, I think this is beastly of you. I don't want not to
see you again."

"I'm sorry. . . . Good-bye, Nina, darling."

"Good-bye, Adam, my sweet. But I think you're rather a cad."

Next day Lottie said to Adam, "You know that chap I said came here
asking for you?"

"The dun?"

"Well, he wasn't a dun. I've just remembered. He's a chap who
used to come here quite a lot until he had a fight with a Canadian. He
was here the night that silly Flossie killed herself on the chandelier."

"Not the drunk Major?"

"He wasn't drunk yesterday. Not so as you'd notice anyway. Red-
faced chap with an eyeglass. You ought to remember him, dear. He was
the one made that bet for you on the November Handicap."

"But I must get hold of him at once. What's his name?"

"Ah, that I couldn't tell you. I *did* know, but it's slipped my memory.

He's gone to Manchester to look for you. Pity your missing him!"

Then Adam rang up Nina. "Listen," he said. "Don't do anything sudden about Ginger. I may be able to buy you back. The drunk Major has turned up again."

"But, darling, it's too late. Ginger and I got married this morning. I'm just packing for our honeymoon. We're going in an aeroplane."

"Ginger wasn't taking any chances, was he? Darling, don't go."

"No, I must. Ginger says he knows a 'top-hole little spot not far from Monte with a very decent nine-hole golf course.' "

"Well?"

"Yes, I know . . . we shall only be away a few days. We're coming back to spend Christmas with papa. Perhaps we shall be able to arrange something when we get back. I do hope so."

"Good-bye."

"Good-bye."

There was rarely more than a quarter of a mile of the black road to be seen at one time. It unrolled like a length of cinema film. At the edges was confusion; a fog spinning past; *"Faster, faster,"* they shouted above the roar of the engine. The road rose suddenly and the white car soared up the sharp ascent without slackening of speed. At the summit of the hill there was a corner. Two cars had crept up, one on each side, and were closing in. "Faster," cried Miss Runcible. "Faster."

"Quietly, dear, quietly. You're disturbing everyone. You must lie quiet or you'll never get well. Everything's quite all right. There's nothing to worry about. Nothing at all."

They were trying to make her lie down. How could one drive properly lying down?

Another frightful corner. The car leant over on two wheels, tugging outwards; it was drawn across the road until it was within a few inches of the bank. One ought to brake down at the corners, but one couldn't see them coming lying flat on one's back like this. The back wheels wouldn't hold the road at this speed. Skidding all over the place.

"Faster. Faster."

The stab of a hypodermic needle.

"Theres nothing to worry about, dear . . . *nothing at all . . . nothing.*"

IV

COLONEL BLOUNT was just having tea — he had finished a brown boiled egg and was spreading a crumpet with honey — when Florin opened the library door and announced, "Captain and Mrs. Littlejohn, sir."

And Adam and Nina came in.

Colonel Blount put down his crumpet and rose to greet them.

"Well, Nina, it's a long time since you came to see your old father. So this is my son-in-law, eh? How do you do, my boy. Come and sit down, both of you. Florin will bring some more cups directly. . . . Well," he said, giving Adam a searching glance, "I can't say I should have recognised you. I used to know your father very well indeed at one time. Used to be a neighbour of mine over at where-was-it. I expect you've forgotten those days. You used to come over here to ride with Nina. You can't have been more than ten or eleven. . . . Funny, something gave me an idea you had red hair . . ."

"I expect you'd heard him called 'Ginger,'" said Nina, "and that made you think of it."

"Something of the kind, I daresay . . . extraordinary thing to call him 'Ginger' when he's got ordinary fair hair . . . anyway, I'm very glad to see you, very glad. I'm afraid it'll be a very quiet weekend. We don't see many people here now. Florin says he's asked a Captain and Mrs. Something-or-other to come and stay, damn his impudence, but I said I wouldn't see them. Why should I entertain Florin's friends? Servants seem to think after they've been with you some time they can do anything they like. There was poor old Lady Graybridge, now — they only found out after her death that her man had been letting lodgings all the time in the North Wing. She never could understand why none of the fruit ever came into the dining-room — the butler and his boarders were eating it all in the servants' hall. And after she was ill, and couldn't leave her room, he laid out a golf links in the park . . . shocking state of affairs. I don't believe Florin would do a thing like that — still, you never know. It's the thin edge of the wedge asking people down for the week-end."

In the kitchen Florin said, "*That's* not the Mr. Littlejohn I used to know."

Mrs. Florin said, "It's the young gentleman that came here to luncheon last month."

Ada said, "He's very nice looking."

In the library Colonel Blount said, "I've got a treat for you to-night, anyway. The last two reels of my cinema film have just come back from being developed. I thought we'd run through it to-night. We shall have to go across to the Rectory, because the Rector's got electric light, the lucky fellow. I told him to expect us. He didn't seem very pleased about it. Said he had to preach three sermons to-morrow, and be up at six for early service. That's not the Christmas spirit. Didn't want to bring the car round to fetch us either. It's only a matter of a quarter of a mile, no trouble to *him*, and how can we walk in the snow carrying all the apparatus? I said to him, 'If you practised a little more Christianity yourself we might be more willing to subscribe to your foreign missions and Boy Scouts and organ funds.' Had him there. Dammit, I put the man in his job myself — if I haven't a right to his car, who has?"

When they went up to change for dinner, Nina said to Adam, "I knew papa would never recognise you."

Adam said, "Look, someone's put mistletoe over our bed."

"I think you gave the Florins rather a surprise."

"My dear, what will the Rector say? He drove me to the station the first time I came. He thought I was mad."

". . . Poor Ginger. I wonder, are we treating him terribly badly? . . . It seemed a direct act of fate that he should have been called up to join his regiment just at this moment."

"I left him a cheque to pay for you."

"Darling, you know it's a bad one."

"No cheque is bad until it's refused by the bank. To-morrow's Christmas, then Boxing Day, then Sunday. He can't pay it in until Monday, and anything may have happened by then. The drunk Major may have turned up. If the worst comes to the worst I can always send you back to him."

"I expect it will end with that. . . . Darling, the honeymoon *was* hell . . . frightfully cold, and Ginger insisted on walking about on a terrace after dinner to see the moon on the Mediterranean — he played golf all day, and made friends with the other English people in the hotel. I can't tell you what it was like . . . too spirit-crushing, as poor Agatha used to say."

"Did I tell you I went to Agatha's funeral? There was practically
no one there except the Chasms and some aunts. I went with Van,
rather tight, and got stared at. I think they felt I was partly responsible
for the accident. . . ."

"What about Miles?"

"He's had to leave the country, didn't you know?"

"Darling, I only came back from my honeymoon today. I haven't
heard anything. . . . You know there seems to be none of us left
now except you and me."

"And Ginger."

"Yes, and Ginger."

Next morning Adam and Nina woke up under Ada's sprig of
mistletoe to hear the bells ringing for Christmas, across the snow. "Come
all to church, good people; good people, come to church." They had
each hung up a stocking the evening before, and Adam had put a
bottle of scent and a scent spray into Nina's, and she had put two
ties and a new kind of safety razor into his. Ada brought them their
tea and wished them a happy Christmas. Nina had remembered to get
a present for each of the Florins, but had forgotten Ada, so she gave
her the bottle of scent.

"Darling," said Adam, "it cost twenty-five shillings — on Archie
Schwert's account at Asprey."

Later they put some crumbs of their bread and butter on the window-
sill and a robin redbreast came to eat them. The whole day was like that.

[That night war was declared.]

V

On a splintered tree stump in the biggest battlefield in the history of
the world, Adam sat down and read a letter from Nina. It had arrived
early the day before, but in the intensive fighting which followed
he had not had a spare minute in which to open it.

Doubting Hall
Aylesbury

DEAREST ADAM, — *I wonder how you are. It is difficult to know
what is happening quite because the papers say such odd things. Van*

has got a divine job making up all the war news, and he invented a lovely story about you the other day, how you'd saved hundreds of people's lives, and there's what they call popular agitation saying why haven't you got a V.C., so probably you will have by now. Isn't it amusing?

Ginger and I are very well. Ginger has a job in an office in Whitehall and wears a very grand sort of uniform, and, my dear, I'm going to have a baby, isn't it too awful? But Ginger has quite made up his mind it's his, and is as pleased as anything, so that's all right. He's quite forgiven you about last Christmas, and says anyway you're doing your bit now, and in war time one lets bygones be bygones.

Doubting is a hospital, did you know? Papa shows his film to the wounded and they adore it. I saw Mr. Benfleet, and he said how awful it was when one had given all one's life in the cause of culture to see everything one's stood for swept away, but that he's doing very well with his "Sword Unsheathed" series of war poets.

There's a new Government order that we have to sleep in gas masks because of the bombs, but no one does. They've put Archie in prison as an undesirable alien, Ginger saw to that, he terrific about spies. I'm sick such a lot because of this baby, but everyone says it's patriotic to have babies in war time. Why?

Lots of love, my angel, take care of your dear self.

N.

He put it back in its envelope and buttoned it into his breast-pocket. Then he took out a pipe, filled it and began to smoke. The scene all round him was one of unrelieved desolation; a great expanse of mud in which every visible object was burnt or broken. Sounds of firing thundered from beyond the horizon, and somewhere above the grey clouds there were aeroplanes. He had had no sleep for thirty-six hours. It was growing dark.

Presently he became aware of a figure approaching, painfully picking his way among the strands of barbed wire which strayed across the ground like drifting cobweb; a soldier clearly. As he came nearer Adam saw that he was levelling towards him a liquid-fire projector. Adam tightened his fingers about his Huxdane-Halley bomb (for the dissemination of leprosy germs), and in this posture of mutual suspicion they met. Through the dusk Adam recognised the uniform of an English staff officer. He put the bomb back in his pocket and saluted.

The newcomer lowered his liquid-fire projector and raised his gas mask. "You're English, are you?" he said. "Can't see a thing. Broken my damned monocle."

"Why," said Adam. "You're the drunk Major."

"I'm not drunk, damn you, sir," said the drunk Major, "and, what's more, I'm a General. What the deuce are *you* doing here?"

"Well," said Adam. "I've lost my platoon."

"Lost your platoon. . . . I've lost my whole bloody division!"

"Is the battle over, sir?"

"I don't know, can't see a thing. It was going on all right last time I heard of it. My car's broken down somewhere over there. My driver went out to try and find someone to help and got lost, and I went out to look for him, and now I've lost the car too. Damn difficult country to find one's way about in. No landmarks. . . . Funny meeting you. I owe you some money."

"Thirty-five thousand pounds."

"Thirty-five thousand and five. Looked for you everywhere before this scrap started. I can give you the money now if you like."

"The pound's not worth much nowadays, is it?"

"About nothing. Still, I may as well give you a cheque. It'll buy you a couple of drinks and a newspaper. Talking of drinks, I've got a case of bubbly in the car if we could only find it. Salvaged it out of an R.A.F. mess that got bombed back at H.Q. Wish I could find that car."

Eventually they did find it. A Daimler limousine sunk to the axles in mud.

"Get in and sit down," said the General hospitably. "I'll turn the light on in a second."

Adam climbed in and found that it was not empty. In the corner, crumpled up in a French military great-coat, was a young woman fast asleep.

"*Hullo*, I'd forgotten all about you," said the General. "I picked up this little lady on the road. I can't introduce you, because I don't know her name. Wake up, mademoiselle."

The girl gave a little cry and opened two startled eyes.

"That's all right, little lady, nothing to be scared about — all friends here. *Parlez anglais?*"

"Sure," said the girl.

"Well, what about a spot?" said the General, peeling the tinfoil from the top of a bottle. "You'll find some glasses in the locker."

The woebegone fragment of womanhood in the corner looked a little
less terrified when she saw the wine. She recognised it as the symbol of
international goodwill.

"Now perhaps our fair visitor will tell us her name," said the
General.

"I dunno," she said.

"Oh, come, little one, you mustn't be shy."

"I dunno. I been called a lot of things. I was called Chastity once.
Then there was a lady at a party, and she sent me to Buenos Aires,
and then when the war came she brought me back again, and I was
with the soldiers training at Salisbury Plain. That was swell. They
called me Bunny — I don't know why. Then they sent me over here
and I was with the Canadians, what they called me wasn't nice, and
then they left me behind when they retreated and I took up with some
foreigners. They were nice too, though they *were* fighting against the
English. Then *they* ran away, and the lorry I was in got stuck in the
ditch, so I got in with some other foreigners who were on the same
side as the English, and they were beasts, but I met an American
doctor who had white hair, and he called me Emily because he said
I reminded him of his daughter back home, so he took me to Paris
and we had a lovely week till he took up with another girl in a night
club, so he left me behind in Paris when he went back to the front,
and I hadn't no money and they made a fuss about my passport, so
they called me *numéro mille soixante dix-huit*, and they sent me and
a lot of other girls off to the East to be with the soldiers there. At least
they would have done only the ship got blown up, so I was rescued and
the French sent me up here in a train with some different girls who were
very unrefined. Then I was in a tin hut with the girls, and then yesterday they had friends and I was alone, so I went for a walk, and when
I came back the hut was gone and the girls were gone, and there didn't
seem anyone anywhere until you came in your car, and now I don't
rightly know where I am. *My*, isn't war awful?"

The General opened another bottle of champagne.

"Well, you're as right as rain now, little lady," he said, "so let's see you
smile and look happy. You mustn't sit there scowling, you know —
far too pretty a little mouth for that. Let me take off that heavy coat.
Look, I'll wrap it round your knees. There, now, isn't that better?
. . . Fine, strong little legs, eh? . . ."

Adam did not embarrass them. The wine and the deep cushions

and the accumulated fatigue of two days' fighting drew him away from them and, oblivious to all the happy emotion pulsing near him, he sank into sleep.

The windows of the stranded motor car shone over the wasted expanse of the battlefield. Then the General pulled down the blinds, shutting out that sad scene.

"Cosier now, eh?" he said.

And Chastity in the prettiest way possible fingered the decorations on his uniform and asked him all about them.

And presently, like a circling typhoon, the sounds of battle began to return.

From Black Mischief

THE MINISTRY OF MODERNISATION

One of the recurrent crises in his affairs prompts Basil Seal, the cad-hero of Black Mischief, *to take off for barbaric Azania, a Negro island-empire off the east coast of Africa, whose new ruler, Seth, was a contemporary of Basil's at Oxford. The naive young Emperor, a fanatic for progress, makes Basil his Minister of Modernisation. The other characters in the episode which follows are:*

General Connolly	*An Irishman who is Commander-in-chief of the Azanian Army and Duke of Ukaka.*
"Black Bitch"	*Connolly's Azanian wife.*
Krikor Youkoumian	*A wily Armenian entrepreneur.*
Madame Ballon	*The wife of the French Minister. It is falsely rumored that she is Connolly's mistress.*
Sir Samson Courteney	*The British Minister.*
Prudence	*Sir Samson's daughter.*
William Bland	*Honorary attaché at the British Legation.*

ON the south side of the Palace Compound, between the kitchen and the stockade, lay a large irregular space where the oxen were slaughtered for the public banquets. A minor gallows stood there which was used for such trivial, domestic executions as now and then became necessary within the royal household. The place was now deserted except for the small cluster of puzzled blacks who were usually congregated round the headquarters of the One Year Plan and a single dog who gnawed her hindquarters in the patch of shadow cast by two corpses, which rotated slowly face to face, half circle East, a half circle West, ten foot high in the limpid morning sunlight.

The Ministry of Modernisation occupied what had formerly been the old Empress's oratory; a circular building of concrete and corrugated iron, its outer wall enriched with posters from all parts of Europe and the United States advertising machinery, fashion and foreign travel. The display was rarely without attendance and to-day the customary loafers were reinforced by five or six gentlemen in the blue cotton cloaks which the official class of Debra-Dowa assumed in times of bereavement. These were mourners for the two criminals — peculators and perjurers both — who had come to give a dutiful tug at their relatives' heels in case life might not yet be extinct, and had stayed to gape, entranced by the manifestations of Progress and the New Age.

On the door was a board painted in Arabic, Sakuyu and French with the inscription:

MINISTRY OF MODERNISATION

HIGH COMMISSIONER & COMPTROLLER GENERAL:

MR. BASIL SEAL

FINANCIAL SECRETARY: MR. KRIKOR

YOUKOUMIAN

A vague smell of incense and candle-grease still possessed the interior; in all other ways it had been completely transformed. Two partitions divided it into unequal portions. The largest was Basil's office, which contained nothing except some chairs, a table littered with maps and memoranda and a telephone. Next door Mr. Youkoumian had induced a more homely note; his work was economically confined to two or three penny exercise books filled with figures and indecipherable jottings, but his personality extended itself and pervaded the room, finding concrete expression in the seedy red plush sofa that he had scavenged from one of the state apartments, the scraps of clothing hitched negligently about the furniture, the Parisian photographs pinned to the walls, the vestiges of food on enamelled tin plates, the scent spray, cigarette ends, spittoon, and the little spirit-stove over which perpetually simmered a brass pan of coffee. It was his idiosyncrasy to prefer working in stockinged feet, so that when he was at his post a pair of patent leather, elastic-sided boots proclaimed his presence from the window ledge.

In the vestibule sat a row of native runners with whose services the modernising party were as yet unable to dispense.

At nine in the morning both Basil and Mr. Youkoumian were at their desks. Instituted a month previously by royal proclamation, the Ministry of Modernisation was already a going concern. Just how far it was going, indeed, was appreciated by very few outside its circular, placarded walls. Its function as defined in Seth's decree was *"to promote the adoption of modern organisation and habits of life throughout the Azanian Empire"* which, liberally interpreted, comprised the right of interference in most of the public and private affairs of the nation. As Basil glanced through the correspondence that awaited him and the rough agenda for the day he felt ready to admit that anyone but himself and Mr. Youkoumian would have bitten off more than he could chew. Reports from eight provincial viceroys on a questionnaire concerning the economic resources and population of their territory — documents full of ponderous expressions of politeness and the minimum of trustworthy information; detailed recommendations from the railway authorities at Matodi; applications for concessions from European prospectors; enquiries from tourist bureaux about the possibilities of big game hunting, surf bathing and mountaineering; applications for public appointments; protests from missions and legations; estimates for building; details of court etiquette and precedence — everything seemed to find its way to Basil's table. The other ministers of the crown had not yet begun to feel uneasy about their own positions. They regarded Basil's arrival as a direct intervention of heaven on their behalf. Here was an Englishman who was willing to leave them their titles and emoluments and take all the work off their hands. Each was issued with the rubber stamp, REFER TO BUREAU OF MODERNISATION, and in a very few days the Minister of the Interior, the Lord Chamberlain, the Justiciar, the City Governor and even Seth himself, acquired the habit of relegating all decisions to Basil, with one firm stab of indelible ink. Two officials alone, the Nestorian Patriarch and the Commander-in-Chief of the army, failed to avail themselves of the convenient new institution, but continued to muddle through the routine of their departments in the same capricious, dilatory, but independent manner as before the establishment of the new régime.

Basil had been up very late the night before working with the Emperor on a codification of the criminal law, but the volume of business before him left him undismayed.

"Youkoumian."

" 'Ullo. Mr. Seal?"

The financial secretary padded in from the next room.

"Connolly won't have boots."

"Won't ave boots? But, Mr. Seal, he got to ave boots. I bought them from Cape Town. They come next ship. I bought them, you understand, as a personal enterprise, out of my own pocket. What in ell can I do with a thousand pair boots if Connolly won't take them?"

"You ought to have waited."

"Waited? And then when the order is out and everyone knows guards to ave boots, what'll appen then? Some pig wanting to make money will go to the Emperor and say I get you boots damned cheaper than Youkoumian. Where am I then? They might as well go barefoot all same as they do now like the dirty niggers they are. No, Mr. Seal, that is not business. I fix it so that one morning the Army Order says guards must have boots. Everyone say but where are boots? No one got enough boots in this stinking hole. Someone say I get you boots in three weeks, month, five weeks, so long. I came up and say I got boots. How many pairs you want? Thousand? O.K. I fix it. That is business. What does the General say?"

Basil handed him the letter. It was emphatic and almost ungenerously terse, coming as it did in answer to a carefully drafted recommendation beginning: *The Minister of Modernisation presents his compliments to the Commander-in-Chief of the Imperial Army and in pursuance of the powers granted him by royal decree begs to advise . . .*

It consisted of a single scrap of lined paper torn from a note-book across which Connolly had scrawled in pencil: *The Minister of Damn All can go to blazes. My men couldn't move a yard in boots. Try and sell Seth top hats next time. Ukaka C. in C.*

"Well," said Mr. Youkoumian doubtfully, "I *could* get top ats."

"That is one of Connolly's jokes, I'm afraid."

"Jokes is it? And ere am I with a thousand pair black boots on my ands. Ha. Ha. Like ell it's a joke. There isn't a thousand people in the whole country that wears boots. Besides, these aren't the kind of boots people buys for themselves. Government stuff. Damn rotten. See what I mean?"

"Don't you worry," Basil said. "We'll find a use for them. We might have them served out to the clergy." He took back the General's note, glanced through it frowning and clipped it into the file of correspondence; when he raised his head his eyes were clouded in an expression characteristic to him, insolent, sulky and curiously childish. "But as a matter of fact," he added, "I shouldn't mind a showdown with Connolly. It's nearly time for one."

"They are saying that the General is in love with Madame Ballon."

"I don't believe it."

"I am convinced," said Mr. Youkoumian. "It was told me on very igh authority by the barber who visits the French Legation. Everyone in the town is speaking of it. Even Madame Youkoumian has heard. I tell you ow it is," he added complacently. "Madame Ballon drinks. That is ow Connolly first ad er."

Quarter of an hour later both Basil and Mr. Youkoumian were engaged in what seemed more important business.

A morning's routine at the Ministry of Modernisation.

"Now, look, Mister, I tell you exactly how we are fixed. We have His Majesty's interests to safeguard. See what I mean. You think there is tin in the Ngumo mountains in workable quantities. So do we. So do other companies. They want concession too. Only to-day two gentlemen come to ask me to fix it for them. What do I do? I say, we can only give concession to company we have confidence in. Look. How about if on your board of directors you had a man of financial status in the country; someone who His Majesty trusts . . . see what I mean . . . someone with a fair little block of share allocated to him. He would protect His Majesty's interests and interests of company too . . . see?"

"That's all very well, Mr. Youkoumian, but it isn't so easy to find anyone like that. I can't think of anyone at the moment."

"No, can't you? Can't you think?"

"Unless, of course, you yourself? But I can hardly suggest that. You are far too busy?"

"Mister, I have learned how to be busy and still have time for things that please me . . ."

Next door: Basil and the American commercial attaché: "The situation is this, Walker. I'm — the Emperor is spending quarter of a million sterling on road construction this year. It can't come out of the ordinary revenue. I'm floating a loan to raise the money. You're acting over here for Cosmopolitan Oil Trust and for Stetson cars. Every mile of road we make is worth five hundred cars a year and God knows how many gallons of oil. If your companies like to take up the loan I'm prepared to give them a ten years monopoly . . ."

Later, the editor of the *Courier d'Azanie*.

Monsieur Bertrand did not look a man of any importance — nor, in fact, was he. The *Courier* consisted of a single sheet, folded quarto, which was issued weekly to rather less than a thousand subscribers in Debra-Dowa and Matodi. It retailed in French the chief local events of the week — the diplomatic entertainments, official appointments, court circular, the programmes of the cinemas, and such few items of foreign news as came through on the wireless. It occupied one day a week of Monsieur Bertrand's time, the remainder of which was employed in printing menus, invitation cards, funeral and wedding announcements, in acting as local correspondent for a European news-agency, and in selling stationery over the counter of his little office. It was in the hope of a fat order for crested note-paper that he presented himself in answer to Basil's invitation at the offices of the new Ministry.

"Good morning, Monsieur Bertrand. It's good of you to come. We may as well get to business at once. I want to buy your paper."

"Why, certainly, Monsieur Seal. I have a very nice cream laid line suitable for office use or a slightly more expensive quality azure tinted with a linen surface. I suppose you would want the name of the Ministry embossed at the head?"

"I don't think you understand me. I mean the *Courier d'Azanie*."

Monsieur Bertrand's face showed disappointment and some vexation. It was really unpardonably high-handed of this young man to demand a personal call from the proprietor and editor-in-chief whenever he bought a copy of his journal.

"I will tell my clerk. You wish to subscribe regularly?"

"No, no, you don't understand. I wish to become the proprietor — to own the entire concern. What is your price?"

Slowly the idea took root, budded and blossomed; then Monsieur Bertrand said: "Oh, no, that would be quite impossible. I don't want to sell."

"Come, come. It can't be worth much to you and I am willing to pay a generous price."

"It is not that, sir, it is a question of prestige, you understand," he spoke very earnestly. "You see as the proprietor and editor of the *Courier* I am *someone*. Twice a year Madame Bertrand and I dine at the French Legation; once we go to the garden party, we go to the Court and the polo club. That is something. But if I became Bertrand, job-printer, who will regard me then? Madame Bertrand would not forgive it."

"I see," said Basil. To be someone in Debra-Dowa . . . it seemed a modest ambition; it would be a shame to deprive Monsieur Bertrand. "I see. Well, suppose that you retained the position of editor and were nominally proprietor. That would fulfil my purpose. You see I am anxious to enlarge the scope of your paper. I wish it to publish leading articles explaining the political changes. Listen . . ." and for a quarter of an hour Basil outlined his intentions for the *Courier's* development . . . three sheets, advertisements of European firms and government services to meet increased cost of production; enlarged circulation; features in Sakuyu and Arabic; intelligent support of government policy . . . At the end of the interview Monsieur Bertrand left, slightly bewildered, carrying with him a fair-sized cheque and the notes for a leading article forecasting possible changes in the penal code . . . convict settlements to replace local prisons . . . What extraordinary subjects to mention in the *Courier!*

At eleven the Anglican Bishop came to protest against the introduction of State Lotteries.

At quarter-past, William came from Sir Sampson Courteney to discuss the possibility of making a road out to the Legation. William and Basil did not like each other.

At half-past, the Lord Chamberlain came to consult about cookery. A banquet was due to some Wanda notables next week. Seth had forbidden raw beef. What was he to give them? "Raw beef," said Basil. "Call it steak tartare."

"That is in accordance with modern thought?"

"Perfectly."

At noon Basil went to see the Emperor.

The heat, rarely intolerable in the hills, was at this time of day penetrating and devitalising. The palace roofs glared and shimmered. A hot breeze lifted the dust and powdered the bodies of the dangling courtiers and carried across the yard a few waste shreds of paper, baked crisp and brittle as dead leaves. Basil sauntered with half-shut eyes to the main entrance.

Soldiers stood up and saluted clumsily; the captain of the guard trotted after him and plucked at his sleeve.

"Good morning, captain."

"Good morning, Excellency. You are on your way to the Emperor?"

"As usual."

"There is a small matter. If I could interest your Excellency . . . It is about the two gentlemen who were hanged. One was my cousin."

"Yes?"

"His post has not yet been filled. It has always been held by my family. My uncle has made a petition to His Majesty . . ."

"Yes, yes. I will speak on his behalf."

"But that is exactly what you must not do. My uncle is a wicked man, Excellency. It was he who poisoned my father. I am sure of it. He wanted my mother. It would be most unjust for him to have the post. There is my little brother — a man of supreme ability and devotion . . ."

"Very well, captain, I'll do what I can."

"The angels preserve your Excellency."

The Emperor's study was strewn with European papers and catalogues; his immediate concern was a large plan of Debra-Dowa on which he was working with ruler and pencil.

"Come in, Seal, I'm just rebuilding the city. The Anglican Cathedral will have to go, I think, and all the South quarter. Look, here is Seth Square with the avenues radiating from it. I'm calling this Boulevard Basil Seal."

"Good of you, Seth."

"And this Avenue Connolly."

"Ah, I wanted to talk about him." Basil sat down and approached his subject discreetly. "I wouldn't say anything against him. I know you like him and in his rough-and-tumble way he's a decent soldier. But d'you ever feel that he's *not quite modern?*"

"He never made full use of our tank."

"Exactly. He's opposed to progress throughout. He wants to keep the army under *his* control. Now there's the question of boots. I don't think we told you, but the matter came before the Ministry and we sent in a recommendation that the guards should be issued with boots. It would increase their efficiency a hundred per cent. Half the sick list is due to hookworm, which as you know comes from going about barefooted. Besides, you know, there's the question of prestige. There's not a single guards' regiment in Europe without boots. You've seen them for yourself at Buckingham Palace. You'll never get the full respect of the powers until you give your troops boots."

"Yes, yes, by all means. They shall have boots at once."

"I was sure you'd see it that way. But the trouble is that Connolly's standing out against it. Now we've no power at present to issue an army ordinance. That has to come through him — or through you as commander-in-chief of the army."

"I'll make out an order to-day. Of course they must have boots. I'll hang any man I see barefooted."

"Fine. I thought you'd stand by us, Seth. You know," he added reflectively, "we've got a much easier job now than we should have had fifty years ago. If we'd had to modernise a country then it would have meant constitutional monarchy, bicameral legislature, proportional representation, women's suffrage, independent judicature, freedom of the press, referendums . . ."

"What is all that?" asked the Emperor.

"Just a few ideas that have ceased to be modern."

Then they settled down to the business of the day.

"The British Legation are complaining again about their road."

"That is an old question. I am tired of it. Besides you will see from the plan I have orientated all the roads leading out of the capital; they go by the points of the compass. I cannot upset my arrangements."

"The Minister feels very strongly about it."

"Well, another time . . . no, I tell you what I will do. Look, we will name this street after him. Then he will be satisfied."

The Emperor took up his indiarubber and erased Connolly's name from the new metropolis. *Avenue Sir Samson Courteney* he wrote in its place.

"I wish we had a tube railway," he said. "Do you think it would pay?"

"No."

"So I feared. But one day we will have one. Listen. You can tell Sir Samson that. When there is a tube railway he shall have a private station in the Legation compound. Now listen; I have had a letter from the Society for the Prevention of Cruelty to Animals. They want to send out a Commission to investigate Wanda methods of hunting. Is it cruel to spear lions, do you think?"

"No."

"No. However, here is the letter. From Dame Mildred Porch. Do you know her?"

"I've heard of her. An intolerable old gas-bag."

"What is gas-bag? An orator?"

"Yes, in a way."

"Well, she is returning from South Africa and wishes to spend a week here. I will say yes?"

"I shouldn't."

"I will say yes . . . And another thing. I have been reading in my papers about something very modern called birth control. What is it?"

Basil explained.

"I must have a lot of that. You will see to it. Perhaps it is not a matter for an ordinance, what do you think? We must popularise it by propaganda — educate the people in sterility. We might have a little pageant in its honour . . ."

Sir Samson accepted the rebuff to his plans with characteristic calm. "Well, well, I don't suppose young Seth will keep his job long. There's bound to be another revolution soon. The boy's head over heels in debt they tell me. I daresay the next government, whoever they are, will be able to afford something. And anyway, you may laugh at me, Prudence, but I think it's uncommonly decent of the young fellow to name that avenue after me. I've always liked him. You never know. Debra-Dowa may become a big city one day. I like to think of all the black johnnies in a hundred years' time driving up and down in their motor cars and going to the shops and saying, 'Number a hundred Samson Courteney' and wondering who I was. Like, like . . ."

"Like the Avenue Victor Hugo, Envoy."

"*Exactly,* or St. James's Square."

But the question of the boots was less easily settled.

On the afternoon of the day when the new ordinance was issued, Basil and Mr. Youkoumian were in conference. A major difficulty had arisen with regard to the plans for the new guest house at the palace. The Emperor had been captivated by some photographs he had discovered in a German architectural magazine and had decided to have the new building constructed of steel and vita-glass. Basil had spent half the morning in a vain attempt to persuade the royal mind that this was not a style at all suitable to his tropical climate and he was now at work with his financial secretary on a memorandum of the prohibitive extravagance of the new plans, when the door was pushed noisily open and the Duke of Ukaka strode into the room.

"Clear out, Youkoumian," he said. "I want to talk to your boss."

"O.K., General. I'll op off. No offence."

"Nonsense. Mr. Youkoumian is financial secretary of the Ministry. I should like him to be present at our interview."

"What me, Mr. Seal? I got nothing to say to the General."

"I wish you to stay."

"Quick," said the Duke, making a menacing motion towards him.

"Very sorry, gentlemen," said Mr. Youkoumian and shot through the door into his own office.

First trick to Connolly.

"I notice even that little dago has the sense to take off his boots."

Second trick to Connolly.

But in the subsequent interview Basil held his own. The General began: "Sorry to have to sling that fellow out. Can't stand his smell. Now let's talk. What's all this infernal nonsense about boots?"

"His Majesty's ordinance seemed perfectly explicit to me."

"*His Majesty's trousers.* For the Lord's sake come off the high horse, old boy, and listen to me. I don't give a hoot in hell about your modernisation. It's none of my business. You can set every damn coon in the place doing crossword puzzles for all I care. But I'm not going to have any monkeying about with my men. You'll lame the whole army in a day if you try to make 'em wear boots. Now look here, there's no reason why we should scrap over this. I've been in the country long enough to see through Youkoumian's game. Selling junk to the government has been the staple of industry of Debra-Dowa as long as I can remember it. I'd as soon you got the boodle as anyone else. Listen. If I tip the wink to the people on the line I can have the whole consignment of boots carried off by Sakuyu. You'll get compensation, the ordinance will be forgotten and no one will be any the worse off. What do you say? Is it a deal?"

For an appreciable time Basil hesitated in a decision of greater importance than either of them realised. The General sat jauntily on the edge of the table bending his rising cane over his knee; his expression was one of cordiality and of persuasive good sense. Basil hesitated. Was it some atavistic sense of a caste, an instinct of superiority, that held him aloof? Or was it vexed megalomania because Mr. Youkoumian had trotted so obediently from the room in his stockinged feet?

"You should have made your representations before," he said. "The tone of your first note made discussion impossible. The boots will be issued to the war department next week."

"Bloody young fool," said Connolly and took his leave.

As the door opened Mr. Youkoumian hastily stepped back from the keyhole. The General pushed past him and left the Ministry.

"Oh, Mr. Seal, why the ell do you want a bust up with im for? Look, how about I go after im and fix it, eh, Mr. Seal?"

"You won't do anything of the sort. We'll carry right on with the plans for the pageant of contraception."

"Oh dear, oh dear, Mr. Seal, there ain't no sense at all in aving bust ups."

News of the rupture spread like plague through the town. It was first-class gossip. The twenty or so spies permanently maintained by various interests in the Imperial Household carried tidings of the split through the legations and commercial houses; runners informed the Earl of Ngumo; Black Bitch told her hairdresser; an Eurasian bank clerk told his manager and the bank manager told the Bishop; Mr. You-koumian recounted the whole incident in graphic gesture over the bar of the Empereur Seth; Connolly swore hideously about it at the Per-roquet to Prince Fyodor; the Minister of the Interior roared out a fantastically distorted version to the assembled young ladies of the leading maison de société. That evening there was no dinner table of any importance in Debra-Dowa where the subject was not discussed in detail.

"Pity," remarked Sir Samson Courteney. "I suppose this'll mean that young Seal will be coming up here more than ever. Sorry, Prudence, I daresay he's right, but the truth is I can never find much to say to the chap . . . interested in different things . . . always going on about local politics. . . . Damn fool thing to quarrel about anyway. Why shouldn't he wear boots if he wants to?"

"That wasn't quite the point, Envoy."

"Well, it was something of the kind, I know."

"Ha! Ha!" said Monsieur Ballon. "Here is a thing Sir Samson did *not* foresee. Where is his fine web now, eh? Gossamer in the wind. Connolly is our man."

"Alas, blind, trusting husband, if he only knew," murmured the first to the second secretary.

"The Seal-Courteney faction and their puppet emperor have lost the allegiance of the army. We must consolidate our party."

It was in this way it happened that next morning there occurred an event unique in Black Bitch's experience. She was in the yard in front of her house laundering some of the General's socks (for she could not bear another woman to touch her man's clothes), chewing nut and meditatively spitting the dark juice into the soap-suds, when a lancer dismounted before her in the crimson and green uniform of the French Legation.

"Her Grace, the Duchess of Ukaka."

She lifted her dress, so as not to soil it, and wiped her hands on her knickers. "Me," she said.

The man saluted, handed her a large envelope; saluted again, mounted and rode away.

The Duchess was left alone with her large envelope; she squatted on her heels and examined it, turning it this way and that, holding it up to her ear and shaking it, her head sagely cocked on one side. Then she rose, padded into the house and across the hall to her bed-room; there, after circumspection, she raised a loose corner of the fibre matting and slipped the letter beneath it.

Two or three times during the next hour she left her wash-tub to see if her treasure was safe. At noon the General returned to luncheon and she handed it over to him, to await his verdict.

"Hullo, Black Bitch, what do you suppose this is? Madame Ballon wants us to dine at the French Legation to-morrow."

"You go?"

"But it's for both of us, old girl. The invitation is addressed to you. What d'you think of that?"

"Oh, my! Me dine with Madame Ballon! Oh, my, that's good!"

The Duchess could not contain her excitement; she threw back her head, lolled her eyes, and emitting deep gurgles of pleasure began spinning about the room like a teetotum.

"Good for the old geyser," said the Duke, and later when the ac-ceptance was written and despatched by the hand of the Imperial Guard's most inspiring sergeant-major, and Connolly had answered numerous questions about the proper conduct of knife, fork, glass and gloves, and the Duchess had gone bustling off to Mr. Youkoumian's store for ribbon and gold braid and artificial peonies to embellish her party frock, he went back to barracks with unusual warmth at heart towards the French Legation, remarking again, "Good for the old geyser. He's the first person who's troubled to ask Black Bitch to anything in eight years. And wasn't she pleased as Punch about it too, bless her black heart?"

As the time approached Black Bitch's excitement became almost alarming and her questions on etiquette so searching that the General was obliged to thump her soundly on the head and lock her in a cupboard for some hours before she could be reduced to a condition sufficiently subdued for diplomatic society. The dinner party, however, was a great success. The French Legation were there in full force, the director of the railway with his wife and daughters, and Lord Boaz, the Minister for the Interior. Black Bitch as Duchess of Ukaka took precedence and sat beside Monsieur Ballon who spoke to her in English in praise of her husband's military skill, influence and discretion. Any small errors in deportment which she may have committed were completely eclipsed by the Minister for the Interior who complained of the food, drank far too much, pinched the ladies on either side of him, pocketed a dozen cigars and a silver pepper mill which happened to take his fancy, and later in the drawing-room insisted on dancing by himself to the gramophone until his slaves appeared to hoist him into his car and carry him back to Madame Fifi, of whose charms he had been loudly boasting throughout the evening with a splendour of anatomical detail which was, fortunately, unintelligible to many of the people present.

In the dining-room when the succession of wines finally ended with the few ceremonial spoonfuls of sweet champagne and the men were left alone — the Minister for the Interior being restrained with difficulty from too precipitately following the ladies — Monsieur Ballon signalled for a bottle of eau de vie and moving round to the General's side, filled his glass and prompted him to some frank criticism of the Emperor and the present régime.

In the drawing-room the French ladies crowded about their new friend and before the evening was out several of them, including Madame Ballon, had dropped the "Duchess" and were on terms of calling her "Black Bitch." They asked her to come and see their gardens and children, they offered to teach her tennis and picquet, they advised her about an Armenian dressmaker in the town and a Hindu fortune teller; they were eager to lend her the patterns of their pyjamas; they spoke seriously of pills; best of all they invited her to sit on the committee which was being organised in the French colony to decorate a car for the forthcoming Birth-Control Gala. There was no doubt about it; the Connollys had made the French set.

Ten days later the boots arrived at Debra-Dowa; there were some formalities to be observed but these were rendered simple by the fact that the departments involved were now under the control of the Ministry of Modernisation. Mr. Youkoumian drew up an application to himself from the Ministry of War for the delivery of the boots; he made out a chit from the War Office to Ministry of Supplies; passed it on to the Treasury, examined and countersigned it, drew himself a cheque and in the name of the Customs and Excise Department allowed his own claim to rebate of duty on the importation of articles of "national necessity." The whole thing took ten minutes. A few hours later a thousand pairs of black boots had been dumped in the square of the Guards barracks where a crowd of soldiers rapidly collected and studied them throughout the entire afternoon with vivid but nervous interest.

That evening there was a special feast in honour of the boots. Cook-pots steaming over the wood fires; hand drums beating; bare feet shuffling unforgotten tribal rhythms; a thousand darkies crooning and swaying on their haunches, white teeth flashing in the fire light.

They were still at it when Connolly returned from dinner at the French consulate.

"What in hell are the boys making whoopee for to-night? It's not one of their days, is it?"

"Yes, General, very big day," said the sentry. "Boots day."

The singing reached Basil as he sat at his writing table at the Ministry, working long after midnight at the penal code.

"What's going on at the barracks?" he asked his servant.

"Boots."

"They like em, eh?"

"They like em fine."

"That's one in the eye for Connolly," he said, and next day, meeting the General in the Palace Yard he could not forbear to mention it. "So the boots went down all right with your men after all, Connolly."

"They went down."

"No cases of lameness yet I hope?"

The General leant over in his saddle and smiled pleasantly. "No cases of lameness," he replied. "One or two of belly ache though. I'm just writing a report on the matter to the Commissioner of Supplies — that's our friend Youkoumian, isn't it? You see my adjutant made rather a silly mistake. He hadn't had much truck with boots before and the silly fellow thought they were extra rations. My men ate the whole bag of tricks last night."

Dust in the air; a light wind rattling the leaves in the eucalyptus trees. Prudence sat over the *Panorama of Life* gazing through the window across the arid legation croquet lawn; dun grass rubbed bare between the hoops, a few sapless stalks in the beds beyond. She drew little arabesques in the corners of the page and thought about love.

It was the dry season before the rains when the cattle on the hills strayed miles from their accustomed pastures and herdsmen came to blows over the brackish dregs of the drinking holes; when, preceded by a scutter of children, lions would sometimes appear, parading the streets of the town in search of water; when Lady Courteney remarked that her herbaceous borders were a positive eyesore.

How out of tune with nature is the spirit of man! wrote Prudence in her sprawling, schoolroom characters. *When the earth proclaims its fertility, in running brooks, bursting seed, mating of birds and frisking of lambs then the thoughts of man turn to athletics and horticulture, water colour painting and amateur theatricals. Now in the arid season when nature seems all dead under the cold earth, there is nothing to think about except sex.* She bit her pen and read it through, substituting *hot soil* for *cold earth*. I am sure I've got something wrong in the first part, she thought and called to Lady Courteney who, watering-can in hand, was gloomily surveying a withered rose tree. "Mum, how soon after the birds mate are the lambs born?"

"Eggs, dear, not lambs," said her mother and pottered off towards some azalea roots which were desperately in need of water.

"Damn the panorama of life," said Prudence, and she began drawing a series of highly stylised profiles which by an emphasis of the chin and disordering of the hair had ceased during the last six weeks to be portraits of William and had come to represent Basil Seal. "To think that I wanted to be in love so much," she thought, "that I even practised on William."

"Luncheon," said her mother, repassing the window. "And I shall be late again. Do go in and be bright to your father."

But when Lady Courteney joined them in the dining-room she found father, daughter and William sitting in moody silence.

"Tinned asparagus," said Sir Samson. "And a letter from the Bishop."

"He's not coming out to dinner again?"

"No, no, it isn't as bad as that. But apparently Seth wants to pull down his Cathedral for some reason. What does he expect *me* to do about it I should like to know? Shocking ugly building anyhow. I wish, Prudence and William, you'd take the ponies out this afternoon. They haven't had any proper exercise for days."

"Too hot," said Prudence.

"Too busy," said William.

"Oh, well," said Sir Samson Courteney. And later he remarked to his wife: "I say, there isn't any trouble between those two, is there? They used to be such pals."

"I've been meaning to mention it for some time, Sam, only I was so worried about the antirrhinums. I don't think Prudence is at all herself. D'you think it's good for a girl of her age living at this height all the year round? It might be an idea to send her back to England for a few months. Harriet could put her up in Belgrave Place. I'm not sure it wouldn't be a good thing for her to go out in London for a season and meet some people of her own age. What d'you think?"

"I daresay you're right. All that What-d'you-call-it of Life she keeps working away at . . . Only you must write to Harriet. I'm far too busy at the moment. Got to think of something to say to the Bishop."

But next day Prudence and William went out with the ponies. She had an assignation with Basil.

"Listen, William, you're to go out of the city by the lane behind the Baptist school and the Jewish abattoirs, then past the Parsee death house and the fever hospital."

"Not exactly the prettiest ride."

"Darling. Don't be troublesome. You might get seen the other way. Once you're clear of the Arab cemetery you can go where you like. And you're to fetch me at Youkoumian's at five."

"Jolly afternoon for me, leading Mischief all the time."

"Now, William, you know you manage him perfectly. You're the only person I'd trust to take him. I can't leave him outside Youkoumian's, can I, because of *discretion*."

"What you don't seem to see is that it's pretty dim for me, floundering about half the day, I mean, in a dust heap with two ponies while you neck with the chap who's cut me out."

"*William*, don't be *coarse*. And anyway 'cut you out' nothing. You had me all to yourself for six months and weren't you just bored blue with it?"

"Well, I daresay he'll be bored soon."

"Cad."

Basil still lived in the large room over Mr. Youkoumian's Store. There was a veranda, facing onto a yard littered with scrap iron and general junk, accessible by an outside staircase. Prudence passed through the shop, out and up. The atmosphere of the room was rank with tobacco smoke. Basil, in shirt sleeves, rose from the deck chair to greet her. He threw the butt of his Burma cheroot into the tin hip bath which stood unemptied at the side of the bed; it sizzled and went out and floated throughout the afternoon, slowly unfurling in the soapy water. He bolted the door. It was half dark in the room. Dusty parallels of light struck through the shutters onto the floor boards and the few, shabby mats. Prudence stood isolated, waiting for him, her hat in her hand. At first neither spoke. Presently she said, "You might have shaved," and then, "Please help with my boots."

Below, in the yard, Madame Youkoumian upbraided a goat. Strips of sunlight traversed the floor as an hour passed. In the bath water, the soggy stub of tobacco emanated a brown blot of juice.

Banging on the door.

"Heavens," said Prudence, "that can't be William already."

"Mr. Seal, Mr. Seal."

"Well, what is it? I'm resting."

"Well you got to stop," said Mr. Youkoumian. "They're looking for you all over the town. Damn fine rest I've had this afternoon, like ell I aven't."

"What is it?"

"Emperor must see you at once. E's got a new idea. Very modern and important. Some damn fool nonsense about Swedish drill."

Basil hurried to the Palace to find his master in a state of high excitement.

"I have been reading a German book. We must draft a decree at once . . . communal physical exercises. The whole population, every morning, you understand. And we must get instructors from Europe.

Cable for them. Quarter of an hour's exercise a morning. And community singing. That is very important. The health of the nation depends on it. I have been thinking it over. Why is there no cholera in Europe? Because of community singing and physical jerks . . . and bubonic plague . . . and leprosy."

Back in her room Prudence reopened the *Panorama of Life* and began writing: *a woman in love* . . .

"A woman," said Mr. Youkoumian. "That's what Seth needs to keep im quiet. Always sticking is nose in too much everywhere. You listen to me, Mr. Seal— if we can fix Seth with a woman our modernisation will get along damn fine."

"There's always Fifi."

"Oh, Mr. Seal, e ad er when e was a little boy. Don't you worry. I'll fix it O.K."

Royal interruptions of the routine of the Ministry were becoming distressingly frequent in the last few days as the Emperor assimilated the various books that had arrived for him by the last mail. Worst of all the Pageant of Birth Control was proving altogether more trouble than it was worth; in spite of repeated remonstrances, however, it continued to occupy the mind of the Emperor in precedence of all other interests. He had already renamed the site of the Anglican Cathedral, Place Marie Stopes.

"Heaven knows what will happen if he ever discovers psycho-analysis," remarked Basil, gloomily foreseeing a Boulevard Krafft-Ebing, an Avenue Oedipus and a pageant of coprophagists.

"He'll discover every damn modern thing," said Mr. Youkoumian, "if we don't find him a woman damn quick . . . ere's another letter from the Vicar Apostolic. If I adn't ordered all that stuff from Cario I'd drop the whole pageant. But you can't use it for nothing else but what it's for — so far as I can see, not like boots what they can eat."

The opposition to the pageant was firm and widespread. The conservative party rallied under the leadership of the Earl of Ngumo. This nobleman, himself one of a family of forty-eight (most of whom he had been obliged to assassinate on his succession to the title) was the father of over sixty sons and uncounted daughters. This progeny was a favourite boast of his; in fact he maintained a concert party of seven minstrels for no other purpose than to sing at table about this topic when he entertained friends. Now in ripe age, with his triumphs behind him, he found himself like some scarred war veteran surrounded by pacifists, his prestige assailed and his proudest achievements held up to vile detraction. The new proposals struck at the very roots of sport and decency and he expressed the general feeling of the landed gentry when he threatened amid loud grunts of approval to dismember any man on his estates whom he found using the new-fangled and impious appliances.

The smart set, composed (under the leadership of Lord Boaz) of cosmopolitan blacks, courtiers, younger sons and a few of the decayed Arab intelligentsia, though not actively antagonistic, were tepid in their support; they discussed the question languidly in Fifi's salon and, for the most part, adopted a sophisticated attitude maintaining that of course *they* had always known about these things, but why invite trouble by all this publicity; at best it would only make contraception middle class. In any case this circle was always suspect to the popular mind and their allegiance was unlikely to influence public opinion in the Emperor's favour.

The Churches came out strong on the subject. No one could reasonably accuse the Nestorian Patriarch of fanatical moral inflexibility — indeed there had been incidents in his Beatitude's career when all but grave scandal had been caused to the faithful — but whatever his personal indulgence, his theology had always been unimpeachable. Whenever a firm lead was wanted on a question of opinion, the Patriarch had been willing to forsake his pleasures and pronounce freely and intransigently for the tradition he had inherited. There had been the ugly affair of the Metropolitan of Matodi who had proclaimed himself fourth member of the Trinity; there was the parish priest who was unsound about the Dual Will; there was the ridiculous heresy that sprang up in the province of Mhomala that the prophet Esias had wings and lived in a tree; there was the painful case of the human sacrifices at the Bishop of Popo's consecration — on all these and other uncertain topics the Patriarch had given proof of a sturdy orthodoxy.

Now, on the question of birth control, his Beatitude left the faithful in no doubt as to where their duty lay. As head of the established Church he called a conference which was attended by the Chief Rabbi, the Mormon Elder and the chief representatives of all the creeds of the empire; only the Anglican Bishop excused himself, remarking in a courteous letter of refusal, that his work lay exclusively among the British community who, since they were already fully informed and equipped in the matter, could scarcely be injured in any way by the Emperor's new policy; he wished his Beatitude every success in the gallant stand he was making for the decencies of family life, solicited his prayers and remarked that he was himself too deeply embroiled with the progressive party, who were threatening the demolition of his Cathedral, to confuse the issue with any other cause, however laudable it might be in itself.

As a result of the conference, the Patriarch composed an encyclical in rich, oratorical style and despatched copies of it by runners to all parts of the island. Had the influence of the established Church on the popular mind been more weighty, the gala should have been doomed, but as has already been mentioned the Christianising of the country was still so far incomplete that the greater part of the Empire retained with a minimum of disguise their older and grosser beliefs and it was, in fact, from the least expected quarter, the tribesmen and villagers, that the real support of Seth's policy suddenly appeared.

This development was due directly and solely to the power of advertisement. In the dark days when the prejudice of his people compassed him on every side and even Basil spoke unsympathetically of the wisdom of postponing the gala, the Emperor found among the books that were mailed to him monthly from Europe a collection of highly inspiring Soviet posters. At first the difficulties of imitation appeared to be insuperable. The *Courier* office had no machinery for reproducing pictures. Seth was contemplating the wild expedient of employing slave labour to copy his design when Mr. Youkoumian discovered that some years ago an enterprising philanthropist had by bequest introduced lithography into the curriculum of the American Baptist school. The apparatus survived the failure of the attempt. Mr. Youkoumian purchased it from the pastor and resold it at a fine profit to the Department of Fine Arts in the Ministry of Modernisation. An artist was next found in the Armenian colony who, on Mr. Youkoumian's introduction, was willing to elaborate Seth's sketches. Finally there resulted a large, highly coloured poster well calculated to convey to the illiterate the benefits of birth control. It was in many ways the highest triumph of the new ministry and Mr. Youkoumian was the hero. Copies were placarded all over Debra-Dowa; they were sent down the line to every station latrine, capital and coast; they were sent into the interior to vice-regal lodges and headmen's huts, hung up at prisons, barracks, gallows and juju trees, and wherever the poster was hung there assembled a cluster of inquisitive, entranced Azanians.

It portrayed two contrasted scenes. On one side a native hut of hideous squalor, overrun with children of every age, suffering from every physical incapacity — crippled, deformed, blind, spotted and insane; the father prematurely aged with paternity squatted by an empty cook-pot; through the door could be seen his wife, withered and bowed with child bearing, desperately hoeing at their inadequate crop. On the other side a bright parlour furnished with chairs and table; the mother, young and beautiful, sat at her ease eating a huge slice of raw meat; her husband smoked a long Arab hubble-bubble (still a caste mark of leisure throughout the land), while a single, healthy child sat between them reading a newspaper. Inset between the two pictures was a detailed drawing of some up-to-date contraceptive apparatus and the words in Sakuyu: WHICH HOME DO YOU CHOOSE?

Interest in the pictures was unbounded; all over the island woolly heads were nodding, black hands pointing, tongues clicking against filed teeth in unsyntactical dialects. Nowhere was there any doubt about the meaning of the beautiful new pictures.

See: on right hand: there is rich man: smoke pipe like big chief: but his wife she no good: sit eating meat: and rich man no good: he only one son.

See: on left hand: poor man: not much to eat: but his wife she very good, work hard in field: man he good too: eleven children: one very mad, very holy. And in the middle: Emperor's juju. Make you like that good man with eleven children.

And as a result, despite admonitions from squire and vicar, the peasantry began pouring into town for the gala, eagerly awaiting initiation to the fine new magic of virility and fecundity.

Once more, wrote Basil Seal, in a lead article in the *"Courier,"* the *people of the Empire have overridden the opposition of a prejudiced and interested minority, and with no uncertain voice have followed the Emperor's lead in the cause of Progress and the New Age.*

So brisk was the demand for the Emperor's juju that some time before the day of the carnival Mr. Youkoumian was frantically cabling to Cairo for fresh supplies.

Meanwhile the Nestorian Patriarch became a very frequent guest at the French Legation.

"We have the army, we have the Church," said Monsieur Ballon. "All we need now is a new candidate for the throne."

"If you ask me," said Basil, one morning soon after the distribution of the poster, "loyalty to the throne is one of the hardest parts of our job."

"Oh, gosh, Mr. Seal, don't you ever say a thing like that. I seen gentlemen poisoned dead for less. What's e done now?"

"Only this." He handed Mr. Youkoumian a chit which had just arrived from the Palace:

For your information and necessary action; I have decided to abolish the following:
Death penalty.
Marriage.
The Sakuyu language and all native dialects.
Infant mortality.
Totemism.
Inhumane butchery.
Mortgages.
Emigration.
Please see to this. Also organise system of reservoirs for city's water supply and draft syllabus for competitive examination for public services. Suggest compulsory Esperanto.

Seth

"E's been reading books again, Mr. Seal, that's what it is. You won't get no peace from im not till you fix im with a woman. Why can't e drink or something?"

In fact the Ministry's triumph in the matter of birth control was having highly embarrassing consequences. If before, Basil and Mr. Youkoumian had cause to lament their master's tenacity and single-ness of purpose, they were now harassed from the opposite extreme of temperament. It was as though Seth's imagination like a volcanic lake had in the moment of success become suddenly swollen by the irruption of unsuspected, subterranean streams until it darkened and seethed and overflowed its margins in a thousand turbulent cascades. The earnest and rather puzzled young man became suddenly capricious and volatile; ideas bubbled up within him, bearing to the surface a confused sediment of phrase and theory, scraps of learning half understood and fantastically translated.

"It's going to be awkward for us if the Emperor goes off his rocker."

"Oh, my, Mr. Seal, you do say the most damned dangerous things."

That afternoon Basil called at the Palace to discuss the new proposals, only to find that since his luncheon the Emperor's interests had veered suddenly towards archaeology.

"Yes, yes, the abolitions. I sent you a list this morning, I think. It is a mere matter of routine. I leave the details to the Ministry. Only you must be quick please . . . it is not that which I want to discuss with you now. It is our Museum."

"Museum?"

"Yes, of course we must have a Museum. I have made a few notes to guide you. The only serious difficulty is accommodation. You see it must be inaugurated before the arrival of the Cruelty to Animals Commission at the beginning of next month. There is hardly time to build a house for it. The best thing will be to confiscate one of the town palaces. Ngumo's or Boaz's would do after some slight adjustments. But that is a matter for the Ministry to decide. On the ground floor will be the natural history section. You will collect examples of all the flora and fauna of the Empire, lions, butterflies, birds' eggs, specimens of woods, everything. That should easily fill the ground floor. I have been reading," he added earnestly, "about ventilation. That is very important. The air in the cases must be continually renewed — a cubic metre an hour is about the right draught — otherwise the specimens suffer. You will make a careful note of that. Then on the first floor will be the anthropological and historical section — examples of native craft, Portuguese and Arab work, a small library. Then in the Central Hall, the relics of the Royal House. I have some of the medals of Amurath upstairs under one of the beds in a box — photographs of myself, some of my uniforms, the cap and gown I wore at Oxford, the model of the Eiffel Tower which I brought back from Paris. I will lend some pages of manuscript in my own hand to be exhibited. It will be most interesting."

For some days Mr. Youkoumian busied himself with the collection of specimens. Word went round that there was a market for objects of interest at the Ministry of Modernisation and the work of the office was completely paralysed by the hawkers of all races who assembled in and around it, peddling brass pots and necklaces of carved nut, snakes in baskets and monkeys in cages, cloth of beaten bark and Japanese cotton, sacramental vessels pouched by Nestorian deacons, ironwood clubs, homely household deities, tanned human scalps, cauls and navel strings and wonder-working fragments of meteorite, amulets to ward off the evil eye from camels, Monsieur Ballon's masonic apron purloined by the legation butler, and a vast monolithic phallus borne by three oxen from a shrine in the interior. Mr. Youkoumian bargained briskly and bought almost everything he was offered, reselling them later to the Ministry of Fine Arts of which Basil had created him the director. But when, at a subsequent interview, Basil mentioned their progress to the Emperor he merely nodded a listless approval and even while he unscrewed the cap of his fountain pen to sign the order evicting the Earl of Ngumo from his town house, began to speak of the wonders of astronomy.

"Do you realise the magnitude of the fixed stars? They are immense. I have read a book which says that the mind boggles at their distances. I did not know that word, boggles. I am immediately founding an Institute for Astronomical Research. I must have Professors. Cable for them to Europe. Get me tip-top professors, the best procurable."

But next day he was absorbed in ectogenesis. "I have read here," he said, tapping a volume of speculative biology, "that there is to be no more birth. The ovum is fertilised in the laboratory and then the foetus is matured in bottles. It is a splendid idea. Get me some of those bottles . . . and no boggling."

Even while discussing the topic that immediately interested him, he would often break off in the middle of a sentence, with an irrelevant question. "How much are autogyros?" or "Tell me exactly, please, what is Surréalism" or "Are you convinced of Dreyfus' innocence?" and then, without pausing for the reply would resume his adumbrations of the New Age.

The days passed rapturously for Mr. Youkoumian who had found in the stocking of the Museum work for which early training and all his natural instincts richly equipped him; he negotiated endlessly between the Earl of Ngumo and Viscount Boaz, armed with orders for the dispossession of the lowest bidder; he bought and resold, haggled, flattered and depreciated, and ate and slept in a clutter of dubious antiques. But on Basil the strain of modernity began to leave its traces. Brief rides with Prudence through the tinder-dry countryside, assignations furtively kept and interrupted at a moment's notice by some peremptory, crazy summons to the Palace, alone broke the unquiet routine of his day.

"I believe that odious Emperor is slowly poisoning you. It's a thing he does do," said Prudence. "And I never saw anyone look so ill."

"You know it sounds absurd but I miss Connolly. It's rather a business living all the time between Seth and Youkoumian."

"Of course you wouldn't remember that there's me too, would you," said Prudence. "Not just to cheer me up you wouldn't?"

"You're a grand girl, Prudence. What Seth calls tip-top. But I'm so tired I could die."

And a short distance away the Legation syce moodily flicked with his whip at a train of ants while the ponies shifted restlessly among the stones and shelving earth of a dry water-course.

Two mornings later the Ministry of Modernisation received its sharpest blow. Work was going on as usual. Mr. Youkoumian was interviewing a coast Arab who claimed to possess some "very old, very genuine" Portuguese manuscripts; Basil, pipe in his mouth, was considering how best to deal with the Emperor's latest memorandum, *Kindly insist straw hats and gloves compulsory peerage,* when he received an unexpected and disturbing call from Mr. Jagger, the contractor in charge of the demolition of the Anglican Cathedral; a stocky, good-hearted little Britisher who after a succession of quite honourable bankruptcies in Cape Town, Mombasa, Dar-es-salaam and Aden had found his way to Debra-Dowa where he had remained ever since, occupied with minor operations in the harbour and along the railway line. He threaded his way through the antiquities which had lately begun to encroach on Basil's office, removed a seedy-looking caged vulture from the chair and sat down; his manner was uncertain and defiant.

"It's not playing the game, Mr. Seal," he said. "I tell you that fair and square and I don't mind who knows it, not if it's the Emperor himself."

"Mr. Jagger," said Basil impressively, "you should have been long enough in this country to know that that is a very rash thing to say. Men have been poisoned for less. What is your trouble?"

"This here's my trouble," said Mr. Jagger, producing a piece of paper from a pocket full of pencils and foot rules and laying it on the table next to the mosaic portrait of the late Empress recently acquired by the Director of Fine Arts. "What is it, eh, that's what I want to know."

"What indeed?" said Basil. He picked it up and examined it closely.

In size, shape and texture it resembled an English five-pound note and was printed on both sides with intricate engraved devices of green and red. There was an Azanian eagle, a map of the Empire, a soldier in the uniform of the Imperial Guard, an aeroplane, and a classical figure bearing a cornucopia but the most prominent place was taken by a large, medallion portrait of Seth in top hat and European tail coat. The words *Five Pounds* lay in flourished script across the middle; above them THE IMPERIAL BANK OF AZANIA and below them a facsimile of Seth's signature.

The normal currency of the capital and the railway was in Indian rupees, although East African shillings, French and Belgian colonial francs and Marie Therese thalers circulated with equal freedom; in the interior the mediums of exchange were rock-salt and cartridges.

"This is a new one on me," said Basil. "I wonder if the Treasury knows anything about it. Mr. Youkoumian, come in here a minute, will you?"

The Director of Fine Arts and First Lord of the Treasury trotted through the partition door in his black cotton socks; he carried a model dhow he had just acquired.

"No, Mr. Seal," he pronounced, "I ain't never seen a thing like that before. Where did the gentleman get it?"

"The Emperor's just given me a whole packet of them for the week's wages bill. What is the Imperial Bank of Azania anyway. I never see such a thing all the time I been in the country. There's something here that's not on the square. You must understand, Mr. Seal, that it's not anyone's job breaking up that Cathedral. Solid granite shipped all the way from Aberdeen. Why Lord love you the pulpit alone weighs seven and a half ton. I had two boys hurt only this morning through the font swinging loose as they were hoisting it into a lorry. Smashed up double one of them was. The Emperor ain't got no right to try putting that phoney stuff across me."

"You may be quite confident," said Basil with dignity, "that in all your dealings with His Majesty you will encounter nothing but the highest generosity and integrity. However I will institute enquiries on your behalf."

"No offence meant, I'm sure," said Mr. Jagger.

Basil watched him across the yard and then snatched up his topee from a fossilised tree-fern. "What's that black lunatic been up to this time?" he asked, starting off towards the Palace.

"Oh, Mr. Seal, you'll get into trouble one day with the things you say."

The Emperor rose to greet him with the utmost cordiality.

"Come in, come in. I'm very glad you've come. I'm in some perplexity about *Nacktkultur*. Here have I spent four weeks trying to enforce the edict prescribing trousers for the official classes, and now I read that it is more modern not to wear any at all."

"Seth, what's the Imperial Bank of Azania?"

The Emperor looked embarrassed.

"I thought you might ask. . . . Well, actually it is not quite a bank at all. It is a little thing I did myself. I will show you."

He led Basil to a huge cupboard which occupied half the wall on one side of the library, and opening it showed him a dozen or so shelves stacked with what might have been packets of writing paper.

"What is that?"

"Just under three million pounds," said the Emperor proudly. "A little surprise. I had them done in Europe."

"But you can't possibly do this."

"Oh, yes, I assure you. It was easy. All these on this shelf are for a thousand pounds each. And now that the plates have been made, it is quite inexpensive to print as many more as we require. You see there were a great many things which needed doing and I had not a great many rupees. Don't look angry, Seal. Look, I'll give you some." He pressed a bundle of fivers into Basil's hand. "And take some for Mr. Youkoumian, too. Pretty fine picture of me, eh? I wondered about the hat. You will see that in the fifty-pound notes I wear a crown."

For some minutes Basil attempted to remonstrate; then quite suddenly he abandoned the argument.

"I knew you would understand," said the Emperor. "It is so simple. As soon as these are used up we will send for some more. And to-morrow you will explain to me about *Nacktkultur*, eh?"

Basil returned to his office very tired.

"There's only one thing to hope for now. That's a fire in the Palace to get rid of the whole lot."

"We must change these quick," said Mr. Youkoumian. "I know a damn fool Chinaman might do it. Anyway the Ministry of Fine Arts can take one at par for the historical section."

It was on that afternoon that Basil at last lost his confidence in the permanence of the One Year Plan.

Excursion in Reality

THE commissionaire at Espinoza's restaurant seems to maintain under his particular authority all the most decrepit taxicabs in London. He is a commanding man; across his great chest the student of military medals may construe a tale of heroism and experience; Boer farms sink to ashes, fanatical Fuzzie-Wuzzies hurl themselves to paradise, supercilious mandarins survey the smashing of their porcelain and rending of fine silk, in that triple row of decorations. He has only to run from the steps of Espinoza's to call to your service a vehicle as crazy as all the enemies of the King-Emperor.

Half a crown into the white cotton glove, because Simon Lent was too tired to ask for change. He and Sylvia huddled into the darkness on broken springs, between draughty windows. It had been an unsatisfactory evening. They had sat over their table until two because it was an extension night. Sylvia would not drink anything because Simon had said he was broke. So they sat for five or six hours, sometimes silent, sometimes bickering, sometimes exchanging listless greeting with the passing couples. Simon dropped Sylvia at her door; a kiss, clumsily offered, coldly accepted; then back to the attic flat, over a sleepless garage, for which Simon paid six guineas a week.

Outside his door they were sluicing a limousine. He squeezed round it and climbed the narrow stairs that had once echoed to the whistling of ostlers, stamping down to stables before dawn. (Woe to young men in Mewses! Oh woe, to bachelors half in love, living on £800 a year!) There was a small heap of letters on his dressing-table, which had arrived that evening while he was dressing. He lit his gas fire and began to open them. Tailor's bill £56, hosier £43; a reminder that his club subscription for that year had not been paid; his account from Espinoza's with a note informing him that the terms were strict, net cash monthly, and that no further credit would be extended to him; "it appeared from the books" of his bank that his last cheque overdrew his account £10 16s. beyond the limit of his guaranteed overdraft; a demand from the income-tax collector for particulars of his employees and their wages (Mrs. Shaw, who came in to make his bed and orange juice for 4s. 6d. a day); small bills for books, spectacles, cigars, hair lotion and Sylvia's last four birthday presents. (Woe to shops that serve young men in Mewses!)

The other part of his mail was in marked contrast to this. There was a box of preserved figs from an admirer in Fresno, California; two letters from young ladies who said they were composing papers about his work for their college literary societies, and would he send a photograph; press cuttings describing him as a "popular," "brilliant," "meteorically successful," and "enviable" young novelist; a request for the loan of £200 from a paralysed journalist; an invitation to luncheon from Lady Metroland; six pages of closely reasoned abuse from a lunatic asylum in the North of England. For the truth, which no one who saw into Simon Lent's heart could possibly have suspected, was that he was in his way and within his limits quite a famous young man.

There was a last letter with a typewritten address which Simon opened with little expectation of pleasure. The paper was headed with the name of a film studio in one of the suburbs of London. The letter was brief and businesslike.

Dear Simon Lent [a form of address, he had noted before, largely favoured by the theatrical profession],

I wonder whether you have ever considered writing for the films. We should value your angle on a picture we are now making. Perhaps you would meet me for luncheon to-morrow at the Garrick Club and let me know your reactions to this. Will you leave a message with my night secretary some time before 8 A.M. to-morrow morning or with my day secretary after that hour?

Cordially yours,

Below this were two words written in pen and ink which seemed to be *Jewee Mecceee* with below them the explanatory typescript (*Sir James Macrae*).

Simon read this through twice. Then he rang up Sir James Macrae and informed his night secretary that he would keep the luncheon appointment next day. He had barely put down the telephone before the bell rang.

"This is Sir James Macrae's night secretary speaking. Sir James would be very pleased if Mr. Lent would come round and see him this evening at his house in Hampstead."

Simon looked at his watch. It was nearly three. "Well . . . it's rather late to go so far to-night . . ."

"Sir James is sending a car for you."

Simon was no longer tired. As he waited for the car the telephone rang again. "Simon," said Sylvia's voice, "are you asleep?"

"No; in fact I'm just going out."

"Simon . . . I say, was I beastly to-night?"

"Lousy."

"Well, I thought you were lousy, too."

"Never mind. See you some time."

"Aren't you going to go on talking?"

"Can't, I'm afraid. I've got to do some work."

"*Simon*, what *can* you mean?"

"Can't explain now. There's a car waiting."

"When am I seeing you — to-morrow?"

"Well, I don't really know. Ring me up in the morning. Good night."

A quarter of a mile away, Sylvia put down the telephone, rose from the hearthrug, where she had settled herself in the expectation of twenty minutes' intimate explanation, and crept disconsolately into bed.

Simon bowled off to Hampstead through deserted streets. He sat back in the car in a state of pleasant excitement. Presently they began to climb the steep hill and emerged into an open space with a pond and the tops of trees, black and deep as a jungle in the darkness. The night butler admitted him to the low Georgian house and led him to the library, where Sir James Macrae was standing before the fire, dressed in ginger-coloured plus fours. A table was laid with supper.

"Evening, Lent. Nice of you to come. Have to fit in business when I can. Cocoa or whisky? Have some rabbit pie; it's rather good. First chance of a meal I've had since breakfast. Ring for some more cocoa, there's a good chap. Now what was it you wanted to see me about?"

"Well, I thought *you* wanted to see *me*."

"Did I? Very likely. Miss Bentham'll know. She arranged the appointment. You might ring the bell on the desk, will you?"

Simon rang and there instantly appeared the neat night secretary.

"Miss Bentham, what did I want to see Mr. Lent about?"

"I'm afraid I couldn't say, Sir James. Miss Harper is responsible for Mr. Lent. When I came on duty this evening I merely found a note from her asking me to fix an appointment as soon as possible."

"Pity," said Sir James. "We'll have to wait until Miss Harper comes on to-morrow."

"I think it was something about writing for films."

"Very likely," said Sir James. "Sure to be something of the kind. I'll let you know without delay. Thanks for dropping in." He put down his cup of cocoa and held out his hand with unaffected cordiality. "Good night, my dear boy." He rang the bell for the night butler. "Sanders, I want Benson to run Mr. Lent back."

"I'm sorry, sir. Benson has just gone down to the studio to fetch Miss Grits."

"Pity," said Sir. James. "Still, I expect you'll be able to pick up a taxi or something."

Simon got to bed at half-past four. At ten minutes past eight the telephone by his bed was ringing.

"Mr. Lent? This is Sir James Macrae's secretary speaking. Sir James's car will call for you at half-past eight to take you to the studio."

"I shan't be ready as soon as that, I'm afraid."

There was a shocked pause; then the day secretary said: "Very well, Mr. Lent. I will see if some alternative arrangement is possible and ring you in a few minutes."

In the intervening time Simon fell asleep again. Then the bell woke him once more and the same impersonal voice addressed him.

"Mr. Lent? I have spoken to Sir James. His car will call for you at eight forty-five."

Simon dressed hastily. Mrs. Shaw had not yet arrived, so there was no breakfast for him. He found some stale cake in the kitchen cupboard and was eating it when Sir James's car arrived. He took a slice down with him, still munching.

"You needn't have brought that," said a severe voice from inside the car. "Sir James has sent you some breakfast. Get in quickly; we're late."

In the corner, huddled in rugs, sat a young woman in a jaunty red hat; she had bright eyes and a very firm mouth.

"I expect that you are Miss Harper."

"No. I'm Elfreda Grits. We're working together on this film, I believe. I've been up all night with Sir James. If you don't mind I'll go to sleep for twenty minutes. You'll find a thermos of cocoa and some rabbit pie in the basket on the floor."

"Does Sir James live on cocoa and rabbit pie?"

"No; those are the remains of his supper. Please don't talk. I want to sleep."

Simon disregarded the pie, but poured some steaming cocoa into the metal cap of the thermos flask. In the corner Miss Grits composed herself for sleep. She took off the jaunty red hat and laid it between them on the seat, veiled her eyes with two blue-pigmented lids and allowed the firm lips to relax and gape a little. Her platinum-blonde wind-swept head bobbed and swayed with the motion of the car as they swept out of London through converging and diverging tram lines. Stucco gave place to brick and the façades of the tube stations changed from tile to concrete; unoccupied building plots appeared and newly planted trees along unnamed avenues. Five minutes exactly before their arrival at the studio Miss Grits opened her eyes, powdered her nose, touched her lips with red, and pulling her hat on to the side of her scalp, sat bolt upright, ready for another day.

Sir James was at work on the lot when they arrived. In a white-hot incandescent hell two young people were carrying on an infinitely tedious conversation at what was presumably the table of a restaurant. A dozen emaciated couples in evening dress danced listlessly behind them. At the other end of the huge shed some carpenters were at work building the façade of a Tudor manor house. Men in eyeshades scuttled in and out. Notices stood everywhere. DO NOT SMOKE. DO NOT SPEAK. KEEP AWAY FROM THE HIGH-POWER CABLE.

Miss Grits, in defiance of these regulations, lit a cigarette, kicked some electric apparatus out of her path, said, "He's busy. I expect he'll see us when he's through with this scene," and disappeared through a door marked NO ADMITTANCE.

Shortly after eleven o'clock Sir James caught sight of Simon. "Nice of you to come. Shan't be long now," he called out to him. "Mr. Briggs, get a chair for Mr. Lent."

At two o'clock he noticed him again. "Had any lunch?"

"No," said Simon.

"No more have I. Just coming."

At half-past three Miss Grits joined him and said: "Well, it's been an easy day so far. You mustn't think we're always as slack as this. There's a canteen across the yard. Come and have something to eat."

An enormous buffet was full of people in a variety of costume and make-up. Disappointed actresses in languorous attitudes served cups of tea and hard-boiled eggs. Simon and Miss Grits ordered sandwiches and were about to eat them when a loud-speaker above their heads suddenly announced with alarming distinctness, "Sir James Macrae calling Mr. Lent and Miss Grits in the Conference Room."

"Come on, quick," said Miss Grits. She bustled him through the swing doors, across the yard, into the office buildings and up a flight of stairs to a solid oak door marked CONFERENCE. KEEP OUT.

Too late.

"Sir James has been called away," said the secretary. "Will you meet him at the West End office at five-thirty."

Back to London, this time by tube. At five-thirty they were at the Piccadilly office ready for the next clue in their treasure hunt. This took them to Hampstead. Finally at eight they were back at the studio. Miss Grits showed no sign of exhaustion.

"Decent of the old boy to give us a day off," she remarked. "He's easy to work with in that way — after Hollywood. Let's get some supper."

But as they opened the canteen doors and felt the warm breath of light refreshments, the loud-speaker again announced: "Sir James Macrae calling Mr. Lent and Miss Grits in the Conference Room."

This time they were not too late. Sir James was there at the head of an oval table; round him were grouped the chiefs of his staff. He sat in a great-coat with his head hung forward, elbows on the table and his hands clasped behind his neck. The staff sat in respectful sympathy. Presently he looked up, shook himself and smiled pleasantly.

"Nice of you to come," he said. "Sorry I couldn't see you before. Lots of small things to see to on a job like this. Had dinner?"

"Not yet."

"Pity. Have to eat, you know. Can't work at full pressure unless you eat plenty."

Then Simon and Miss Grits sat down and Sir James explained his plan. "I want, ladies and gentlemen, to introduce Mr. Lent to you. I'm sure you all know his name already and I daresay some of you know his work. Well, I've called him in to help us and I hope that when he's heard the plan he'll consent to join us. I want to produce a film of *Hamlet*. I daresay you don't think that's a very original idea —

but it's *angle* that counts in the film world. I'm going to do it from an entirely new angle. That's why I've called in Mr. Lent. I want him to write dialogue for us."

"But surely," said Simon, "there's quite a lot of dialogue there already?"

"Ah, you don't see my angle. There have been plenty of productions of Shakespeare in modern dress. We are going to produce him in modern speech. How can you expect the public to enjoy Shakespeare when they can't make head or tail of the dialogue. D'you know I began reading a copy the other day and blessed if *I* could understand it. At once I said, 'What the public wants is Shakespeare with all his beauty of thought and character translated into the language of every-day life.' Now Mr. Lent here was the man whose name naturally sug- gested itself. Many of the most high-class critics have commended Mr. Lent's dialogue. Now my idea is that Miss Grits here shall act in an advisory capacity, helping with the continuity and the technical side, and that Mr. Lent shall be given a free hand with the scenario . . ."

The discourse lasted for a quarter of an hour; then the chiefs of staff nodded sagely; Simon was taken into another room and given a contract to sign by which he received £50 a week retaining fee and £250 advance.

"You had better fix up with Miss Grits the times of work most suitable to you. I shall expect your first treatment by the end of the week. I should go and get some dinner if I were you. Must eat."

Slightly dizzy, Simon hurried to the canteen where two languorous blondes were packing up for the night.

"We've been on since four o'clock this morning," they said, "and the supers have eaten everything except the nougat. Sorry."

Sucking a bar of nougat Simon emerged into the now-deserted studio. On three sides of him, to the height of twelve feet, rose in appalling completeness the marble walls of the scene-restaurant; at his elbow a bottle of imitation champagne still stood in its pail of melted ice; above and beyond extended the vast gloom of rafters and ceiling.

"*Fact*," said Simon to himself, "the world of action . . . the pulse of life . . . Money, hunger . . . *Reality*."

Next morning he was called with the words, "Two young ladies wait- ing to see you."

"Two?"

Simon put on his dressing-gown and, orange-juice in hand, entered his sitting-room. Miss Grits nodded pleasantly.

"We arranged to start at ten," she said. "But it doesn't really matter. I shall not require you very much in the early stages. This is Miss Dawkins. She is one of the staff stenographers. Sir James thought you would need one. Miss Dawkins will be attached to you until further notice. He also sent two copies of *Hamlet*. When you've had your bath, I'll read you my notes for our first treatment."

But this was not to be; before Simon was dressed Miss Grits had been recalled to the studio on urgent business.

"I'll ring up and tell you when I am free," she said.

Simon spent the morning dictating letters to everyone he could think of; they began — *Please forgive me for dictating this, but I am so busy just now that I have little time for personal correspondence . . .*" Miss Dawkins sat deferentially over her pad. He gave her Sylvia's number.

"Will you get on to this number and present my compliments to Miss Lennox and ask her to luncheon at Espinoza's . . . And book a table for two there at one forty-five."

"Darling," said Sylvia, when they met, "why were you out all yesterday, and *who* was that voice this morning?"

"Oh, that was Miss Dawkins, my stenographer."

"Simon, what *can* you mean?"

"You see, I've joined the film industry."

"*Darling*. Do give me a job."

"Well, I'm not paying much attention to casting at the moment — but I'll bear you in mind."

"Goodness. How you've changed in two days!"

"Yes!" said Simon, with great complacency. "Yes, I think I have. You see, for the first time in my life I have come into contact with Real Life. I'm going to give up writing novels. It was a mug's game anyway. The written word is dead — first the papyrus, then the printed book, now the film. The artist must no longer work alone. He is part of the age in which he lives; he must share — only of course, my dear Sylvia, in very different proportions — the weekly wage envelope of the proletarian. Vital art implies a corresponding set of social relationships. Co-operation . . . co-ordination . . . the hive endeavour of the community directed to a single end . . ."

Simon continued in this strain at some length, eating meantime a luncheon of Dickensian dimensions, until, in a small miserable voice, Sylvia said: "It seems to me that you've fallen for some ghastly film star."

"Oh God," said Simon, "only a virgin could be as vulgar as that."

They were about to start one of their old, interminable quarrels when the telephone boy brought a message that Miss Grits wished to resume work instantly.

"So that's her name," said Sylvia.

"If you only knew how funny that was," said Simon scribbling his initials on the bill and leaving the table while Sylvia was still groping with gloves and bag.

As things turned out, however, he became Miss Grits's lover before the week was out. The idea was hers. She suggested it to him one evening at his flat as they corrected the transcript of the final version of their first treatment.

"No, really," Simon said aghast. "No, really. It would be quite impossible. I'm sorry, but . . ."

"Why? Don't you like women?"

"Yes, but . . ."

"Oh, come along," Miss Grits said briskly. "We don't get much time for amusement . . ." And later, as she packed their manuscripts into her attaché case she said, "We must do it again if we have time. Besides I find it's so much easier to work with a man if you're having an *affaire* with him."

For three weeks Simon and Miss Grits — he always thought of her by this name in spite of all subsequent intimacies — worked together in complete harmony. His life was redirected and transfigured. No longer did he lie in bed, glumly preparing himself for the coming day; no longer did he say every morning, "I *must* get down to the country and finish that book," and every evening find himself slinking back to the same urban flat; no longer did he sit over supper tables with Sylvia, idly bickering; no more listless explanations over the telephone. Instead he pursued a routine of incalculable variety, summoned by telephone at all hours to conferences which rarely assembled; sometimes to Hampstead, sometimes to the studios, once to Brighton. He spent long periods of work pacing up and down his sitting-room, with Miss Grits pacing backwards and forwards along the other wall and Miss Dawkins obediently perched between them, as the two dictated, corrected and redrafted their scenario. There were meals at improbable times and vivid, unsentimental passages of love with Miss Grits. He ate irregular and improbable meals, bowling through the suburbs in Sir James's car, pacing the carpet dictating to Miss Dawkins, perched in deserted lots upon scenery which seemed made to survive the collapse of civilisation. He lapsed, like Miss Grits, into brief spells of deathlike unconsciousness, often awakening, startled, to find that a street or desert or factory had become into being about him while he slept.

The film meanwhile grew rapidly, daily putting out new shoots and changing under their eyes in a hundred unexpected ways. Each conference produced some radical change in the story. Miss Grits in her precise, invariable voice would read out the fruits of their work. Sir James would sit with his head in his hand, rocking slightly from side to side and giving vent to occasional low moans and whimpers; round him sat the experts — production, direction, casting, continuity, cutting and costing managers, bright eyes, eager to attract the great man's attention with some apt intrusion.

"Well," Sir James would say, "I think we can O.K. that. Any suggestions, gentlemen?"

There would be a pause, until one by one the experts began to deliver their contributions . . . "I've been thinking, sir, that it won't do to have the scene laid in Denmark. The public won't stand for travel stuff. How about setting it in Scotland — then we could have some kilts and clan gathering scenes?"

"Yes, that's a very sensible suggestion. Make a note of that, Lent . . ."

"I was thinking we'd better drop this character of the Queen. She'd much better be dead before the action starts. She hangs up the action. The public won't stand for him abusing his mother."

"Yes, make a note of that, Lent."

"How would it be, sir, to make the ghost the Queen instead of the King . . ."

"Don't you think, sir, it would be better if Ophelia were Horatio's sister. More poignant, if you see what I mean."

"Yes, make a note of that, Lent."

"I think we are losing sight of the essence of the story in the last sequence. After all, it is first and foremost a ghost story, isn't it? . . ."

"Yes, make a note of that, Lent . . ."

And so from simple beginnings the story spread majestically. It was in the second week that Sir James, after, it must be admitted, considerable debate, adopted the idea of incorporating with it the story of *Macbeth*. Simon was opposed to the proposition at first, but the appeal of the three witches proved too strong. The title was then changed to *The White Lady of Dunsinane,* and he and Miss Grits settled down to a prodigious week's work in rewriting their entire scenarios.

The end came as suddenly as everything else in this remarkable episode. The third conference was being held at an hotel in the New Forest where Sir James happened to be staying; the experts had assembled by train, car and motor bicycle at a moment's notice and were tired and unresponsive. Miss Grits read the latest scenario; it took some time, for it had now reached the stage when it could be taken as "white script" ready for shooting. Sir James sat sunk in reflection longer than usual. When he raised his head, it was to utter the single word:

"No."

"No?"

"No, it won't do. We must scrap the whole thing. We've got much too far from the original story. I can't think why you need introduce Julius Caesar and King Arthur at all."

"But, sir, they were your own suggestions at the last conference."

"Were they? Well, I can't help it. I must have been tired and not paying full attention . . . Besides, I don't like the dialogue. It misses all the poetry of the original. What the public wants is Shakespeare, the whole of Shakespeare and nothing but Shakespeare. Now this scenario you've written is all very well in its way — but it's not Shakespeare. I'll tell you what we'll do. We'll use the play exactly as he wrote it and record from that. Make a note of it, Miss Grits."

"Then you'll hardly require my services any more?" said Simon.

"No, I don't think I shall. Still, nice of you to have come."

Next morning Simon woke bright and cheerful as usual and was about to leap from his bed when he suddenly remembered the events of last night. There was nothing for him to do. An empty day lay before him. No Miss Grits, no Miss Dawkins, no scampering off to conferences or dictating of dialogue. He rang up Miss Grits and asked her to lunch with him.

"No, quite impossible, I'm afraid. I have to do the continuity for a scenario of St. John's Gospel before the end of the week. Pretty tough job. We're setting it in Algeria so as to get the atmosphere. Off to Hollywood next month. Don't suppose I shall see you again. Good-bye."

Simon lay in bed with all his energy slowly slipping away. Nothing to do. Well, he supposed, now was the time to go away to the country and get on with his novel. Or should he go abroad? Some quiet café-restaurant in the sun where he could work out those intractable last chapters. That was what he would do . . . sometime . . . the end of the week perhaps.

Meanwhile he leaned over on his elbow, lifted the telephone, and asking for Sylvia's number, prepared himself for twenty-five minutes' acrimonious reconciliation.

From A Handful of Dust

DU CÔTÉ DE CHEZ TODD

A Handful of Dust grew out of a short story entitled The Man Who Liked Dickens, which reappeared with slight modifications as the sardonic climax of the novel — perhaps the most famous passage in all of Waugh's work. The version which Mr. Waugh prefers — that incorporated in the novel (in the chapter, "Du Côté de Chez Todd") — calls for a brief summary of the preceding action. Tony Last — a dull, decent man whose whole life had been devoted to keeping up his Gothic country house — has been deserted by his wife, Brenda, after seven years of marriage. Brenda has fallen in love with John Beaver, a dim young sponger-about-town dominated by his go-getting mother, a fashionable interior decorator. Seeing his world in ruins, Tony joins Dr. Messinger in an expedition to the Amazonian back-of-beyond in search of a legendary lost city. The expedition comes to grief, Dr. Messinger is drowned, and Tony, delirious with fever, stumbles on alone through the jungle.

ALTHOUGH Mr. Todd had lived in Amazonas for nearly sixty years, no one except a few families of Pie-wie Indians was aware of his existence. His house stood in a small savannah, one of those little patches of sand and grass that crop up occasionally in that neighbourhood, three miles or so across, bounded on all sides by forest.

The stream which watered it was not marked on any map; it ran through rapids, always dangerous and at most seasons of the year impassable, to join the upper waters of the river where Dr. Messinger had come to grief. None of the inhabitants of the district, except Mr. Todd, had ever heard of the governments of Brazil or Dutch Guiana, both of which, from time to time claimed its possession.

Mr. Todd's house was larger than those of his neighbours, but similar in character — a palm thatch roof, breast high walls of mud and wattle, and a mud floor. He owned the dozen or so head of puny cattle which grazed in the savannah, a plantation of cassava, some banana and mango trees, a dog and, unique in the neighbourhood, a single-barrelled breech-loading shotgun. The few commodities which he employed from the outside world came to him through a long succession of traders, passed from hand to hand, bartered for in a dozen languages at the extreme end of one of the longest threads in the web of commerce that spreads from Manáos into the remote fastness of the forest.

One day while Mr. Todd was engaged in filling some cartridges, a Pie-wie came to him with the news that a white man was approaching through the forest, alone and very sick. He closed the cartridge and loaded his gun with it, put those that were finished into his pocket and set out in the direction indicated.

The man was already clear of the bush when Mr. Todd reached him, sitting on the ground, clearly in a very bad way. He was without hat or boots, and his clothes were so torn that it was only by the dampness of his body that they adhered to it; his feet were cut and grossly swollen; every exposed surface of skin was scarred by insect and bat bites; his eyes were wild with fever. He was talking to himself in delirium but stopped when Todd approached and addressed him in English.

"You're the first person who's spoken to me for days," said Tony. "The others won't stop. They keep bicycling by . . . I'm tired . . . Brenda was with me at first but she was frightened by a mechanical mouse, so she took the canoe and went off. She said she would come back that evening but she didn't. I expect she's staying with one of her new friends in Brazil . . . You haven't seen her have you?"

"You are the first stranger I have seen for a very long time."

"She was wearing a top hat when she left. You can't miss her." Then he began talking to someone at Mr. Todd's side, who was not there.

"Do you see that house over there? Do you think you can manage to walk to it? If not I can send some Indians to carry you."

Tony squinted across the savannah at Mr. Todd's hut.

"Architecture harmonizing with local character," he said, "indigenous material employed throughout. Don't let Mrs. Beaver see it or she will cover it with chromium plating."

"Try and walk." Mr. Todd hoisted Tony to his feet and supported him with a stout arm.

"I'll ride your bicycle. It *was* you I passed just now on a bicycle wasn't it? . . . except that your beard is a different colour. His was green . . . green as mice."

Mr. Todd led Tony across the hummocks of grass towards the house.

"It is a very short way. When we get there I will give you something to make you better."

"Very kind of you . . . rotten thing for a man to have his wife go away in a canoe. That was a long time ago. Nothing to eat since." Presently he said, "I say, you're English. I'm English too. My name is Last."

"Well, Mr. Last, you aren't to bother about anything more. You're ill and you've had a rough journey. I'll take care of you."

Tony looked round him. "Are you all English?"

"Yes, all of us."

"That dark girl married a Moor . . . It's very lucky I met you all. I suppose you're some kind of cycling club?"

"Yes."

"Well, I feel too tired for bicycling . . . never liked it much . . . you fellows ought to get motor bicycles you know, much faster and noisier . . . Let's stop here."

"No, you must come as far as the house. It's not very much further."

"All right . . . I suppose you would have some difficulty getting petrol here."

They went very slowly, but at length reached the house.

"Lie there in the hammock."

"That's what Messinger said. He's in love with John Beaver."

"I will get something for you."

"Very good of you. Just my usual morning tray — coffee, toast, fruit. And the morning papers. If her ladyship has been called I will have it with her . . ."

Mr. Todd went into the back room of the house and dragged a tin canister from under a heap of skins. It was full of a mixture of dried leaf and bark. He took a handful and went outside to the fire. When he returned his guest was bolt upright astride the hammock, talking angrily.

Mr. Todd put a hand behind Tony's head and held up the concoction of herbs in the calabash. Tony sipped and turned away his head.

"Nasty medicine," he said, and began to cry.

Mr. Todd stood by him holding the calabash. Presently Tony drank some more, screwing up his face and shuddering slightly at the bitterness. Mr. Todd stood beside him until the draught was finished; then he threw out the dregs on the mud floor. Tony lay back in the hammock sobbing quietly. Soon he fell into a deep sleep.

Tony's recovery was slow. At first, days of lucidity alternated with delirium; then his temperature dropped and he was conscious even when most ill. The days of fever grew less frequent, finally occurring in the normal system of the tropics, between long periods of comparative health. Mr. Todd dosed him regularly with herbal remedies.

"It's very nasty," said Tony, "but it does do good."

"There is medicine for everything in the forest," said Mr. Todd; "to make you well and to make you ill. My mother was an Indian and she taught me many of them. I have learned others from time to time from my wives. There are plants to cure you and give you fever, to kill you and send you mad, to keep away snakes, to intoxicate fish so that you can pick them out of the water with your hands like fruit from a tree. There are medicines even I do not know. They say that it is possible to bring dead people to life after they have begun to stink, but I have not seen it done."

"But surely you are English?"

"My father was — at least a Barbadian. He came to Guiana as a missionary. He was married to a white woman but he left her in Guiana to look for gold. Then he took my mother. The Pie-wie women are ugly but very devoted. I have had many. Most of the men and women living in this savannah are my children. That is why they obey — for that reason and because I have the gun. My father lived to a great age. It is not twenty years since he died. He was a man of education. Can you read?"

"Yes, of course."

"It is not everyone who is so fortunate. I cannot."

Tony laughed apologetically. "But I suppose you haven't much opportunity here."

"Oh yes, that is just it. I have a *great* many books. I will show you when you are better. Until five years ago there was an Englishman — at least a black man, but he was well educated in Georgetown. He died. He used to read to me every day until he died. You shall read to me when you are better."

"I shall be delighted to."

"Yes, you shall read to me," Mr. Todd repeated, nodding over the calabash.

During the early days of his convalescence Tony had little conversation with his host; he lay in the hammock staring up at the thatched roof and thinking about Brenda. The days, exactly twelve hours each, passed without distinction. Mr. Todd retired to sleep at sundown, leaving a little lamp burning — a hand-woven wick drooping from a pot of beef fat — to keep away vampire bats.

The first time that Tony left the house Mr. Todd took him for a little stroll around the farm.

"I will show you the black man's grave," he said, leading him to a mound between the mango trees. "He was very kind. Every afternoon until he died, for two hours, he used to read to me. I think I will put up a cross — to commemorate his death and your arrival — a pretty idea. Do you believe in God?"

"I suppose so. I've never really thought about it much."

"I have thought about it a *great* deal and I still do not know . . . Dickens did."

"I suppose so."

"Oh yes, it is apparent in all his books. You will see."

That afternoon Mr. Todd began the construction of a headpiece for the Negro's grave. He worked with a large spokeshave in a wood so hard that it grated and rang like metal.

At last when Tony had passed six or seven consecutive nights without fever, Mr. Todd said, "Now I think you are well enough to see the books."

At one end of the hut there was a kind of loft formed by a rough platform erected in the eaves of the roof. Tony followed, still unsteady after his illness. Mr. Todd sat on the platform and Tony stood at the top of the ladder looking over. There was a heap of small bundles there, tied up with rag, palm leaf and raw hide.

"It has been hard to keep out the worms and ants. Two are practically destroyed. But there is an oil the Indians make that is useful."

He unwrapped the nearest parcel and handed down a calf bound book. It was an early American edition of *Bleak House*.

"It does not matter which we take first."

"You are fond of Dickens?"

"Why, yes, of course. More than fond, far more. You see, they are the only books I have ever heard. My father used to read them and later the black man . . . and now you. I have heard them all several times by now but I never get tired; there is always more to be learned and noticed, so many characters, so many changes of scene, so many words . . . I have all Dickens books here except those that the ants devoured. It takes a long time to read them all — more than two years."

"Well," said Tony lightly, "they will well last out my visit."

"Oh, I hope not. It is delightful to start again. Each time I think I find more to enjoy and admire."

They took down the first volume of *Bleak House* and that afternoon Tony had his first reading.

He had always rather enjoyed reading aloud and in the first year of marriage had shared several books in this way with Brenda, until one day, in a moment of frankness, she remarked that it was torture to her. He had read to John Andrew, late in the afternoon, in winter, while the child sat before the nursery fender eating his supper. But Mr. Todd was a unique audience.

The old man sat astride his hammock opposite Tony, fixing him throughout with his eyes, and following the words, soundlessly, with his lips. Often when a new character was introduced he would say, "Repeat the name, I have forgotten him," or "Yes, yes, I remember her well. She dies, poor woman." He would frequently interrupt with questions; not as Tony would have imagined about the circumstances of the story — such things as the procedure of the Lord Chancellor's Court or the social conventions of the time, though they must have been unintelligible, did not concern him — but always about the characters. "Now why does she say that? Does she really mean it? Did she feel faint because of the heat of the fire or of something in that paper?" He laughed loudly at all the jokes and at some passages which did not seem humorous to Tony, asking him to repeat them two or three times; and later at the description of the sufferings of the outcasts in "Tom-all-alones" tears ran down his cheeks into his beard. His comments on the story were usually simple. "I think that Dedlock is a very proud man," or, "Mrs. Jellyby does not take enough care of her children."

Tony enjoyed the readings almost as much as he did.

At the end of the first day the old man said, "You read beautifully, with a far better accent than the black man. And you explain better. It is almost as though my father were here again." And always at the end of a session he thanked his guest courteously. "I enjoyed that *very* much. It was an extremely distressing chapter. But, if I remember rightly, it will all turn out well."

By the time that they were in the second volume however, the novelty of the old man's delight had begun to wane, and Tony was feeling strong enough to be restless. He touched more than once on the subject of his departure, asking about canoes and rains and the possibility of finding guides. But Mr. Todd seemed obtuse and paid no attention to these hints.

One day, running his thumb through the pages of *Bleak House* that remained to be read, Tony said, "We still have a lot to get through. I hope I shall be able to finish it before I go."

"Oh yes," said Mr. Todd. "Do not disturb yourself about that. You will have time to finish it, my friend."

For the first time Tony noticed something slightly menacing in his host's manner. That evening at supper, a brief meal of farine and dried beef, eaten just before sundown, Tony renewed the subject.

"You know, Mr. Todd, the time has come when I must be thinking about getting back to civilisation. I have already imposed myself on your hospitality for too long."

Mr. Todd bent over the plate, crunching mouthfuls of farine, but made no reply.

"How soon do you think I shall be able to get a boat? . . . I said how soon do you think I shall be able to get a boat? I appreciate all your kindness to me more than I can say but . . ."

"My friend, any kindness I may have shown is amply repaid by your reading of Dickens. Do not let us mention the subject again."

"Well I'm very glad you have enjoyed it. I have, too. But I really must be thinking of getting back . . ."

"Yes," said Mr. Todd. "The black man was like that. He thought of it all the time. But he died here . . ."

Twice during the next day Tony opened the subject but his host was evasive. Finally he said, "Forgive me, Mr. Todd, but I really must press the point. When can I get a boat?"

"There is no boat."

"Well, the Indians can build one."

"You must wait for the rains. There is not enough water in the river now."

"How long will that be?"

"A month . . . two months . . ."

They had finished *Bleak House* and were nearing the end of *Dombey and Son* when the rain came.

"Now it is time to make preparations to go."

"Oh, that is impossible. The Indians will not make a boat during the rainy season — it is one of their superstitions."

"You might have told me."

"Did I not mention it? I forgot."

Next morning Tony went out alone while his host was busy, and, looking as aimless as he could, strolled across the savannah to the group of Indian houses. There were four or five Pie-wies sitting in one of the doorways. They did not look up as he approached them. He addressed them in the few words of Macushi he had acquired during the journey but they made no sign whether they understood him or not. Then he drew a sketch of a canoe in the sand, he went through some vague motions of carpentry, pointed from them to him, then made motions of giving something to them and scratched out the outlines of a gun and a hat and a few other recognisable articles of trade. One of the women giggled but no one gave any sign of comprehension, and he went away unsatisfied.

At their midday meal Mr. Todd said, "Mr. Last, the Indians tell me that you have been trying to speak with them. It is easier that you say anything you wish through me. You realise, do you not, that they would do nothing without my authority. They regard themselves, quite rightly in many cases, as my children."

"Well, as a matter of fact, I was asking them about a canoe."

"So they gave me to understand . . . and now if you have finished your meal perhaps we might have another chapter. I am quite absorbed in the book."

They finished *Dombey and Son;* nearly a year had passed since Tony had left England, and his gloomy foreboding of permanent exile became suddenly acute when, between the pages of *Martin Chuzzlewit,* he found a document written in pencil in irregular characters.

Year 1919.

I James Todd of Brazil do swear to Barnabas Washington of George-town that if he finish this book in fact Martin Chuzzlewit I will let him go away back as soon as finished.

There followed a heavy pencil X and after it: *Mr. Todd made this mark signed Barnabas Washington.*

"Mr. Todd," said Tony, "I must speak frankly. You saved my life, and when I get back to civilisation I will reward you to the best of my ability. I will give you anything within reason. But at present you are keeping me here against my will. I demand to be released."

"But, my friend, what is keeping you? You are under no restraint. Go when you like."

"You know very well that I can't get away without your help."

"In that case you must humour an old man. Read me another chapter."

"Mr. Todd, I swear by anything you like that when I get to Manáos I will find someone to take my place. I will pay a man to read to you all day."

"But I have no need of another man. You read so well."

"I have read for the last time."

"I hope not," said Mr. Todd politely.

That evening at supper only one plate of dried meat and farine was brought in and Mr. Todd ate alone. Tony lay without speaking, staring at the thatch.

Next day at noon a single plate was put before Mr. Todd but with it lay his gun, cocked, on his knee, as he ate. Tony resumed the reading of *Martin Chuzzlewit* where it had been interrupted.

Weeks passed hopelessly. They read *Nicholas Nickleby* and *Little Dorrit* and *Oliver Twist*. Then a stranger arrived in the savannah, a half-caste prospector, one of that lonely order of men who wander for a lifetime through the forests, tracing the little streams, sifting the gravel and, ounce by ounce, filling the little leather sack of gold dust, more often than not dying of exposure and starvation with five hundred dollars' worth of gold hung around their necks. Mr. Todd was vexed at his arrival, gave him farine and *tasso* and sent him on his journey within an hour of his arrival, but in that hour Tony had time to scribble his name on a slip of paper and put it into the man's hand.

From now on there was hope. The days followed their unvarying routine; coffee at sunrise, a morning of inaction while Mr. Todd pottered about on the business of the farm, farine and *tasso* at noon, Dickens in the afternoon, farine and *tasso* and sometimes some fruit for supper, silence from sunset to dawn with the small wick glowing in the beef fat and the palm thatch overhead dimly discernible; but Tony lived in quiet confidence and expectation.

Sometime, this year or next, the prospector would arrive at a Brazilian village with news of his discovery. The disasters of the Messinger expedition would not have passed unnoticed. Tony could imagine the headlines that must have appeared in the popular press; even now probably there were search parties working over the country he had crossed; any day English voices must sound over the savannah and a dozen friendly adventurers come crashing through the bush. Even as he was reading, while his lips mechanically followed the printed pages, his mind wandered away from his eager, crazy host opposite, and he began to narrate to himself incidents of his homecoming — the gradual re-encounters with civilisation (he shaved and bought new clothes at Manáos, telegraphed for money, received wires of congratulation; he enjoyed the leisurely river journey to Belem, the big liner to Europe; savoured good claret and fresh meat and spring vegetables; he was shy at meeting Brenda and uncertain how to address her . . . "*Darling*, you've been much longer than you said. I quite thought you were lost . . .")

And then Mr. Todd interruped. "May I trouble you to read that passage again? It is one I particularly enjoy."

The weeks passed; there was no sign of rescue but Tony endured the day for hope of what might happen on the morrow; he even felt a slight stirring of cordiality towards his jailer and was therefore quite willing to join him when, one evening after a long conference with an Indian neighbour, he proposed a celebration.

"It is one of the local feast days," he explained, "and they have been making *piwari*. You may not like it but you should try some. We will go across to this man's home to-night."

Accordingly after supper they joined a party of Indians that were assembled round the fire in one of the huts at the other side of the savannah. They were singing in an apathetic, monotonous manner and passing a large calabash of liquid from mouth to mouth. Separate bowls were brought for Tony and Mr. Todd, and they were given hammocks to sit in.

"You must drink it all without lowering the cup. That is the etiquette."

Tony gulped the dark liquid, trying not to taste it. But it was not unpleasant, hard and muddy on the palate like most of the beverages he had been offered in Brazil, but with a flavour of honey and brown bread. He leant back in the hammock feeling unusually contented. Perhaps at that very moment the search party was in camp a few hours' journey from them. Meanwhile he was warm and drowsy. The cadence of song rose and fell interminably, liturgically. Another calabash of *piwari* was offered him and he handed it back empty. He lay full length watching the play of shadows on the thatch as the Pie-wies began to dance. Then he shut his eyes and thought of England and Hetton and fell asleep.

He awoke, still in the Indian hut, with the impression that he had outslept his usual hour. By the position of the sun he knew it was late afternoon. No one else was about. He looked for his watch and found to his surprise that it was not on his wrist. He had left it in the house, he supposed, before coming to the party.

"I must have been tight last night," he reflected. "Treacherous drink that." He had a headache and feared a recurrence of fever. He found when he set his feet to the ground that he stood with difficulty; his walk was unsteady and his mind confused as it had been during the first weeks of his convalescence. On the way across the savannah he was obliged to stop more than once, shutting his eyes and breathing deeply. When he reached the house he found Mr. Todd sitting there.

"Ah, my friend, you are late for the reading this afternoon. There is scarcely another half hour of light. How do you feel?"

"Rotten. That drink doesn't seem to agree with me."

"I will give you something to make you better. The forest has remedies for everything; to make you awake and to make you sleep."

"You haven't seen my watch anywhere?"

"You have missed it?"

"Yes. I thought I was wearing it. I say, I've never slept so long."

"Not since you were a baby. Do you know how long? Two days."

"Nonsense. I can't have."

"Yes, indeed. It is a long time. It is a pity because you missed our guests."

"Guests?"

"Why, yes. I have been quite gay while you were asleep. Three men from outside. Englishmen. It is a pity you missed them. A pity for them, too, as they particularly wished to see you. But what could I do? You were so sound asleep. They had come all the way to find you, so — I thought you would not mind — as you could not greet them yourself I gave them a little souvenir, your watch. They wanted something to take back to England where a reward is being offered for news of you. They were very pleased with it. And they took some photographs of the little cross I put up to commemorate your coming. They were pleased with that, too. They were very easily pleased. But I do not suppose they will visit us again, our life here is so retired . . . no pleasures except reading . . . I do not suppose we shall ever have visitors again . . . well, well, I will get you some medicine to make you feel better. Your head aches, does it not? . . . We will not have any Dickens to-day . . . but to-morrow, and the day after that, and the day after that. Let us read *Little Dorrit* again. There are passages in that book I can never hear without the temptation to weep."

From Put Out More Flags

BASIL SEAL DOES HIS BIT

Put Out More Flags *opens at the outbreak of the Second World War; its hero, the iniquitous Basil Seal of* Black Mischief, *is now in his middle thirties. Basil's nonchalant arrogance ruins his slender chances of getting a commission in a smart regiment and no one taps him for the cloak-and-dagger work for which he fancies himself ideally suited. Disgusted by his country's neglect of his talents, Seal retires from London to his sister's place in the country to write a book on how to win the war. But his sister's job as billeting officer for evacué children suggests to him a profitable racket, which he proceeds to put into operation with characteristic audacity and shamelessness. The characters in the episodes which follow are:*

Barbara Sothill	*Basil's sister.*
Freddy Sothill	*Barbara's husband.*
Sir Joseph Mainwaring	*An old and influential friend of Basil's mother, Lady Seal.*
"Poppet" Green	*A woman painter with Communist affiliations.*
Parsnip and Pimpernell	*Two famous left-wing English poets who have recently emigrated to the United States.*
Angela Lyne	*A chic married woman who for years has been incurably in love with Basil.*
Mr. Geoffrey Bentley	*A publisher who is working for the duration at the Ministry of Information.*
Mr. Rampole	*Mr. Bentley's senior partner in publishing.*
Ambrose Silk	*A talented esthete who has found his wartime niche in the Ministry of Information — Religious Department, atheist desk. Ambrose is planning to launch a literary review entitled the* Ivory Tower.
Peter, Lord Pastmaster	*He appeared as a schoolboy, Peter Beste-Chetwynde, in* Decline and Fall.

EVACUATION to Malfrey had followed much the same course as it had in other parts of the country and had not only kept Barbara, as billeting officer, constantly busy, but had transformed her, in four months, from one of the most popular women in the countryside into a figure of terror. When her car was seen approaching, people fled through covered lines of retreat, through side doors and stable yards, into the snow, anywhere to avoid her persuasive, "But surely you could manage *one* more. He's a boy this time and a very well-behaved little fellow" — for the urban authorities maintained a steady flow of refugees well in excess of the stream of returning malcontents. Few survived of the original party who had sat glumly on the village green on the first morning of war. Some had gone back immediately; others more reluctantly in response to ugly rumours of their husbands' goings on; one had turned out to be a fraud, who, herself childless, had kidnapped a baby from a waiting perambulator in order to secure her passage to safety, so impressed had she been by the propaganda of the local officials. It was mostly children now who assembled, less glumly, on the village green, and showed the agricultural community how another part of the world lived. They were tolerated now as one of the troubles of the time. Some had even endeared themselves to their hosts. But everyone, when evacués were spoken of, implicitly excluded for all generalities the family of Connolly.

These had appeared as an act of God apparently without human agency; their names did not appear on any list; they carried no credentials; no one was responsible for them. They were found lurking under the seats of a carriage when the train was emptied on the evening of the first influx. They had been dragged out and stood on the platform where everyone denied knowledge of them, and since they could not be left there, they were included in the party that was being sent by bus to Malfrey village. From that moment they were on a list; they had been given official existence and their destiny was inextricably involved with that of Malfrey.

Nothing was ever discovered about the Connollies' parentage. When they could be threatened or cajoled into speaking of their antecedents they spoke, with distaste, of an "Auntie." To this woman, it seemed, the war had come as a God-sent release. She had taken her dependents to the railway station, propelled them into the crowd of milling adolescence, and hastily covered her tracks by decamping from home. Enquiry by the police in the street where the Connollies professed to have lived produced no other information than that the woman had been there and was not there any longer. She owed a little for milk; otherwise she had left no memorial on that rather unimpressionable district.

There was Doris, ripely pubescent, aged by her own varied accounts anything from ten years to eighteen. An early and ingenious attempt to have her certified as an adult was frustrated by an inspecting doctor who put her at about fifteen. Doris had dark, black bobbed hair, a large mouth and dark pig's eyes. There was something of the Eskimo about her head but her colouring was ruddy and her manner more vivacious than is common among that respectable race. Her figure was stocky, her bust prodigious, and her gait, derived from the cinematograph, was designed to be alluring.

Micky, her junior by the length of a rather stiff sentence for housebreaking, was of lighter build; a scrawny, scowling little boy; a child of few words and those, for the most part, foul.

Marlene was presumed to be a year younger. But for Micky's violent denials she might have been taken for his twin. She was the offspring of unusually prolonged coincident periods of liberty in the lives of her parents, which the sociologist must deplore, for Marlene was simple. An appeal to have her certified imbecile was disallowed by the same inspecting doctor, who expressed an opinion that country life might work wonders with the child.

There the three had stood, on the eve of the war, in Malfrey Parish Hall, one leering, one lowering, and one drooling, as unprepossessing a family as could be found in the kingdom. Barbara took one look at them, looked again to see that her weary eyes were not playing tricks with her, and consigned them to the Mudges of Upper Lamstock, a tough farming family on a remote homestead.

Within a week Mr. Mudge was at the park, with the three children in the back of his milk truck. "It's not for myself, Mrs. Sothill; I'm out and about all day and in the evenings I'm sleepy, and being with animals so much I don't take on so. But it's my old woman. She *do* take on and she won't stand for it. She've locked herself in upstairs and she won't come down till they've gone and when she do say she means it, Mrs. Sothill. We're willing to do anything in reason to help the war, but these brats aren't to be borne and that's flat."

"Oh dear, Mr. Mudge, which of them is giving trouble?"

"Why it's all of 'em, ma'am. There's the boy was the best of 'em at first though you can't understand what he do say, speaking as they do where he come from. Nasty, unfriendly ways he had but he didn't do much that you could call harm not till he'd seen me kill the goose. I took him out to watch to cheer him up like, and uncommon interested he was and I thought I'll make a country lad of you yet. I gave him the head to play with and he seemed quite pleased. Then no sooner was I off down to the root field, than blessed if he didn't get hold of a knife and when I came back supper-time there was six of my ducks dead and the old cat. Yes, mum, blessed if he hadn't had the head off of our old yellow cat. Then the little un, she's a dirty girl begging your pardon, mum. It's not only her wetting the bed; she've wetted every-where, chairs, floor and not only wetting, mum. Never seem to have been taught to be in a house where she comes from."

"But doesn't the elder girl do anything to help?"

"If you ask me, mum, she's the worst of the lot. My old woman would stick it but for her, but it's that Doris makes her take on like she do. Soft about the men, she is, mum. Why she even comes making up to me and I'm getting on to be her grandf'er. She won't leave our Willie alone not for a minute, and he's a bashful boy our Willie and he can't get on with the work, her always coming after him. So there it is, mum. I'm sorry not to oblige but I've promised my old woman I won't come back with 'em and I dusn't go back on what I've said."

Mr. Mudge was the first of a succession of hosts. The longest that the Connollies stayed in any place was ten days; the shortest was an hour and a quarter. In six weeks they had become a legend far beyond the parish. When influential old men at the Turf in London put their heads together and said, "The whole scheme has been a mistake. I was hearing last night some examples of the way some of the evacués are behaving . . . ," the chances were that the scandal originated with the Connollies. They were cited in the House of Commons; there were paragraphs about them in official reports.

Barbara tried separating them, but in their first night apart Doris climbed out of her window and was lost for two days, to be found in a barn eight miles away, stupefied with cider; she gave no coherent account of her adventure. On the same evening Micky bit the wife of the roadman on whom he was quartered, so that the district nurse had to be called in; while Marlene had a species of seizure which aroused unfulfilled hopes that she might be dead. Everyone agreed that the only place for the Connollies was "an institution"; and at last, just before Christmas, after formalities complicated by the obscurity of

their origins, to an institution they were sent; and Malfrey settled back
to entertain its guests with a Christmas tree and a conjuror, with an air
of relief which could be sensed for miles around. It was as though the
All Clear had sounded after a night of terror. And now the Connollies
were back.

"What's happened, Mrs. Fremlin? Surely the Home *can't* send them
away."

"It's being evacuated. All the children are being sent back to the
places they came from. Malfrey was the only address they had for
the Connollies, so here they are. The Welfare Woman brought them
to the Parish Hall. I was there with the Guides so I said I'd bring them
up to you."

"They might have warned us."

"I expect they thought that if we had time we should try and stop
them coming."

"How right they were. Have the Connollies been fed?"

"I think so. At any rate Marlene was terribly sick in the car."

"I'm dying to see these Connollies," said Basil.

"You shall," said his sister grimly.

But they were not in the lobby where they had been left. Barbara
rang the bell. "Benson, you remember the Connolly children?"

"Vividly, madam."

"They're back."

"Here, madam?"

"Here. Somewhere in the house. You'd better institute a search."

"Very good, madam. And when they are found, they will be going
away immediately?"

"Not immediately. They'll have to stay here to-night. We'll find
somewhere for them in the village to-morrow."

Benson hesitated. "It won't be easy, madam."

"It won't be, Benson."

He hesitated again; thought better of whatever he meant to say, and
merely added: "I will start the search, madam."

"I know what that means," said Barbara as the man left them.
"Benson is yellow."

The Connollies were found at last and assembled. Doris had been
in Barbara's bedroom trying out her make-up, Micky in the library
tearing up a folio, Marlene grovelling under the pantry sink eating
the remains of the dogs' dinners. When they were together again,

in the lobby, Basil inspected them. Their appearance exceeded anything he had been led to expect. They were led away to the bachelors'
wing and put together into a large bedroom.

"Shall we lock the door?"

"It would be no good. If they want to get out, they will."

"Could I speak to you for a moment, madam?" said Benson.

When Barbara returned she said, "Benson *is* yellow. He can't take it."

"Wants to leave?"

"It's him or the Connollies, he says. I can't blame him. Freddy will
never forgive me if I let him go."

"Babs, you're blubbing."

"Who wouldn't?" said Barbara, pulling out a handkerchief and weeping in earnest. "I ask you, who wouldn't?"

"Don't be a chump," said Basil, relapsing, as he often did with
Barbara, into the language of the schoolroom. "I'll fix it for you."

"Swank. Chump yourself. Double chump."

"Double chump with knobs on."

"Darling Basil, it is nice to have you back. I do believe if anyone
could fix it, you could."

"Freddy couldn't, could he?"

"Freddy isn't here."

"I'm cleverer than Freddy. Babs, say I'm cleverer than Freddy."

"I'm cleverer than Freddy. Sucks to you."

"Babs, say you love me more than Freddy."

"You love me more than Freddy. Double sucks."

"Say I, Barbara, love you, Basil, more than him, Freddy."

"I won't. Don't . . . Beast, you're hurting."

"Say it."

"Basil stop at once or I shall call Miss Penfold."

They were back twenty years, in the schoolroom again. "Miss Penfold,
Miss Penfold, Basil's pulling my hair."

They scuffled on the sofa. Suddenly a voice said, " 'Ere, Missus."
It was Doris. "Missus!"

Barbara stood up, panting and dishevelled. "Well, Doris, what is it?"

"Marlene's queer again."

"Oh dear. I'll come up. Run along."

Doris looked languishingly at Basil. " 'Aving a lark, eh?" she said.
"I like a lark."

"Run along, Doris. You'll get cold."

" I ain't cold. Pull my hair if you like, mister."

"I wouldn't dream of it," said Basil.

"Dessay I shall. I dream a lot of funny things. Go on, mister, pull it. Hard. I don't mind." She offered her bobbed head to Basil and then with a giggle ran out of the room.

"You see," said Barbara. "A problem child."

When Marlene had been treated for her queerness, Barbara came back to say good night.

"I'll stay up a bit and work on this book."

"All right, darling. Good night." She bent over the back of the sofa and kissed the top of his head.

"Not blubbing any more?"

"No, not blubbing."

He looked up at her and smiled. She smiled back; it was the same smile. They saw themselves, each in the other's eyes. There's no one like Basil, thought Barbara, seeing herself — no one like him, when he's nice.

Next morning Basil was called by Benson, who was the only man-servant indoors since Freddy had drawn in his horns. (He had taken his valet with him to the yeomanry and supported him now, in a very much lower standard of comfort, at the King's expense.) Lying in bed and watching the man put out his clothes, Basil reflected that he still owed him a small sum of money from his last visit.

"Benson, what's this about your leaving?"

"I was cross last night, Mr. Basil. I couldn't ever leave Malfrey, and Mrs. Sothill ought to know that. Not with the Captain away, too."

"Mrs. Sothill was very upset."

"So was I, Mr. Basil. You don't know what those Connollies are. They're not human."

"We'll find a billet for them."

"No one will take the Connollies in these parts. Not if they were given a hundred pounds."

"I have an idea I owe you some money."

"You do, Mr. Basil. Twelve pound ten."

"As much as that? Time I paid it back."

"It is."

"I will, Benson."

"I hope so, sir. I'm sure."

Basil went to his bath pondering. No one will take the Connollies in these parts. Not for a hundred pounds. Not for a hundred pounds.

Since the war began Barbara had taken to breakfasting downstairs in the mistaken belief that it caused less trouble. Instead of the wicker bed-table tray, a table had to be laid in the small dining-room, the fire had to be lit there two hours earlier, silver dishes had to be cleaned and the wicks trimmed under them. It was an innovation deplored by all.

Basil found her crouched over the fire with her cup of coffee; she turned her curly black head and smiled; both of them had the same devastating combination of dark hair and clear blue eyes. Narcissus greeted Narcissus from the watery depths as Basil kissed her.

"Spoony," she said.

"I've squared Benson for you."

"Darling, how clever of you."

"I had to give the old boy a fiver."

"Liar."

"All right, don't believe me then."

"I don't, knowing Benson and knowing you. I remember last time you stayed here I had to pay him over ten pounds that you'd borrowed."

"You paid him?"

"Yes. I was afraid he'd ask Freddy."

"The old double-crosser. Anyway he's staying."

"Yes; thinking it over I knew he would. I don't know why I took it so hard last night. I think it was the shock of seeing the Connollies."

"We must get them settled to-day."

"It's hopeless. No one will take them."

"You've got powers of coercion."

"Yes, but I can't possibly use them."

"*I* can," said Basil. "I shall enjoy it."

After breakfast they moved from the little dining-room to the little parlour. The corridor, though it was one of the by-ways of the house, had a sumptuous cornice and a high, coved ceiling; the door cases were enriched with classic pediments in whose broken entablatures stood busts of philosophers and composers. Other busts stood at regular intervals on marble pedestals. Everything in Malfrey was splendid and harmonious; everything except Doris, who, that morning, lurked in their path rubbing herself on a pilaster like a cow on a stump.

"Hullo," she said.

"Hullo, Doris. Where are Micky and Marlene?"

"Outside. They're all right. They've found the snow-man the others made and they're mucking him up."

"Run along and join them."

"I want to stay here with you — and *him*."

"I bet you do," said Basil. "No such luck. I'm going to find you a nice billet miles and miles away."

"I want to stay with you."

"You go and help muck up the snow-man."

"That's a kid's game. I'm not a kid. Mister, why wouldn't you pull my hair last night? Was it because you thought I had nits? I haven't any more. The nurse combed them all out at the institution and put oil on. That's why it's a bit greasy."

"I don't pull girls' hair."

"You do. I saw you. You pulled *hers*. He's your boy, isn't he?" she said, turning to Barbara.

"He's my brother, Doris."

"Ah," she said, her pig eyes dark with the wisdom of the slums, "but you fancy him, don't you? I saw."

"She really is an atrocious child," said Barbara.

Basil set about the problem of finding a home for the Connollies with zeal and method. He settled himself at a table with an ordnance map, the local newspaper and the little red-leather-covered address book which had been one of old Mrs. Sothill's legacies to Barbara; in this book were registered all her more well-to-do neighbours for a radius of twenty miles, the majority of whom were marked with the initials G.P.O. — which stood for Garden Party Only. Barbara had done her best to keep this invaluable work of reference up to date and had from time to time crossed out those who had died or left the district, and added the names of newcomers.

Presently Basil said, "What about the Harknesses of Old Mill House, North Grappling?"

"Middle-aged people. He retired from some sort of a job abroad. I think she's musical. Why?"

"They're advertising for boarders." He pushed the paper across to her, where she read, in the *Accommodation* column:

Paying Guests accepted in lovely modernised fifteenth century mill. Ideal surroundings for elderly or artistic people wishing to avoid war worries. All home produce. Secluded old world gardens. 6 gns weekly. Highest references given and expected. Harkness, Old Mill House, North Grappling.

"How about that for the Connollies?"

"Basil, you can't."

"Can't I just. I'll get to work on them at once. Do they allow you extra petrol for your billeting work?"

"Yes, but . . ."

"That's grand. I'll take the Connollies over there this morning. D'you know, this is the first piece of serious war-work I've done so far?"

Normally, whenever the car left the garage there was a stampede of evacués to the running boards crying "Give us a ride." This morning, however, seeing the three forbidding Connollies in the back seat, the other children fell back silently. They were not allowed by their mothers to play with the Connollies.

"Mister, why can't I sit in front with you?"

"You've got to keep the other two in order."

"They'll be good."

"That's what you think."

"They'll be good if I tell them, mister."

"Then why aren't they?"

"Cos I tell 'em to be bad. In fun you know. Where are we going?"

"I'm finding a new home for you, Doris."

"Away from you?"

"Far away from me."

"Mister, listen. Micky ain't bad really nor Marlene isn't silly. Are you, Marlene?"

"Not very silly," said Marlene.

"She can be clean if she wants to be, if I tell her. See here, mister, play fair. You let us stay with you and I'll see the kids behave themselves."

"And what about you, Doris?"

"I don't have to behave. I'm not a kid. Is it on?"

"It is not."

"You going to take us away?"

"You bet I am."

"Then just you wait and see what we give them where we're going."

"I shan't wait and see," said Basil, "but I've no doubt I shall hear about it in good time."

North Grappling was ten miles distant, a stone-built village of uneven stone-tile roofs none of which was less than a century old. It lay off the main road in a fold of the hills; a stream ran through it following the line of its single street and crossing it under two old stone bridges. At the upper end of the street stood the church, which declared by its size and rich decoration that in the centuries since it was built, while the rest of the world was growing, North Grappling had shrunk; at the lower end, below the second bridge, stood Old Mill House. It was just such a home of ancient peace as a man might dream of who was forced to earn his living under a fiercer sky. Mr. Harkness had in fact dreamed of it, year in, year out, as he toiled in his office at Singapore, or reclined after work on the club veranda, surrounded by gross vegetation and rude colours. He bought it from his father's legacy while he was still a young man, meaning to retire there when the time came, and his years of waiting had been haunted by only one fear: that he would return to find the place "developed," new red roofs among the grey and a tarmac road down the uneven street. But modernity spared North Grappling; he returned to find the place just as he had first come upon it, on a walking tour, late in the evening with the stones still warm from the afternoon sun and the scent of the gillyflowers sweet and fresh on the breeze.

This morning, half lost in snow, the stones, which in summer seemed grey, were a golden brown; and the bleached limes, which in their leaf hid the low front of the Old Mill, now revealed the mullions and dripstones, the sundial above the long, centre window, and the stone hood of the door carved in the shape of a scallop-shell. Basil stopped the car by the bridge.

"Jesus," said Doris. "You aren't going to leave us here?"

"Sit tight," said Basil. "You'll know soon enough."

He threw a rug over the radiator of the car, opened the little iron gate and walked up the flagged path grimly, a figure of doom. The low winter sun cast his shadow before him, ominously, against the door which Mr. Harkness had had painted apple green. The gnarled trunk of a wistaria rose from beside the door-jamb and twisted its naked length between the lines of the windows. Basil glanced once over his shoulder to see that his young passengers were invisible and then put his hand

to the iron bell. He heard it ring melodiously, not far away, and
presently the door was opened by a maid dressed in apple green, with
an apron of sprigged muslin and a starched white cap that was in
effect part Dutch, part conventual, and wholly ludicrous. This figure
of fancy led Basil up a step, down a step and into a living-room where
he was left long enough to observe the decorations. The floor was
covered in coarse rush matting and in places by bright Balkan rugs.
On the walls were Thornton's flower prints (with the exception of his
masterpiece, "The Night-Flowering Cereus"), samplers and old maps.
The most prominent objects of furniture were a grand piano and a harp.
There were also some tables and chairs of raw-looking beech. From an
open hearth peat smoke billowed periodically into the room, causing
Basil's eyes to water. It was just such a room as Basil had imagined from
the advertisement and Mr. and Mrs. Harkness were just such a couple.
Mrs. Harkness wore a hand-woven woolen garment, her eyes were
large and poetic, her nose long and red with the frost, her hair nondescript in colour and haphazard in arrangement. Her husband had
done all that a man can to disguise the effects of twenty years of club
and bungalow life in the Far East. He had grown a little pointed beard;
he wore a homespun suit of knickerbockers in the style of the pioneers
of bicycling; he wore a cameo ring round his loose silk tie, yet there was
something in his bearing which still suggested the dapper figure in
white ducks who had stood his round of pink gins, evening after evening, to other dapper white figures, and had dined twice a year at
Government House.

They entered from the garden door. Basil half expected Mr. Harkness
to say "take a pew" and clap his hands for the gin. Instead they stood
looking at him with enquiry and some slight distaste.

"My name is Seal. I came about your advertisement in the *Courier*."

"Our advertisement. Ah yes," said Mr. Harkness vaguely. "It was
just an idea we had. We felt a little ashamed here, with so much space
and beauty; the place is a little large for our requirements these days.
We did think that perhaps if we heard of a few people like ourselves —
the same simple tastes — we might, er, join forces as it were during
the present difficult times. As a matter of fact we have one newcomer
with us already. I don't think we *really* want to take anyone else, do
we, Agnes?"

"It was just an idle thought," said Mrs. Harkness. "A green thought
in a green place."

"This is not a Guest House, you know. We take in paying guests. Quite a different thing."

Basil understood their difficulties with a keenness of perception that was rare to him. "It's not for myself that I was enquiring," he said.

"Ah, that's different. I daresay we might take in one or two more if they were *really* . . ."

Mrs. Harkness helped him out. "If we were sure they were the kind of people who would be happy here."

"Exactly. It is essentially a *happy* house."

(It was like his housemaster at school. "We are essentially a keen House, Seal. We may not win many cups but at least we try.")

"I can see it is," he said gallantly.

"I expect you'd like to look round. It looks quite a little place from the road but is surprisingly large, really, when you come to count up the rooms."

A hundred years ago the pastures round North Grappling had all been corn-growing land and the mill had served a wide area. Long before the Harknesses' time it had fallen into disuse and, in the 'eighties, had been turned into a dwelling house by a disciple of William Morris. The stream had been diverted, the old mill pool drained and levelled and made into a sunken garden. The rooms that had held the grind-stones and machinery, and the long lofts where the grain had been stored, had been tactfully floored and plastered and partitioned. Mrs. Harkness pointed out all the features with maternal pride.

"Are your friends who were thinking of coming here artistic people?"

"No, I don't think you could call them that."

"They don't write?"

"No, I don't think so."

"I've always thought this would be an ideal place for someone who wanted to write. May I ask, what *are* your friends?"

"Well, I suppose you might call them evacués."

Mr. and Mrs. Harkness laughed pleasantly at the little joke. "Towns-folk in search of sanctuary, eh?"

"Exactly."

"Well, they will find it here, eh, Agnes?"

They were back in the living-room. Mrs. Harkness laid her hand on the gilded neck of the harp and looked out across the sunken garden with a dreamy look in her large grey eyes. Thus she had looked out across the Malaya golf course, dreaming of home.

"I like to think of this beautiful old house still being of use in the world. After all it was built for *use*. Hundreds of years ago it gave bread to the people. Then with the change of the times it was left forlorn and derelict. Then it became a home, but it was still out of the world, shut off from the life of the people. And now at last it comes into its own again. Fulfilling a *need*. You may think me fanciful," she said, remote and whimsical, "but in the last few weeks I feel sometimes I can see the old house smiling to itself and hear the old timbers whispering, 'They thought we were no use. They thought we were old stick-in-the-muds. But they can't get on without us, all these busy go-ahead people. They come back to us when they're in trouble.'"

"Agnes was always a poet," said Mr. Harkness. "I have had to be the practical housewife. You saw our terms in the advertisement?"

"Yes."

"They may have seemed to you a little heavy, but you must understand that our guests live exactly as we do ourselves. We live simply but we like our comfort. Fires," he said, backing slightly from the belch of aromatic smoke which issued into the room as he spoke. "The garden," he said, indicating the frozen and buried enclosure outside the windows. "In the summer we take our meals under the old mulberry tree. Music. Every week we have chamber music. There are certain *imponderabilia* at the Old Mill which, to be crude, have their market value. I *don't* think," he said coyly, "I *don't* think that in the circumstances" — and the circumstances, Basil felt, surely were meant to include a good fat slice of Mrs. Harkness's poetic imagination — "six guineas is too much to ask."

The moment for which Basil had been waiting was come. This was the time for the grenade he had been nursing ever since he opened the little, wrought-iron gate and put his hand to the wrought-iron bell-pull. "We pay eight shillings and sixpence a week," he said. That was the safety pin; the lever flew up, the spring struck home; within the serrated metal shell the primer spat and, invisibly, flame crept up the finger's-length of fuse. Count seven slowly, then throw. One, two, three, four . . .

"Eight shillings?" said Mr. Harkness. "I'm afraid there's been some misunderstanding."

Five, six, *seven*. Here it comes. *Bang!* "Perhaps I should have told you at once. I am the billeting officer. I've three children for you in the car outside."

It was magnificent. It was war. Basil was something of a specialist in shocks. He could not recall a better.

After the first tremendous silence there were three stages of Harkness reaction: the indignant appeal to reason and justice, then the humble appeal to mercy, then the frigid and dignified acceptance of the inevitable.

First:

"I shall telephone to Mrs. Sothill . . . I shall go and see the County authorities . . . I shall write to the Board of Education and the Lord Lieutenant. This is perfectly ridiculous; there must be a hundred cottagers who would be *glad* to take these children in."

"Not *these* children," said Basil. "Besides, you know, this is a war for democracy. It looks awfully bad if the rich seem to be shirking their responsibilities."

"*Rich.* It's only because we find it so hard to make both ends meet that we taking paying guests at all."

"Besides this is a *most* unsuitable place for children. They might fall into the stream and be drowned. There's no school within four miles . . ."

Second:

"We're not as young as we were. After living so long in the East the English winter is very difficult. Any additional burden . . ."

"Mr. Seal, you've seen for yourself this lovely old house and the kind of life we live here. Don't you *feel* that there is something *different* here, something precious that could so easily be killed?"

"It's just this kind of influence these children need," said Basil cheerfully. "They're rather short on culture at the moment."

Third:

A hostility as cold as the winter hillside above the village. Basil led the Connollies up the flagged path, through the apple-green door, into the passage which smelled of peat smoke and pot-pourri. "I'm afraid they haven't any luggage," he said. "This is Doris, this is Micky, and that — that is little Marlene. I expect after a day or two you'll wonder how you ever got on without them. We meet that over and over again in our work; people who are a little shy of children to begin with, and soon want to adopt them permanently. Good-bye, kids, have a good time. Good-bye, Mrs. Harkness. We shall drop in from time to time just to see that everything is all right."

And Basil drove back through the naked lanes with a deep interior warmth which defied the gathering blizzard.

That night there was an enormous fall of snow, telephone wires were down, the lane to North Grappling became impassable, and for eight days the Old Mill was cut off physically, as for so long it had been cut in spirit, from all contact with the modern world.

Barbara and Basil sat in the orangery after luncheon. The smoke from Basil's cigar hung on the humid air, a blue line of cloud, motionless, breast-high between the paved floor and the exotic foliage overhead. He was reading aloud to his sister.

"So much for the supply services," he said, laying down the last sheet of manuscript. The book had prospered during the past week.

Barbara awoke, so gently that she might never have been asleep. "Very good," she said. "First-class."

"It ought to wake them up," said Basil.

"It ought," said Barbara, on whom the work had so different an effect. Then she added irrelevantly, "I hear they've dug the way through to North Grappling this morning."

"There was providence in that fall of snow. It's let the Connollies and the Harknesses get properly to grips. Otherwise, I feel one or other side might have despaired."

"I daresay we shall hear something of the Harknesses shortly."

And immediately, as though they were on the stage, Benson came to the door and announced that Mr. Harkness was in the little parlour.

"I *must* see him," said Barbara.

"Certainly not," said Basil. "This is my war effort," and followed Benson into the house.

He had expected some change in Mr. Harkness but not so marked a change as he now saw. The man was barely recognisable. It was as though the crust of tropical respectability that had survived below the homespun and tie-ring surface had been crushed to powder; the man was abject. The clothes were the same. It must be imagination which gave that trim beard a raffish look, imagination fired by the haunted look in the man's eyes.

Basil on his travels had once visited a prison in Trans-Jordan where an ingenious system of punishment had been devised. The institution served the double purpose of penitentiary and lunatic asylum. One of the madmen was a tough old Arab of peculiar ferocity who could be subdued by one thing only — the steady gaze of the human eye. Bat an eyelid, and he was at you. Refractory convicts were taken to this man's cell and shut in with him for periods of anything up to forty-eight hours according to the gravity of their offences. Day and night the madman lurked in his corner with his eyes fixed, fascinated, on those of the delinquent. The heat of midday was his best opportunity; then even the wariest convict sometimes allowed his weary eyelids to droop and in that moment he was across the floor, tooth and nail, in a savage attack. Basil had seen a gigantic felon led out after a two days' session. There was something in Mr. Harkness's eyes that brought the scene back vividly to him.

"I am afraid my sister's away," said Basil.

Whatever hope had ever been in Mr. Harkness's breast died when he saw his old enemy. "You are Mrs. Sothill's brother?"

"Yes; we are thought rather alike. I'm helping her here now that my brother-in-law's away. Is there anything I can do?"

"No," he said brokenly. "No. It doesn't matter. I'd hoped to see Mrs. Sothill. When will she be back?"

"You can never tell," said Basil. "Most irresponsible in some ways. Goes off for months at a time. But this time she has me to watch out for her. Was it about your evacués you wanted to see her? She was *very* glad to hear they had been happily settled. It meant she could go away with a clear conscience. That particular family had been something of an anxiety, if you understand me."

Mr. Harkness sat down uninvited. He sat on a gilt chair in that bright little room like a figure of death. He seemed disposed neither to speak nor to move.

"Mrs. Harkness well?" said Basil affably.

"Prostrate."

"And your paying guest?"

"She left this morning — as soon as the road was cleared. Our two maids went with her."

"I hope Doris is making herself useful about the house."

At the mention of that name Mr. Harkness broke. He came clean. "Mr. Seal, I can't stand it. We neither of us can. We've come to the end. You must take those children away."

"You surely wouldn't suggest sending them back to Birmingham to be bombed?"

This was an argument which Barbara often employed with good effect. As soon as Basil spoke he realised it was a false step. Suffering had purged Mr. Harkness of all hypocrisy. For the first time something like a smile twisted his lips.

"There is nothing would delight me more," he said.

"Tut, tut. You do yourself an injustice. Anyway it is against the law. I should like to help you. What can you suggest?"

"I thought of giving them weed-killer," said Mr. Harkness wistfully.

"Yes," said Basil, "that would be one way. Do you think Marlene could keep it down?"

"Or hanging."

"Come, come, Mr. Harkness, this is mere wishful thinking. We must be more practical."

"Everything I've thought of has had death in it; ours or theirs."

"I'm sure there must be a way," said Basil, and then, delicately, watching Mr. Harkness while he spoke for any expression of distrust or resentment, he outlined a scheme which had come to him, vaguely, when he first saw the Connollies, and had grown more precise during the past week. "The difficulty about billeting on the poor," he said, "is that the allowance barely covers what the children eat. Of course where they are nice, affectionate children people are often glad enough to have them. But one wouldn't call the Connollies nice or affectionate — " Mr. Harkness groaned. "They are destructive, too. Well I needn't tell you that. The fact is that it would be inflicting a very considerable hardship — a *financial* hardship — to put them in a cottage. Now if the meagre allowance paid by the Government were *supplemented* — do you follow me?"

"You mean I might *pay* someone to take them. Of course I will, anything — at least almost anything. How much shall I offer? How shall I set about it?"

"Leave it to me," said Basil, suddenly dropping his urbane manner. "What's it worth to you to have those children moved?"

Mr. Harkness hesitated; with the quickening of hope came a stir of self-possession. One does not work in the East without acquiring a nose for a deal. "I should think a pound a week would make all the difference to a poor family," he said.

"How about a lump sum? People — poor people that is — will often be dazzled by the offer of a lump sum who wouldn't consider an allowance."

"Twenty-five pounds."

"Come, Mr. Harkness, that's what you proposed paying over six months. The war is going to last longer than that."

"Thirty. I can't go higher than thirty."

He was not a rich man, Basil reflected; very likely thirty was all he could afford. "I daresay I could find someone to take them for that," he said. "Of course you realise that this is all highly irregular."

"Oh, I realise that." Did he? Basil wondered; perhaps he did. "Will you fetch those children to-day?"

"To-day?"

"Without fail." Mr. Harkness seemed to be dictating terms now. "The cheque will be waiting for you. I will make it out to the bearer."

"What a long time you've been," said Barbara. "Have you pacified him?"

"I've got to find a new home for the Connollies."

"Basil, you've let him off!"

"He was so pathetic. I softened."

"Basil, how very unlike you."

"I must get to work with that address book again. We shall have to have the Connollies here for the night. I'll find them a new home in the morning."

He drove over to North Grappling in the twilight. On either side of the lane the new-dug snow was heaped high, leaving a narrow, passable track. The three Connollies were standing outside the apple-green door waiting for him.

"The man with the beard said to give you this," said Doris.

It was an envelope containing a cheque; nothing more. Neither Harkness appeared to see them off.

"Mister, am I glad to see you again!" said Doris.

"Jump in," said Basil.

"May I come in front with you?"

"Yes, jump in."

"Really? No kidding?"

"Come on, it's cold." Doris got in beside Basil. "You're here on sufferance."

"What does that mean?"

"You can sit here as long as you behave yourself, and as long as Micky and Marlene do too. Understand?"

"Hear that, you brats?" said Doris with sudden authority. "Behave, or I'll tan yer arses for yer. They'll be all right, mister, if I tell 'em." They were all right.

"Doris, I think it's a very good game of yours making the kids be a nuisance, but we're going to play it my way in future. When you come to the house where I live you're to behave, always. See? I may take you to other houses from time to time. There you can usually be as bad as you like, but not until I give the word. See?"

"O.K., partner. Give us a cig."

"I'm beginning to like you, Doris."

"*I love you,*" said Doris with excruciating warmth, leaning back and blowing a cloud of smoke over the solemn children in the back. "I love you more than anyone I ever seen."

"Their week with the Harknesses seems to have had an extraordinary effect on the children," said Barbara after dinner that night. "I can't understand it."

"Mr. Harkness said there were *imponderabilia* at Mill House. Perhaps it's that."

"Basil, you're up to something. I wish I knew what it was."

Basil turned on her his innocent blue eyes, as blue as hers and as innocent; they held no hint of mischief. "Just war-work, Babs," he said.

"Slimy snake."

"I'm not."

"Crawly spider." They were back in the schoolroom, in the world where once they had played pirates. "Artful monkey," said Barbara, very fondly.

Most of Mrs. Sothill's Garden Party Only list were people of late middle age who, on retirement from work in the cities or abroad, had bought the smaller manor houses and the larger rectories; houses that once had been supported on the rent of a thousand acres and a dozen cottages now went with a paddock and walled garden, and their life subsisted on unsupported pensions and savings. To these modest landholders the rural character of the neighbourhood was a matter of particular jealousy. Magnates like Freddy would eagerly sell off outlying farms for development. It was the G.P.O. list who suffered and protested. A narrow corner could not be widened or a tree lopped to clear the telegraph wires without it being noted and regretted in those sunny morning-rooms. These were benevolent, companionable people; their carefully limited families were "out in the world" and came to them only for occasional visits. Their daughters had flats and jobs and lives of their own in London; their sons were self-supporting in the services and in business. The tribute of Empire flowed gently into the agricultural countryside, tithe barns were converted into village halls, the boy scouts had a new bell tent and the district nurse a motor car; the old box pews were taken out of the churches, the galleries demolished, the Royal Arms and the Ten Commandments moved from behind the altar and replaced with screens of blue damask supported at the four corners with gilt Sarum angels; the lawns were close-mown, fertilised and weeded, and from their splendid surface rose clumps of pampas grass and yucca; year in, year out, gloved hands grubbed in the rockeries, gloved hands snipped in the herbaceous borders; baskets of bass stood beside trays of visiting-cards on the hall tables. Now in the dead depths of winter when ice stood thick on the lily ponds, and the kitchen gardens at night were a litter of sacking, these good people fed the birds daily with the crumbs from the dining-room table and saw to it that no old person in the village went short of coal.

It was this unfamiliar world that Basil contemplated in the leather-bound pages of Mrs. Sothill's address book. He contemplated it as a marauder might look down from the hills into the fat pastures below; as Hannibal's infantry had looked down from the snowline as the first elephants tried the etched footholds which led to the Lombardy plains below them and went lurching and trumpeting over the edge.

After the successful engagement at North Grappling, Basil took Doris into the nearest town and fed her liberally on fried fish and chipped potatoes; afterwards he took her to the cinema, allowed her to hold his hand in a fierce and sticky grasp throughout the length of two deeply sentimental films, and brought her back to Malfrey in a state of entranced docility.

"You don't like blondes, do you?" she asked anxiously in the car.

"Yes, very much."

"More than brunettes?"

"I'm not particular."

"They say like goes to like. She's dark."

"Who?"

"Her you call your sister."

"Doris, you must get this idea out of your head. Mrs. Sothill *is* my sister."

"You aren't sweet on her?"

"Certainly not."

"Then you *do* like blondes," said Doris sadly.

Next day she disappeared alone into the village, returned mysteriously with a small parcel, and remained hidden all the morning in the bachelors' wing. Just before luncheon she appeared in the orangery with her head in a towel.

"I wanted you to see," she said, and uncovered a damp mop of hair which was in part pale yellow, in part its original black, and in part mottled in every intervening shade.

"Good heavens, child," said Barbara. "What have you done?"

Doris looked only at Basil. "D'you like it? I'll give it another go this afternoon."

"I wouldn't," said Basil. "I'd leave it just as it is."

"You like it?"

"I think it's fine."

"Not too streaky?"

"Not a bit too streaky."

If anything had been needed to complete the horror of Doris's appearance, that morning's work had done it.

Basil studied the address book with care. "Finding a new home for the Connollies," he said.

"Basil, we must do something to that poor child's head before we pass her on."

"Not a bit of it. It suits her. What d'you know of the Graces, of the Old Rectory, Adderford?"

"It's a pretty little house. He's a painter."

"Bohemian?"

"Not the least. Very refined. Portraits of children in water-colour and pastel."

"Pastel? He sounds suitable."

"She's rather delicate I believe."

"Perfect."

The Connollies stayed two days at the Old Rectory and earned twenty pounds.

"What about Mr. and Mrs. Prettyman-Partridge of the Malt House, Grantley Green?"

Basil was choosing his objectives from the extreme quarters of the Malfrey billeting area. He had struck east and north. Grantley Green lay south where the land of spur and valley fell away and flattened out into a plain of cider orchards and market gardens.

"They're very old, I think," said Barbara. "I hardly know them. Come to think of it, I heard something about Mr. Prettyman-Partridge the other day. I can't remember what."

"Pretty house? Nice things in it?"

"As far as I remember."

"People of regular habits? Fond of quiet?"

"Yes, I suppose so."

"They'll do."

Basil bent over the map tracing the road to Grantley Green which he would take next day.

He found the Malt House without difficulty. It had been a brew house in the seventeenth century and later was converted to a private house. It had a large, regular front of dressed stone, facing the village green. The curtains and the china in the window proclaimed that it was in "good hands." Basil noted the china with approval — large, black Wedgwood urns — valuable and vulnerable and no doubt well-loved. When the door opened it disclosed a view straight through the house to a white lawn and a cedar tree laden with snow.

The door was opened by a large and lovely girl. She had fair curly hair and a fair skin, pale blue eyes, a large, shy mouth. She was dressed in a tweed suit and woollen jumper as though for country exercise, but the soft, fur-lined boots showed that she was spending the morning at home. Everything about this girl was large and soft and round and ample. A dress shop might not have chosen her as a mannequin but she was not a fat girl; a more civilised age would have found her admirably proportioned; Boucher would have painted her half-clothed in a flutter of blue and pink draperies, a butterfly hovering over a breast of white and rose.

"Miss Prettyman-Partridge?"

"No. Please don't say you've come to sell something. It's terribly cold standing here and if I ask you in I shall have to buy it."

"I want to see Mr. and Mrs. Prettyman-Partridge."

"They're dead. At least one is; the other sold us the house last summer. Is that all, please? I don't want to be rude but I must shut the door or freeze."

So that was what Barbara had heard about the Malt House. "May I come in?"

"Oh dear," said this splendid girl, leading him into the room with the Wedgwood urns. "Is it something to buy or forms to fill in or just a subscription? If it's the first two I can't help because my husband's away with the yeomanry; if it's a subscription I've got some money upstairs. I've been told to give the same as Mrs. Andrews, the doctor's wife. If you haven't been to her yet, come back when you find what she's good for."

Everything in the room was new; that is to say the paint was new and the carpets and the curtains, and the furniture had been newly put in position. There was a very large settee in front of the fireplace whose cushions, upholstered in toile-de-Jouy, still bore the impress of that fine young woman; she had been lying there when Basil rang the bell. He knew that if he put his hand in the round concavity where her hip had rested, it would still be warm; and that further cushion had been tucked under her arm. The book she had been reading was on the lambskin hearth-rug. Basil could reconstruct the position, exactly, where she had been sprawling with the languor of extreme youth.

The girl seemed to sense an impertinence in Basil's scrutiny. "Anyway," she said. "Why aren't you in khaki?"

"Work of national importance," said Basil. "I am the district billeting officer. I'm looking for a suitable home for three evacuated children."

"Well, I hope you don't call this suitable. I ask you. I can't even look after Bill's sheepdog. I can't even look after myself very well. What should I do with three children?"

"These are rather exceptional children."

"They'd have to be. Anyway I'm not having any thank you. There was a funny little woman called Harkness came to call here yesterday. I do think people might let up on calling in war-time, don't you? She told me the most gruesome things about some children that were sent to her. They had to bribe the man, literally bribe him with money, to get the brutes moved."

"These are the same children."

"Well for God's sake, why pick on me?"

Her great eyes held him dazzled, like a rabbit before the headlights of a car. It was a delicious sensation.

"Well, actually, I picked on the Prettyman-Partridges . . . I don't even know your name."

"I don't know yours."

"Basil Seal."

"Basil Seal?" There was a sudden interest in her voice. "How very funny."

"Why funny?"

"Only that I used to hear a lot about you once. Weren't you a friend of a girl called Mary Nichols?"

"Was I?" Was he? Mary Nichols? Mary Nichols?

"Well, she used to talk a lot about you. She was much older than me. I used to think her wonderful when I was sixteen. You met her in a ship coming from Copenhagen."

"I daresay. I've been to Copenhagen."

The girl was looking at him now with a keen and not wholly flattering attention. "So you're Basil Seal," she said. "Well I never . . ."

Four years ago in South Kensington, at Mary Nichols's home, there was a little back sitting-room on the first floor which was Mary's room. Here Mary entertained her girl friends to tea. Here she had come, day after day, to sit before the gas fire and eat Fullers' walnut cake and hear the details of Mary's Experience. "But aren't you going to see him again?" she asked. "No, it was something so beautiful, so complete in itself — " Mary had steeped herself in romantic literature since her Experience. "I don't want to spoil it." "I don't think he sounds half good enough for you, darling." "He's absolutely *different*. You mustn't think of him as one of the young men one meets at dances . . ." The girl did not go to dances yet, and Mary knew it. Mary's tales of the young men she met at dances had been very moving, but not as moving as this tale of Basil Seal. The name had become graven on her mind.

And Basil, still standing, searched his memory. Mary Nichols? Copenhagen? No, it registered nothing. It was very consoling, he thought, the way in which an act of kindness, in the fullness of time, returns to bless the benefactor. One gives a jolly-up to a girl in a ship. She goes her way, he goes his. He forgets; he has so many benefactions of the kind to his credit. But she remembers and then one day, when it is least expected, Fate drops into his lap the ripe fruit of his reward, this luscious creature waiting for him, all unaware, in the Malt House, Grantley Green.

"Aren't you going to offer me a drink — on the strength of Mary Nichols?"

"I don't think there's anything in the house. Bill's away you see. He's got some wine downstairs in the cellar, but the door's locked."

"I expect we could open it."

"Oh! I wouldn't do that. Bill would be furious."

"Well, I don't suppose he'll be best pleased to come home on leave and find the Connolly family hacking up his home. By the way, you haven't seen them yet; they're outside in the car; I'll bring them in."

"*Please* don't!" There was genuine distress and appeal in those blue cow-eyes.

"Well, take a look at them through the window."

She went and looked. "Good God," said the girl. "Mrs. Harkness wasn't far wrong. I thought she was laying it on thick."

"It cost her thirty pounds to get rid of them."

"Oh, but I haven't got anything like that" — again the distress and appeal in her wide blue eyes. "Bill makes me an allowance out of his pay. It comes in monthly. It's practically all I've got."

"I'll take payment in kind," said Basil.

"You mean the sherry?"

"I'd like a glass of sherry very much," said Basil.

When they got to work with the crowbar on the cellar door, it was clear that this high-spirited girl thoroughly enjoyed herself. It was a pathetic little cellar: a poor man's treasury. Half a dozen bottles of hock, a bin of port, a dozen or two of claret. "Mostly wedding presents," explained the girl. Basil found some sherry and they took it up to the light.

"I've no maid now," she explained. "A woman comes in once a week."

They found glasses in the pantry and a corkscrew in the dining-room.

"Is it any good?" she asked anxiously, while Basil tasted the wine.

"Delicious."

"I'm so glad. Bill knows about wine. I don't."

So they began to talk about Bill, who was married in July to this lovely creature, who had a good job in an architect's office in the near-by town, had settled at Grantley Green in August, and in September had gone to join the yeomanry as a trooper . . .

Two hours later Basil left the Malt House and returned to his car. It was evidence of the compelling property of love that the Connolly children were still in their seats.

"Gawd, mister, you haven't half been a time," said Doris. "We're fair froze. Do we get out here?"

"No."

"We aren't going to muck up this house?"

"No, Doris, not this time. You're coming back with me."

Doris sighed blissfully. "I don't care how froze we are if we can come back with you," she said.

When they returned to Malfrey, and Barbara once more found the children back in the bachelors' wing, her face fell. "Oh, Basil," she said. "You've failed me."

"Well not exactly. The Prettyman-Partridges are dead."

"I knew there was something about them. But you've been a long time."

"I met a friend. At least the friend of a friend. A very nice girl. I think you ought to do something about her."

"What's her name?"

"D'you know, I never discovered. But her husband's called Bill. He joined Freddy's regiment as a trooper."

"Who's she a friend of?"

"Mary Nichols."

"I've never heard of her."

"Old friend of mine. Honestly, Babs, you'll like this girl."

"Well, ask her to dinner." Barbara was not enthusiastic; she had known too many of Basil's girls.

"I have. The trouble is she hasn't got a car. D'you mind if I go and fetch her?"

"Darling, we simply haven't the petrol."

"We can use the special allowance."

"Darling, I can't. This has nothing to do with billeting."

"Believe it or not Babs, it has."

Two events decided Basil to return to London. First, the yeomanry moved back to the country under canvas. Freddy telephoned to Barbara:

"Good news," he said; "we're coming home."

"Freddy, how splendid," said Barbara, her spirits falling a little. "When?"

"I arrive to-morrow. I'm bringing Jack Cathcart; he's our second-in-command now. We're going to lay out a camp. We'll stay at Malfrey while we're doing it."

"Lovely," said Barbara.

"We'll be bringing servants, so we'll be self-supporting as far as that goes. There'll be a couple of sergeants. Benson can look after them. And I say, Barbara, what do you say to having the camp in the park?"

"Oh no, Freddy, for God's sake."

"We could open up the saloon and have the mess there. I could live in. You'd have to have old Colonel Sproggin and probably Cathcart, too, but you wouldn't mind that, would you?"

"Please, Freddy, don't decide anything in a hurry."

"Well I have practically decided. See you to-morrow. I say, is Basil still with you?"

"Yes."

"I can't see him getting on terribly well with Cathcart. Couldn't you give him a gentle hint?"

Barbara hung up sadly and went to make arrangements for Freddy's and Major Cathcart's reception.

Basil was at Grantley Green. He returned to Malfrey after dinner, to find Barbara still up.

"Darling, you've got to go away."

"Yes, how did you know?"

"Freddy's coming home."

"Oh damn Freddy; who cares for him? *Bill's* coming home."

"What does she say?"

"Believe it or not, she's as pleased as Punch."

"Ungrateful beast," said Barbara; and, after a pause, "You never wrote that book either."

"No, but we've had a lovely time, haven't we, Babs? Quite like the old days."

"I suppose you'll want some money."

"I could always do with some more, but as it happens I'm quite rich at the moment."

"Basil, how?"

"One thing and another. I tell you what I will do before I go. I'll get the Connollies off your hands again. I'm afraid I've been neglecting them rather in the last few weeks."

That led to the second deciding event.

On his way to and from Grantley Green, Basil had noticed a pretty stucco house standing in paddock and orchard, which seemed exactly suited to harbour the Connollies. He had asked Barbara about it, but she could tell him nothing. Basil was getting lax and confident now in his methods, and no longer bothered himself with much research before choosing his victims. The stucco house was marked down and next day he packed the Connollies into the car and drove over to do his business.

It was ten in the morning but he found the proprietor at breakfast. He did not appear to be quite the type that Basil was used to deal with. He was younger than the G.P.O. list. A game leg, stuck awkwardly askew, explained why he was not in uniform. He had got this injury in a motor race, he explained later to Basil. He had ginger hair and a ginger moustache and malevolent pinkish eyes. His name was Mr. Todhunter.

He was eating kidneys and eggs and sausages and bacon and an overcooked chop; his tea-pot stood on the hob. He looked like a drawing by Leech for a book by Surtees.

"Well," he said, cautious but affable. "I know about you. You're Mrs. Sothill's brother at Malfrey. I don't know Mrs. Sothill but I know all about her. I don't know Captain Sothill but I know about him. What can I do for you?"

"I'm the billeting officer for this district," said Basil.

"*Indeed*. I'm interested to meet you. Go on. You don't mind my eating, I'm sure."

Feeling a little less confident than usual, Basil went through his now stereotyped preface: . . . Getting harder to find billets, particularly since the anti-aircraft battery had come to South Grappling and put their men in the cottages there . . . important to stop the backwash to the towns . . . bad impression if the bigger houses seemed not to be doing their share . . . natural reluctance to employ compulsory powers but these powers *were* there, if necessary . . . three children who had caused some difficulty elsewhere . . .

Mr. Todhunter finished his breakfast, stood with his back to the fire and began to fill his pipe. "And what if I don't want these hard cases of yours?" he said. "What if I'd sooner pay the fine?"

Basil embarked on the second part of his recitation: . . . Official allowance barely covered cost of food . . . serious hardship to poor families . . . poor people valued their household gods even more than the rich . . . possible to find a cottage where a few pounds would make all the difference between dead loss and a small and welcome profit . . .

Mr. Todhunter heard him in silence. At last he said, "So *that's* how you do it. Thank you. That was most instructive, very instructive indeed. I like the bit about household gods."

Basil began to realize that he was dealing with a fellow of broad and rather dangerous sympathies; someone like himself. "In more cultured circles I say *Lares et Penates*."

"Household gods is good enough. Household gods is very good indeed. What d'you generally count on raising?"

"Five pounds is the worst, thirty-five the best I've had so far."

"So far? Do you hope to carry on long with this trade?"

"I don't see why not."

"Don't you? Well, I'll tell you something. D'you know who's billeting officer in this district? I am. Mrs. Sothill's district ends at the main road. You're muscling in on my territory when you come past the crossing. Now what have you got to say for yourself?"

"D'you mean to say that Grantley Green is yours?"

"Certainly."

"How damned funny."

"Why funny?"

"I can't tell you," said Basil. "But it *is* — exquisitely funny."

"So I'll ask you to keep to your own side of the road in future. Not that I'm ungrateful for your visit. It's given me some interesting ideas. I always felt there was money in this racket somehow, but I could never quite see my way to get it. Now I know. I'll remember about the household gods."

"Wait a minute," said Basil. "It isn't quite as easy as all that, you know. It isn't just a matter of having the idea; you have to have the Connollies too. You don't understand it, and I don't understand it, but the fact remains that quite a number of otherwise sane human beings are perfectly ready to take children in; they like them; it makes them feel virtuous; they like the little pattering feet about the house — I know it sounds screwy but it's the truth. I've seen it again and again."

"So have I," said Mr. Todhunter. "There's no sense in it, but it's a fact — they make household gods of them."

"Now the Connollies are something quite special; no one could make a household god of them. Come and have a look."

He and Mr. Todhunter went out into the circle of gravel in front of the porch, where Basil had left the car.

"Doris," he said. "Come out and meet Mr. Todhunter. Bring Micky and Marlene too."

The three frightful children stood in a line to be inspected.

"Take that scarf off your head, Doris. Show him your hair."

In spite of himself Mr. Todhunter could not disguise the fact that he was profoundly moved. "Yes," he said. "I give you that. They *are* special. If it's not a rude question, what did you pay for them?"

"I got them free. But I've put a lot of money into them since — fried fish and cinemas."

"How did you get the girl's hair that way?"

"She did it herself," said Basil, "for love."

"They certainly are special," repeated Mr. Todhunter with awe.

"You haven't seen anything yet. You should see them in action."

"I can imagine it," said Mr. Todhunter. "Well, what d'you want for them?"

"Five pounds a leg and that's cheap, because I'm thinking of closing down the business anyhow."

Mr. Todhunter was not a man to haggle when he was on a good thing. "Done," he said.

Basil addressed the Connollies. "Well, children, this is your new headquarters."

"Are we to muck 'em about?" asked Doris.

"That's up to Mr. Todhunter. I'm handing you over to him now. You'll be working for him in future."

"Ain't we never going to be with you again?" asked Doris.

"Never again, Doris. But you'll find you like Mr. Todhunter just as much. He's very handsome, isn't he?"

"Not as handsome as you."

"No, perhaps not, but he's got a fine little red moustache, hasn't he?"

"Yes, it's a lovely moustache," Doris conceded; she looked from her old to her new master, critically. "But he's shorter than you."

"Dammit, girl," said Basil impatiently. "Don't you realise there's a war on? We've all got to make sacrifices. There's many a little girl would be very grateful for Mr. Todhunter. Look at his fine red nob."

"Yes, it *is* red."

Mr. Todhunter tired of the comparison and stumped indoors to fetch his cheque-book.

"Can't we muck his house up, just a bit?" said Micky wistfully.

"Yes, I don't see why not, just a bit."

"Mister," said Doris, near tears. "Kiss me once before you go."

"No. Mr. Todhunter wouldn't like it. He's terribly jealous."

"Is he?" she said lightening. "I love jealous men."

When Basil left her, her fervent, volatile affections were already plainly engaged with her new host. Marlene remained passive throughout the interview; she had few gifts, poor child, and those she was allowed to employ only on rare occasions. "Mayn't I be sick here, Doris? Just once?"

"Not here, ducky. Wait till the gentleman billets you."

"Will that be long?"

"No," said Mr. Todhunter decisively, "not long."

So the scourge of the Malfrey area moved south into the apple-growing country and the market gardens; and all over the park at Malfrey, dispersed irregularly under the great elms, tents sprang up; and the yeomanry officers set up their mess in the Grinling Gibbons saloon; and Barbara had Colonel Sproggin and Major Cathcart to live in the house; and Freddy made an agreeable sum of money out of the arrangement; and Bill spent many blissful uxorious hours in the Malt House, Grantley Green (he was quite satisfied with the explanation he was given about the cellar door). And Basil returned to London.

He decided to pay one of his rare, and usually rather brief, visits to his mother. He found her busy and optimistic, serving on half a dozen benevolent committees connected with comforts for the troops, seeing her friends regularly. The defeat of Finland had shocked her, but she found it a compensation that Russia was at last disclosed in the true light. She welcomed Basil to the house, heard his news of Barbara and gave him news of Tony. "I want to have a little talk with you sometime," she said, after half an hour's gossip.

Basil, had he not been inured to his mother's euphemisms, might have supposed that a little talk was precisely what she had just had; but he knew what a little talk meant; it meant a discussion of his "future."

"Have you arranged anything for to-night?"

"No, Mother, not yet."

"Then we will dine in. Just the two of us."

And that night after dinner she said, "Basil, I never thought I should have to say this to you. I've been pleased, of course, that you were able to be of help to Barbara with her evacués, but now that you have returned to London, I must tell you that I do not think it is *man's* work. At a time like this you ought to be *fighting*."

"But Mother, as far as I know, no one's fighting much at the moment."

"Don't quibble, dear, you know what I mean."

"Well, I went to see that colonel when you asked me to."

"Yes. Sir Joseph explained that to me. They only want very young officers in the Guards. But he says that there are a number of other excellent regiments that offer a far better career. General Gordon was a Sapper, and I believe quite a number of the generals in this war were originally only Gunners. I don't want you just lounging about London in uniform like your friend Peter Pastmaster. He seems to spend his whole time with girls. That goose Emma Granchester is seriously thinking of him for Molly. So is Etty Flintshire and so is poor Mrs. Van Atrobus for *their* daughters. I don't know what they're thinking of. I knew his poor father. Margot led him a terrible dance. That was long before she married Metroland of course — before he was called Metroland, in fact. No," said Lady Seal, abruptly checking herself in the flow of reminiscence. "I want to see you doing something *important*. Now Sir Joseph has got me one of the forms you fill in to become an officer. It is called the Supplementary Reserve. Before you go to bed I want you to sign it. Then we'll see about getting it sent to the proper quarter. I'm sure that everything will be much easier now that that disgraceful Mr. Belisha has been outed."

"But you know, Mother, I don't really fancy myself much as a subaltern."

"No, dear," said Lady Seal decisively, "and if you had gone into the Army when you left Oxford you would be a major by now. Promotion is very quick in war-time because so many people get killed. I'm sure once you're in, they'll find great use for you. But you must begin somewhere. I remember Lord Kitchener told me that even he was once a subaltern."

Thus it was that Basil found himself again in danger of being started on a career. "Don't worry," said Peter. "No one ever gets taken off the Supplementary Reserve." But Basil did worry. He had a rooted distrust of official forms. He felt that at any moment a telegram might summon him to present himself at some remote barracks, where he would spend the war, like Alastair's Mr. Smallwood, teaching fieldcraft to thirty militiamen. It was not thus that he had welcomed the war as the ne'er-do-well's opportunity. He fretted about it for three days and then decided to pay a visit to the War Office.

He went there without any particular object in view, impelled by the belief that somewhere in that large organisation was a goose who would lay eggs for him. In the first days of the war, when he was seeking to interest the authorities in the annexation of Liberia, he had more than once sought an entrance. Perhaps, he felt now, he had pitched a little too high. The Chief of the Imperial General Staff was a busy man. This time he would advance humbly.

The maelstrom which in early September had eddied round the vestibule of the building seemed to have subsided very little. There was a similar — perhaps, he reflected sadly, an identical — crowd of officers of all ranks attempting to gain admission. Among them he saw a single civilian figure, whom he recognised from his visit to the Ministry of Information.

"Hullo," he said. "Still hawking bombs?"

The little lunatic with the suitcase greeted him with great friendliness. "They won't pay any attention. It's a most unsatisfactory office," he said. "They won't let me in. I was sent on here from the Admiralty."

"Have you tried the Air Ministry?"

"Why, bless you, it was them sent me to the Ministry of Information. I've tried them all. I will say for the Ministry of Information they were uncommon civil. Not at all like they are here. At the M. of I. they were never too busy to see one. The only thing was, I felt I wasn't getting anywhere."

"Come along," said Basil. "We'll get in."

Veterans of the Ashanti and the Zulu campaigns guarded the entrance. Basil watched them stop a full general. "If you'll fill in a form, sir, please, one of the boys will take you up to the Department." They were a match for anyone in uniform but Basil and the bagman were a most uncertain quantity; a full general was just a full general, but a civilian might be anyone.

"Your passes, gentlemen, please."

"That's all right, Sergeant," said Basil. "I'll vouch for this man."

"Yes sir, but who are you, sir?"

"You ought to know by this time. M.I.9. We don't carry passes or give our names in my department."

"Very good, sir; beg pardon, sir. D'you know the way or shall I send a boy up with you?"

"Of course I know my way," said Basil sharply, "and you might take a look at this man. He won't give his name or show a pass, but I expect you'll see him here often."

"Very good, sir."

The two civilians passed through the seething military into the calm of the corridors beyond.

"I'm sure I'm very obliged," said the man with the suitcase; "where shall I go now?"

"The whole place lies open to you," said Basil. "Take your time. Go where you like. I think if I were you I should start with the Chaplain General."

"Where's he?"

"Up there," said Basil vaguely. "Up there and straight on."

The little man thanked him gravely, trotted off down the corridor with the irregular, ill co-ordinated steps of the insane, and was lost to view up the bend in the staircase. Not wishing to compromise himself further by his act of charity, Basil took the opposing turning. A fine vista lay before him of twenty or more closed doors, any one of which might open upon prosperity and adventure. He strolled down the passage in a leisurely but purposeful manner; thus, he thought, an important agent might go to keep an appointment; thus, in fact, Soapy Sponge might have walked in the gallery of Jawleyford Court.

It was a vista full of potentiality; but lacking, at the moment, in ornament — a vista of linoleum and sombre dado; the light came solely from the far end, so that a figure approaching appeared in silhouette, and in somewhat indistinct silhouette; a figure now approached and it was not until she was within a few yards of Basil that he realised that here was the enrichment which the austere architectural scheme demanded: a girl dressed in uniform with a lance-corporal's stripe on her arm — with a face of transparent, ethereal silliness which struck deep into Basil's heart. The classical image might have been sober fact, so swift and silent and piercing was the dart of pleasure. He turned in his tracks and followed the lance-corporal down the lane of linoleum, which seemed, momentarily, as buoyant as the carpet of a cinema or theatre.

The lance-corporal led him a long way; she stopped from time to time to exchange greetings with passers-by, showing to all ranks from full general to second-class scout the same cheerful affection; she was clearly a popular girl in these parts. At length she turned into a door

marked ADDIS; Basil followed her in. There was another lance-corporal —
male — in the room.

This lance-corporal sat behind a typewriter; he had a white, pimply
face, large spectacles, and a cigarette in the corner of his mouth. He
did not look up. The female lance-corporal smiled and said, "So now
you know where I live. Drop in any time you're passing."

"What is ADDIS?" asked Basil.

"It's Colonel Plum."

"What's Colonel Plum?"

"He's a perfect lamb. Go and take a peek at him if you like. He's in
there." She nodded towards a glass door marked KEEP OUT.

"Assistant Deputy Director Internal Security," said the male lance-
corporal without looking up from his typing.

"I think I'd like to come and work in this office," said Basil.

"Yes, everyone says that. It was the same when I was in Pensions."

"I might take *his* job."

"You're welcome," said the male lance-corporal sourly. "Suspects,
suspects, suspects, all day long — all with foreign names, none of them
ever shot."

A loud voice from beyond the glass door broke into the conversation.
"Susie, you slut, come here."

"That's him, the angel. Just take a peek while the door's open. He's
got the sweetest little moustache."

Basil peered round the corner and caught a glimpse of a lean, military
face and, as Susie had said, the sweetest little moustache. The Colonel
caught a glimpse of Basil.

"Who the devil's that?"

"I don't know," said Susie lightly. "He just followed me in."

"Come here you," said the Colonel. "Who are you and what d'you
want in my office?"

"Well," said Basil, "what the lance-corporal says is strictly true.
I just followed her in. But since I'm here I can give you some valuable
information."

"If you can you're unique in this outfit. What is it?"

Until now the word "Colonel" for Basil had connoted an elderly rock-
gardener on Barbara's G.P.O. list. This formidable man of his own age
was another kettle of fish. Here was a second Todhunter. What could
he possibly tell him which would pass for valuable information? "Can
I speak freely before the lance-corporal?" he asked, playing for time.

"Yes, of course. She doesn't understand a word of any language."

Inspiration came. "There's a lunatic loose in the War Office," Basil said.

"Of course there is. There are some hundreds of them. Is that all you came to tell me?"

"He's got a suitcase full of bombs."

"Well, I hope he finds his way to the Intelligence Branch. I don't suppose you know his name? No; well, make out a card for him, Susie, with a serial number, and index him under Suspects. If his bombs go off we shall know where he is; if they don't it doesn't matter. These fellows usually do more harm to themselves than to anyone else. Run along, Susie, and shut the door. I want to talk to Mr. Seal."

Basil was shaken. When the door shut he said, "Have we met before?"

"You bet we have. Djibouti 1936, St. Jean de Luz 1937, Prague 1938. You wouldn't remember me. I wasn't dressed up like this then."

"Were you a journalist?"

Vaguely at the back of Basil's mind was the recollection of an unobtrusive, discreet face among a hundred unobtrusive, discreet faces that had passed in and out of his ken from time to time. During the past ten years he had usually managed to find himself, on one pretext or another, on the outer fringe of contemporary history — in that half-world there were numerous slightly sinister figures whose orbits crossed and recrossed, ubiquitous men and women camp-followers of diplomacy and the press; among those shades he dimly remembered seeing Colonel Plum.

"Sometimes. We got drunk together once at the Basquebar, the night you fought the United Press correspondent."

"As far as I remember he won."

"You bet he did. I took you back to your hotel. What are you doing now besides making passes at Susie?"

"I thought of doing counter-espionage."

"Yes," said Colonel Plum. "Most people who come here seem to have thought of that. Hallo — " he added as a dull detonation shook the room slightly — "that sounds as if your man has had a success with his bombs. That was a straight tip, anyway. I daresay you'd be no worse in the job than anyone else."

Here it was at last, the scene that Basil had so often rehearsed; the scene, very slightly adapted by a later hand, in order to bring it up to date, from the adventure stories of his youth. Here was the lean, masterful man, who had followed Basil's career saying, "One day his country will have a use for him . . ."

"What are your contacts?"

What were his contacts? Alastair Digby-Vane-Trumpington, Angela Lyne, Margot Metroland, Peter Pastmaster, Barbara, the bride of Grantley Green, Mr. Todhunter, Poppet Green — *Poppet Green;* there was his chicken.

"I know some very dangerous Communists," said Basil.

"I wonder if they're on our files. We'll look in a minute. We aren't doing much about Communists at the moment. The politicians are shy of them for some reason. But we keep an eye on them, on the side, of course. I can't pay you much for Communists."

"As it happens," said Basil with dignity, "I came here to serve my country. I don't particularly want money."

"The devil you don't? Well, what *do* you want, then? You can't have Susie. I had the hell of a fight to get her away from the old brute in charge of Pensions."

"We can fight that out later. What I really want most at the moment is a uniform."

"Good God! Why?"

"My mother is threatening to make me a platoon commander."

Colonel Plum accepted this somewhat surprising statement with apparent understanding. "Yes," he said. "There's a lot to be said for a uniform. For one thing you'll have to call me 'sir' and if there's any funny stuff with the female staff I can take disciplinary action. For another thing it's the best possible disguise for a man of intelligence. No one ever suspects a soldier of taking a serious interest in the war. I think I can fix that."

"What'll my rank be?"

"Second Lieutenant, Crosse and Blackwell's regiment."

"Crosse and Blackwell?"

"General Service List."

"I say, can't you do anything better than that?"

"Not for watching Communists. Catch a fascist for me and I'll think about making you a Captain of Marines." At this moment the telephone bell rang. "Yes, ADDIS speaking . . . oh, yes, the bomb . . . yes, we know all about that . . . the Chaplain General? I say, that's bad . . . oh, only the Deputy Assistant Chaplain General and you think he'll recover. Well what's all the fuss about? . . . Yes, we know all about the man in this branch. We've had him indexed a long time. He's nuts — yes, N for nuts, U for uncle, nuts, you've got it. No I don't want to see him. Lock him up. There must be plenty of padded cells in this building, I should imagine."

News of the attempt to assassinate the Chaplain General reached the Religious Department of the Ministry of Information late in the afternoon, just when they were preparing to pack up for the day. It threw them into a fever of activity.

"Really," said Ambrose pettishly. "You fellows get all the fun. I shall be *most* embarrassed when I have to explain this to the editor of the *Godless Sunday at Home*."

Lady Seal was greatly shocked.

"Poor man," she said, "I understand that his eyebrows have completely gone. It must have been Russians."

Basil's job at the War Office looked as if it were going the way of all the others; once secured, it had few attractions for him. Susie was proving a disappointment; in spite of continued remonstrance, she still seemed to prefer Colonel Plum.

"Good evening, handsome," she said. "Plummy has been asking for you."

Basil went through the door marked KEEP OUT.

"Good evening, Colonel."

"You can call me 'sir.'"

"None of the best regiments call their commanding officers 'sir.'"

"You're not in one of the best regiments. You're General Service. What have you been doing all day?"

"You don't think it will improve the tone of the Department if I called you 'Colonel,' sir?"

"I do not. Where have you been and what have you been doing?"

"You think I've been drinking, don't you?"

"I bloody well know you have."

"But you don't know the reason. You wouldn't understand if I told you. I've been drinking out of chivalry. That doesn't make any sense to you, does it?"

"No."

"I thought it wouldn't. Coarse-grained, sir. If they put on my grave,

'He drank out of chivalry' it would simply be the sober truth. But you wouldn't understand. What's more you think I've been idle, don't you?"

"I do."

"Well, sir, that's where you're wrong. I have been following up a very interesting trail. I hope to have some valuable information very soon."

"What have you got up to date?"

"You wouldn't sooner wait until I can give you the whole case cut-and-dried?"

"No."

"Well, I'm on to a very dangerous woman who calls herself Green. Among her intimates she's known as 'Poppet.' She pretends to be a painter, but you have only to look at her work to realise it is a cloak for other activities. Her studio is the meeting place for a Communist cell. She has an agent in the United States named Parsnip; he has the alias of Pimpernell; he puts it about that he is a poet, two poets in fact, but there again, the work betrays him. Would you like me to quote some Parsnip to you?"

"No."

"I have reason to believe that Green is the head of an underground organisation by which young men of military age are smuggled out of the country. Those are the lines I have been working on. What d'you think of them?"

"Rotten."

"I was afraid you might say that. It's your own fault. Give me time and I would have had a better story."

"Now you can do some work. Here's a list of thirty-three addresses of suspected fascists. Check them up."

"Now?"

"Now."

"Shan't I keep track of the woman Green?"

"Not in office hours."

"I can't think what you see in your Plum," said Basil when he regained the outer office. "It must simply be snobbery."

"It's not: it's love. The officer in the Pensions office was a full Colonel, so there."

"I expect you'll be reduced to subalterns, yet. And by the way, Lance-Corporal, you can call me 'sir.' "

Susie giggled. "I believe you're drunk," she said.

"Drunk with chivalry," said Basil.

Basil went to the Café Royal to keep his watch on "the woman Green." He found her sitting among her cronies and was greeted with tepid affection.

"So you're in the Army, now," she said.

"No, the great uniformed bureaucracy. How are all the Reds?"

"Very well thank you, watching your imperialists making a mess of your war."

"Been to many Communist meetings lately?"

"Why?"

"Just wondering."

"You sound like a police spy."

"That's the very last impression I want to make," and, changing the subject hastily, added, "Seen Ambrose lately?"

"He's over there now, the lousy fascist."

Basil looked where she indicated and saw Ambrose at a table by the rail of the opposing gallery, sitting with a little, middle-aged man of nondescript appearance.

"Did you say 'fascist'?"

"Didn't you know? He's gone to the Ministry of Information and he's bringing out a fascist paper next month."

"This is very interesting," said Basil. "Tell me some more."

Ambrose sat, upright and poised, with one hand on the stem of his glass and one resting stylishly on the balustrade. There was no particular feature of his clothes which could be mentioned as conspicuous; he wore a dark, smooth suit that fitted perhaps a little closely at waist and wrists, a shirt of plain, cream-coloured silk; a dark, white spotted bow tie; his sleek black hair was not unduly long (he went to the same barber as Alastair and Peter); his pale Semitic face gave no hint of special care, and yet it always embarrassed Mr. Bentley somewhat to be seen with him in public. Sitting there, gesticulating very slightly as he talked, wagging his head very slightly, raising his voice occasionally in a suddenly stressed uncommon epithet or in a fragment of slang absurdly embedded in his precise and literary diction, giggling between words now and then as something which he had intended to say changed shape and became unexpectedly comic in the telling — Ambrose, like this, caused time to slip back to an earlier age than his own youth or Mr. Bentley's, when amid a more splendid décor of red plush and gilt caryatides *fin-de-siècle* young worshippers crowded to the tables of Oscar and Aubrey.

Mr. Bentley smoothed his sparse grey hairs and fidgeted with his tie and looked about anxiously for fear he was observed.

The Café Royal, perhaps because of its distant associations with Oscar and Aubrey, was one of the places where Ambrose preened himself, spread his feathers and felt free to take wing. He had left his persecution mania downstairs with his hat and umbrella. He defied the universe.

"The decline of England, my dear Geoffrey," he said, "dates from the day we abandoned coal fuel. No, I'm not talking about distressed areas, but about distressed *souls,* my dear. We used to live in a fog, the splendid, luminous, tawny fogs of our early childhood. The golden aura of the golden age. Think of it, Geoffrey, there are children now coming to manhood who never saw a London fog. We designed a city which was meant to be seen in a fog. We had a foggy habit of life and a rich, obscure, choking literature. The great catch in the throat of English lyric poetry is just *fog,* my dear, on the vocal cords. And out of the fog we could rule the world; we were a Voice, like the Voice on Sinai smiling through the clouds. Primitive peoples always choose a God who speaks from a cloud. *Then* my dear Geoffrey," said Ambrose, wagging an accusing finger and fixing Mr. Bentley with a black accusing eye, as though the poor publisher were personally responsible for the whole thing, *"then,* some busybody invents electricity or oil fuel or whatever it is they use nowadays. The fog lifts, the world sees us as we are, and worse still we see ourselves as we are. It was a carnival ball, my dear, which when the guests unmasked at midnight was found to be composed entirely of impostors. Such a *rumpus,* my dear."

Ambrose drained his glass with a swagger, surveyed the café haughtily and saw Basil, who was making his way towards them.

"We are talking of Fogs," said Mr. Bentley.

"They're eaten hollow with Communism," said Basil, introducing himself in the part of *agent provocateur.* "You can't stop a rot that's been going on twenty years by imprisoning a handful of deputies. Half the thinking men in France have begun looking to Germany as their real ally."

"Please Basil, don't start politics. Anyway we were talking of Fogs, not Frogs."

"Oh, Fogs." Basil attempted to tell of a foggy adventure of his own, sailing a yawl round Bear Island, but Ambrose was elated to-night and in no mood for these loose leaves of Conrad drifting in the high wind of his talk. "We must return to the Present," he said prophetically.

"Oh dear," said Mr. Bentley. "Why?"

"Everyone is either looking back or forward. Those with reverence and good taste, like you, my dear Geoffrey, look back to an Augustan Age; those with generous hearts and healthy lives and the taste of the devil, like Poppet Green over there, look forward to a Marxian Jerusalem. We must accept the Present."

"You would say, wouldn't you," said Basil, persevering, "that Hitler was a figure of the Present?"

"I regard him as a page for *Punch*," said Ambrose. "To the Chinese scholar the military hero was the lowest of human types, the subject for ribaldry. We must return to Chinese scholarship."

"It's a terribly difficult language, I believe," said Mr. Bentley.

"I knew a Chink in Valparaiso . . ." began Basil; but Ambrose was now in full gallop.

"European scholarship has never lost its monastic character," he said. "Chinese scholarship deals with taste and wisdom, not with the memorising of facts. In China the man whom we make a don sat for the Imperial examinations and became a bureaucrat. Their scholars were lonely men of few books and fewer pupils, content with a single concubine, a pine tree and the prospect of a stream. European culture has become conventual; we must make it coenobitic."

"I knew a hermit in the Ogaden Desert once . . ."

"Invasions swept over China; the Empire split up into warring kingdoms. The scholars lived their frugal and idyllic lives undisturbed, occasionally making exquisite private jokes which they wrote on leaves and floated downstream."

"I read a lot of Chinese poetry once," said Mr. Bentley, "in the translation, of course. I became fascinated by it. I would read of a sage who, as you say, lived frugally and idyllically. He had a cottage and a garden and a view. Each flower had its proper mood and phase of the climate; he would smell the jasmine after recovering from the toothache and the lotus when drinking tea with a monk. There was a little clearing where the full moon cast no shadow, where his concubine would sit and sing to him when he got drunk. Every aspect of this little garden corresponded to some personal mood of the most tender and re-fined sort. It was quite intoxicating to read."

"It is."

"This sage had no tame dog, but he had a cat and a mother. Every morning he greeted his mother on his knees and every evening, in winter, he put charcoal under her mattress and himself drew the bed-curtains. It sounded the most exquisite existence."

"It was."

"And then," said Mr. Bentley, "I found a copy of the *Daily Mirror* in a railway carriage and I read an article there by Godfrey Winn about his cottage and his flowers and his moods, and for the life of me, Ambrose, I couldn't see the difference between that young gentleman and Yuan Ts'e-tsung."

It was cruel of Mr. Bentley to say this, but it may be argued for him that he had listened to Ambrose for three hours and now that Basil had joined their table he wanted to go home to bed.

The interruption deflated Ambrose and allowed Basil to say, "These scholars of yours, Ambrose — they didn't care if their empire was invaded?"

"Not a hoot, my dear, not a *tinker's* hoot."

"And you're starting a paper to encourage this sort of scholarship."

Basil sat back and ordered a drink, as an advocate in a film will relax, saying in triumph, "Mr. District Attorney, *your* witness."

When Mr. Bentley, in the first flush of patriotic zeal, left publishing and took service with the Ministry of Information, it was agreed between him and the senior partner that his room should be kept for his use and that he should come in whenever he could to keep an eye on his interests. Mr. Rampole, the senior partner, would see to the routine of the office.

Rampole and Bentley was not a large or a very prosperous firm; it owed its continued existence largely to the fact that both partners had a reasonable income derived from other sources. Mr. Bentley was a publisher because ever since he was a boy, he had had a liking for books; he thought them a Good Thing; the more of them the merrier. Wider acquaintance had not increased his liking for authors, whom he found as a class avaricious, egotistical, jealous and ungrateful, but he had always the hope that one day one of these disagreeable people would turn out to be a messiah of genius. And he liked the books themselves; he liked to see in the window of the office the dozen bright covers which were that season's new titles; he liked the sense of vicarious authorship which this spectacle gave him. Not so old Rampole. Mr. Bentley often wondered why his senior partner had even taken to publishing and why, once disillusioned, he persisted in it. Old Rampole deplored the propagation of books. "It won't do," he always said whenever Mr. Bentley produced a new author, "no one ever reads first novels."

Once or twice a year old Rampole himself introduced an author, always with well-justified forecasts of the book's failure. "Terrible thing," he would say. "Met old So-and-so at the club. Got button-holed. Fellow's just retired from Malay States. Written his reminiscences. We shall have to do them for him. No getting out of it now. One comfort, he won't ever write another book." That was one superiority he had over Mr. Bentley which he was fond of airing. His authors never came back for more, like Mr. Bentley's young friends.

The idea of the *Ivory Tower* was naturally repugnant to old Rampole. "I've never known a literary review succeed yet," he said.

He had a certain grudging regard for Ambrose because he was one of the few writers on their list who were incontestably profitable. Other writers always involved an argument, Mr. Bentley having an ingenious way of explaining over-advances and overhead charges and stock in hand in such a way that he seemed to prove that obvious failures had indeed succeeded. But Ambrose's books sold fifteen thousand copies. He didn't like the fellow but he had to concede him a certain knack of writing. It shocked him that Ambrose should be so blind to his own interests as to propose such a scheme.

"Has the fellow got money?" he asked Mr. Bentley privately.

"Very little, I think."

"Then what is he thinking of? What's he *after?*"

To Ambrose he said, "But a literary review, now of all times!"

"Now *is* the time of all times," said Ambrose. "Don't you *see?*"

"No, I don't. Costs are up and going higher. Can't get paper. Who'll want to read this magazine anyway? It isn't a woman's paper. It isn't, as I see it, a man's. It isn't even topical. Who's going to advertise in it?"

"I wasn't thinking of having advertisements. I thought of making it something like the old *Yellow Book.*"

"Well, that was a failure," said old Rampole triumphantly, "in the end."

But presently he gave his consent. He always gave his consent in the end to all Mr. Bentley's suggestions. That was the secret of their long partnership. He had registered his protest. No one could blame him. It was all Bentley's doing. Often he had opposed Mr. Bentley's projects out of habit, on the widest grounds that publication of any kind was undesirable. In the case of the *Ivory Tower* he stood on firm ground and knew it. It gave him positive satisfaction to detect his partner in such indefensible folly. So Mr. Bentley's room, which was the most ornamental in the fine old building which they used as their offices, became the editorial room of Ambrose's paper.

There was not, at this stage, much editorial work to be done.

"There's one criticism I foresee," said Mr. Bentley, studying the proof sheets: "the entire issue seems to be composed by yourself."

"No one's to guess that," said Ambrose. "If you like we'll put some pseudonyms in." Ambrose had always rather specialized in manifestoes. He had written one at school; he had written a dozen at the University; once, in the late twenties, he and his friends Hat and Malpractice had even issued the invitation to a party in the form of a manifesto. It was one of his many reasons for shunning Communism — that its manifesto had been written for it, once and for all, by somebody else. Surrounded, as he believed himself to be, by enemies of all kinds, Ambrose found it exhilarating from time to time to trumpet his defiance. The first number of the *Ivory Tower* somewhat belied the serenity and seclusion which it claimed, for Ambrose had a blow for every possible windmill.

"The Minstrel Boys, or *Ivory Tower* v. *Manhattan Skyscraper*" defined once and for all Ambrose's attitude in the great Parsnip-Pimpernell controversy. "Hermit or Choirmaster" was an expansion of Ambrose's theme at the Café Royal: "Culture must be coenobitic not conventual." He struck ferocious unprovoked blows at those who held that literature was of value to the community. Mr. J. B. Priestley came in for much personal abuse in these pages. There followed "The Bakelite Tower," an onslaught on David Lennox and the decorative school of fashionable artists. "Majors and Mandarins" followed, where was defined the proper degrees of contempt and abhorrence due to the military, and among the military Ambrose included by name all statesmen of an energetic and warlike disposition.

"It's all very controversial," said Mr. Bentley sadly. "When you first told me about it, I thought you meant it to be a purely artistic paper."

"We must show people where we stand," said Ambrose. "Art will follow — anyway, there's 'Monument to a Spartan.'"

"Yes," said Mr. Bentley. "There's that."

"It covers fifty pages, my dear. All Pure Art."

He said this with a facetious, shop assistant's intonation as though he were saying "All Pure Silk"; he said it as though it were a joke, but in his heart he believed — and he knew Mr. Bentley understood him in this sense — he was speaking the simple truth. It *was* all pure art.

He had written it two years ago on his return from Munich after his parting with Hans. It was the story of Hans. Now, after the passage of two years, he could not read it without tears. To publish it was a symbolic action of the laying down of an emotional burden he had carried too long.

"Monument to a Spartan" described Hans, as Ambrose had loved him, in every mood; Hans immature, the provincial petit-bourgeois youth floundering and groping in the gloom of Teutonic adolescence, unsuccessful in his examinations, world-weary, brooding about suicide among the conifers, uncritical of direct authority, unreconciled to the order of the universe; Hans affectionate, sentimental, roughly sensual, guilty; above all Hans guilty, haunted by the taboos of the forest; Hans credulous, giving his simple and generous acceptance to all the nonsense of Nazi leaders; Hans reverent to those absurd instructors who harangued the youth camps, resentful at the injustices of man to man, at the plots of the Jews and the encirclement of his country, at the blockade and disarmament; Hans loving his comrades, finding in a deep tribal emotion an escape from the guilt of personal love, Hans singing with his Hitler youth comrades, cutting trees with them, making roads, still loving his old friend, puzzled that he could not fit the old love into the scheme of the new; Hans growing a little older, joining the Brown Shirts, lapped in a kind of benighted chivalry, bemused in a twilight where the demagogues and party hacks loomed and glittered like Wagnerian heroes; Hans faithful to his old friend, like a woodcutter's boy in a fairy tale who sees the whole forest peopled with the great ones of another world and, rubbing his eyes, returns at evening to his hut and his fireside. The Wagnerians shone in Ambrose's story as they did in Hans's eyes. He austerely denied himself any hint of satire. The blustering, cranky, boneheaded party men were all heroes and philosophers. All this Ambrose had recorded with great delicacy and precision at a time when his heart was consumed by the final tragedy. Hans's Storm Troop comrades discover that his friend is a Jew; they have resented this friend before because in their gross minds they know him to represent something personal and private in a world where only the mob and the hunting pack have the right to live. So the mob and the hunting pack fall on Hans's friendship. With a mercy they are far from feeling they save Hans from facing the implications of his discovery. For him, alone, it would have been the great climacteric of his retarded adolescence; the discovery that his own, personal conviction conflicted with the factitious convictions drummed into him by the crooks and humbugs he took for his guides. But the hunting pack and the mob left Hans no time to devise his own, intense punishment; that at least was spared him in the swift and savage onslaught; that was left to Ambrose returning by train to England.

It was a story which a popular writer would have spun out to 150,000 words; Ambrose missed nothing; it as all there, delicately and precisely, in fifty pages of the *Ivory Tower*.

"Quite frankly, Geoffrey, I regard this as a major work of art."

"Yes, Ambrose, I know you do. So do I. I only wish we were publishing it without all the controversial stuff."

"Not controversial, Geoffrey. We invite acceptance, not argument. We are showing our credentials and *laissez-passer*. That's all."

"Old Rampole won't like it," said Mr. Bentley.

"We won't let old Rampole see it," said Ambrose.

"I'm on to a very good thing, Colonel."

"Will you kindly address me as 'sir' in this office?"

"You wouldn't prefer to be called 'chief'?"

"You'll call me 'sir' or get out of that uniform."

"Its funny," said Basil. "I should much sooner be called 'chief.' In fact that's what Susie does call me. However, sir, may I tell you about my discovery?"

When Basil had told him, Colonel Plum said: "That's all right as far as it goes. We can't take any action, of course. This fellow Silk is a well-known writer, working in the Ministry of Information."

"He's a most dangerous type. I know him well. He was living in Munich before the war — never out of the Brown House."

"That's as may be, but this isn't Spain. We can't go arresting people for what they say in a private conversation in a café. I've no doubt we shall come to that eventually, but at the present stage of our struggle for freedom, it just can't be done."

"But this paper he's starting."

"Yes, that's another matter. But Rampole and Bentley are a perfectly respectable little firm. I can't apply for a search warrant until I've got something to go on. We've got pretty wide powers, but we have to be careful how we use them. We'll keep an eye on this paper and if it seems dangerous we'll stop it. Meanwhile get to work. Here's an anonymous denunciation of a retired admiral in South Kensington. There won't be anything in it. See what the police know about him."

"Don't we ever investigate night clubs? I'm sure they're bursting with enemy agents."

Susie said, "I do. You don't."

A quiet day at the Ministry of Information . . . The more energetic neutral correspondents had mostly left the country by now, finding Axis sources a happier hunting-ground for front-page news. The Ministry could get on with its work undisturbed. That afternoon a film was showing in the Ministry theatre; it dealt with otter-hunting and was designed to impress neutral countries with the pastoral beauty of English life. The Religious Department were all keen film-goers. Basil found the room empty. On Ambrose's table lay two sets of galley-proofs of the new magazine. Basil pocketed one of them. There was also a passport; Basil took it with interest. He had never seen an Irish one before. It was made out for a Father Flanagan, S.J., Professor of Dublin University. The photograph showed a cadaverous face of indeterminate age. Father Flanagan was in his leisure from higher education the correspondent of an Irish newspaper. He wanted to visit the Maginot Line during his vacation and after numerous disappointments had found his way to the Religious Department of the Ministry of Information, where the Roman Catholic director had promised to try and get him a visa. Basil took this too; an additional passport often came in useful. Then he sauntered away.

He took the proofs home and read until dinner, marking a passage here and there as material to his brief. The style throughout was homogeneous but the authors' names were multiform. Ambrose rather let himself go on names: "Hucklebury Squib," "Bartholomew Grass," "Tom

Barebones-Abraham." Only "Monument to a Spartan" bore Ambrose's own name. Later that evening Basil sought Ambrose where he was sure to find him, at the Café Royal.

"I've been reading your magazine," he said.

"So it *was* you. I thought one of those nasty Jesuits had stolen it. They're always flapping in and out of the Department like jackdaws. Geoffrey Bentley was in a great stew about it. He doesn't want old Rampole to see a copy until the thing's out."

"Why should the Jesuits want to show your magazine to old Rampole?"

"They're up to any mischief. What d'you think of it?"

"Well," said Basil. "I think you might have made it a bit stronger. You know what you want to do is to shock people a bit. That's the way to put a new magazine across. You can't shock people nowadays with sex, of course; I don't mean that. But suppose you had a little poem in praise of Himmler — something like that?"

"I don't believe that would be a good idea; besides as far as I know no one has written a poem like that."

"I daresay I could rake one up for you."

"No," said Ambrose. "What did you think of 'Monument to a Spartan'?"

"All the first part is first-rate. I suppose they made you put on that ending?"

"Who?"

"The Ministry of Information."

"They've had nothing to do with it."

"Haven't they? Well, of course, you know best. I can only say how it reads to an outsider. What I felt was: Here is a first-class work of art; something no one but you could have written. And then, suddenly, it degenerates into mere propaganda. Jolly good propaganda, of course; I wish half the stuff your Ministry turns out was as good — but propaganda. An atrocity story — the sort of stuff American journalists turn out by the ream. It glares a bit, you know, Ambrose. Still, of course, we all have to make sacrifices in war-time. Don't think I don't respect you for it. But artistically, Ambrose, it's shocking."

"Is it?" said Ambrose, dismayed. "Is that how it reads?"

"Leaps to the eye, old boy. Still it ought to give you a leg up in the Department."

"Basil," said Ambrose solemnly, "if I thought that was how people would take it, I'd scrap the whole thing."

"Oh, I shouldn't do that. The first forty-five pages are grand. Why don't you leave it like that, with Hans still full of his illusions marching into Poland?"

"I might."

"And you could bring Himmler in, just at the end, in a kind of apotheosis of Nazism."

"No."

"Well, Himmler isn't necessary. Just leave Hans in the first exhilaration of victory."

"I'll think about it . . . D'you really mean that intelligent readers would think I was writing propaganda?"

"They couldn't think anything else, old boy, could they?"

A week later, by the simple process of going to Rampole and Bentley's office and asking for one, Basil obtained an advance copy of the new magazine. He turned eagerly to the last page and found that "Monument to a Spartan" now ended as he had suggested; he read it again with relish; to anyone ignorant of Ambrose's private history it bore one plain character — the triumphant paean of Hitler youth; Doctor Ley himself might have been the author. Basil took the magazine with him to the War Office; before approaching Colonel Plum he marked with a red chalk the "Monument to a Spartan" and passages in the preceding articles which cast particular ridicule upon the Army and the War Cabinet and which urged on the artist the duty of non-resistance to violence. Then he laid it on Colonel Plum's desk.

"I think, sir, you promised to make me a Captain of Marines if I caught a fascist."

"It was a figurative expression."

"Meaning what?"

"That you might have done something to excuse your presence in my office. What have you got there?"

"Documentary evidence. A fifth column nest."

"Well, put it down. I'll have a look at it when I've time."

It was not Colonel Plum's habit to show enthusiasm before subordinates, but as soon as Basil was gone he began reading the marked passages with close attention. Presently he called for Basil.

"I believe you're on to something here," he said. "I'm taking this round to Scotland Yard. Who are these men Squib, Grass and Barebones-Abraham?"

"Don't you think they sound like pseudonyms?"

"Nonsense. When a man chooses an alias he calls himself Smith or Brown."

"Have it your own way, sir. I shall be interested to see them in the dock."

"There won't be any dock. We shall get this bunch under a special warrant."

"Shall I come round to Scotland Yard with you?"

"No."

"Just for that I won't introduce him to Barebones-Abraham," said Basil when the Colonel was gone.

"Have we really caught some fifth column at last?" asked Susie.

"I don't know about 'we'; I have."

"Will they be shot?"

"Not all of them I should think."

"Seems a shame really," said Susie. "I expect they're only a bit touched."

In the pleasure of setting his trap, Basil had not looked forward to its consequences. When Colonel Plum returned to his office two hours later, things seemed to have gone far beyond Basil's control. "They're pleased as Punch at Scotland Yard," he said. "Handing out some very handsome bouquets. The whole thing is buttoned-up. We've taken out a special warrant for authors, publishers and printers, but I don't think we need worry the printers much. To-morrow morning the man Silk will be arrested at the Ministry of Information; simultaneously Rampole and Bentley's will be surrounded and entered, all copies of the paper and all correspondence seized. All the office staff will be held pending investigation. What we need now is a description of the men Grass, Squibb and Barebones-Abraham. You might get on to that. I'm going round to see the Home Secretary now."

There was, at first hearing, a lot about this speech which displeased Basil, and more still when he began to turn the thing over in his mind. In the first place Colonel Plum seemed to be getting all the credit and all the fun. It was he himself, Basil felt, who should be going to see the Home Secretary; *he* should have been to Scotland Yard to make arrangements for the morrow's raid; *he* should have had the handsome bouquets of which Colonel Plum had spoken. It was not for this that he had planned the betrayal of an old friend. Colonel Plum was putting on altogether too much dog.

In the second place the sensation of being on the side of the law was novel to Basil and not the least agreeable. Police raids, for Basil, had in the past always meant escaping over the tiles or through the area; it made him ashamed to hear these things spoken of with tolerance and familiarity.

In the third place he was not absolutely happy in his mind about what Ambrose might say. Even though he was to be deprived of the right of public trial, there would presumably be some kind of investigation at which he would be allowed to give an account of himself. Basil's share in editing "Monument to a Spartan" was, he felt, better kept as a good story to tell in the right company at the right time — not to be made the subject of official and semi-legal enquiry.

And in the fourth place Basil had from long association an appreciable softness of disposition towards Ambrose. Other things being equal, he wished him well rather than ill.

These considerations, in that order of importance, worked in Basil's mind.

Ambrose's flat lay in the neighbourhood of the Ministry of Information; it was the top floor of a large Bloomsbury mansion; where the marble stairs changed to deal, Ambrose ascended into what had once been the servants' bedrooms; it was an attic and, so-called, satisfied the ascetic promptings which had affected Ambrose in the year of the great slump. There was, however, little else about the flat to suggest hardship. He had the flair of his race for comfort and for enviable possessions. There were expensive continental editions of works on architecture, there were deep armchairs, an object like an ostrich egg sculptured by Brancusi, a gramophone with a prodigious horn, and a library of records — these and countless other features made the living-room dear to him. It is true that the bath was served only by a gas-burning apparatus which at the best gave a niggardly trickle of warm water and, at the worst, exploded in a cloud of poisonous vapours, but apparatus of this kind is the hall-mark of the higher intellectuals all the world over. Ambrose's bedroom compensated for the dangers and discomforts of the bathroom. In this flat he was served by a motherly old Cockney who teased him at intervals for not marrying.

To this flat Basil came very late that night. He had delayed his arrival on purely artistic grounds. Colonel Plum might deny him the excitements of Scotland Yard and the Home Office, but there should be every circumstance of melodrama here. Basil knocked and rang for

some time before he made himself heard. Then Ambrose came to the
door in a dressing-gown.

"Oh God," he said. "I suppose you're drunk" — for no friend of
Basil's who maintained a fixed abode in London could ever consider
himself immune from his occasional nocturnal visits.

"Let me in. We haven't a moment to spare." Basil spoke in a
whisper. "The police will be here at any moment."

Slightly dazed with sleep, Ambrose admitted him. There are those
for whom the word "police" holds no terror. Ambrose was not of them.
All his life he had been an outlaw and the days in Munich were still
fresh in his memory, when friends disappeared suddenly in the night,
leaving no address.

"I've brought you this," said Basil, "and this and this." He gave Ambrose a clerical collar, a black clerical vest ornamented with a double
line of jet buttons, and an Irish passport. "You are Father Flanagan
returning to Dublin University. Once in Ireland you'll be safe."

"But surely there's no train at this time."

"There's one at eight. You mustn't be found here. You can sit in
the waiting-room at Euston till it comes in. Have you got a breviary?"

"Of course not."

"Then read a racing paper. I suppose you've got a dark suit."

It was significant both of Basil's fine urgency of manner, and of
Ambrose's constitutionally guilty disposition, that he was already clothed
as a clergyman before he said, "But what have I done? Why are they
after me?"

"Your magazine. It's being surpressed. They're rounding up everyone connected with it."

Ambrose asked no more. He accepted the fact as a pauper accepts
the condition of being perpetually "moved on." It was something
inalienable from his state; the artist's birthright.

"How did you hear about it?"

"In the War Office."

"What am I to do about all this?" asked Ambrose helplessly. "The
flat, and the furniture, and my books, and Mrs. Carver?"

"I tell you what. If you like I'll move in and take care of it for
you until it's safe to come back."

"Would you really, Basil?" said Ambrose, touched. "You're being
very kind."

For some time now Basil had felt himself unfairly handicapped in

his pursuit of Susie by the fact of his living with his mother. He had
not thought of this solution. It had come providentially, with rapid
and exemplary justice all too rare in life; goodness was being rewarded
quite beyond his expectations, if not beyond his deserts.

"I'm afraid the geyser is rather a bore," said Ambrose apologetically.

They were not far from Euston Station. Packing was the work of
a quarter of an hour.

"But, Basil, I *must* have *some* clothes."

"You are an Irish priest. What d'you think the Customs are going
to say when they open a trunk full of Charvet ties and crêpe-de-Chine
pyjamas?"

Ambrose was allowed one suitcase.

"I'll look after all this for you," said Basil, surveying the oriental
profusion of expensive underclothes which filled the many drawers
and presses of the bedroom. "You'll have to walk to the station,
you know."

"Why, for God's sake?"

"Taxi might be traced. Can't take any chances."

The suitcase had seemed small enough when Basil first selected it
as the most priestly of the rather too smart receptacles in Ambrose's
box-room; it seemed enormous as they trudged northward through
the dark streets of Bloomsbury. At last they reached the classic columns
of the railway terminus. It is not a cheerful place at the best of times,
striking a chill in the heart of the gayest holiday-maker. Now in
war-time, before dawn on a cold spring morning, it seemed the entrance
to a sepulchre.

"I'll leave you here," said Basil. "Keep out of sight until the train
is in. If anyone speaks to you, tell your beads."

"I haven't any beads."

"Then contemplate. Go into an ecstasy. But don't open your mouth
or you're done."

"I'll write to you when I get to Ireland."

"Better not," said Basil, cheerfully.

He turned away and was immediately lost in the darkness. Ambrose
entered the station. A few soldiers slept on benches, surrounded by
their kit and equipment. Ambrose found a corner darker, even, than
the general gloom. Here, on a packing-case that seemed by its smell
to contain fish of a sort, he sat waiting for dawn; black hat perched
over his eyes, black overcoat wrapped close about his knees, mournful,

black eyes open, staring into the blackness. From the fishy freight below him water oozed slowly onto the pavement making a little pool, as though of tears.

Mr. Rampole was not, as many of his club acquaintances supposed, a bachelor, but a widower of long standing. He lived in a small but substantial house at Hampstead and there maintained in servitude a spinster daughter. On this fateful morning his daughter saw him off from the front gate as had been her habit years without number, at precisely 8:45. Mr. Rampole paused in the flagged path to comment on the buds which were breaking everywhere in the little garden.

Look well at those buds, old Rampole; you will not see the full leaf.

"I'll be back at six," he said.

Presumptuous Rampole, who shall tell what the day will bring forth? Not his daughter, who returned, unmoved by the separation, to eat a second slice of toast in the dining-room; not old Rampole, who strode at a good pace towards the Hampstead Underground.

He showed his season ticket to the man at the lift.

"I shall have to get it renewed the day after to-morrow," he said affably, and tied a knot in the corner of his large white handkerchief to remind him of the fact.

There is no need for that knot, old Rampole; you will never again travel in the Hampstead Underground.

He opened his morning paper as he had done, five days a week, years without number. He turned first to the Deaths, then to the correspondence, then, reluctantly, to the news of the day.

Never again, old Rampole, never again.

The police raid on the Ministry of Information, like so many similar enterprises, fell flat. First, the plain-clothes men had the utmost difficulty in getting past the gate-keeper.

"Is Mr. Silk expecting you?"

"We hope not."

"Then you can't see him."

When finally they were identified and allowed to pass, there was a confused episode in the Religious Department, where they found only the non-conformist minister, whom, too zealously, they proceeded to handcuff. It was explained that Ambrose was unaccountably absent from duty that morning. Two constables were left to await his arrival.

All through the day they sat there, casting a gloom over the Religious Department. The plain-clothes men proceeded to Mr. Bentley's room, where they were received with great frankness and charm.

Mr. Bentley answered all their questions in a manner befitting an honest citizen. Yes, he knew Ambrose Silk both as a colleague at the Ministry and, formerly, as one of their authors at Rampole's. No, he had almost nothing to do with publishing these days; he was too busy with all this (an explanatory gesture which embraced the dripping sink, the Nollekens busts and the page of arabesques beside the telephone). Mr. Rampole was in entire charge of the publishing firm. Yes, he thought he had heard of some magazine which Silk was starting. The *Ivory Tower?* Was that the name? Very likely. No, he had no copy. Was it already out? Mr. Bentley had formed the impression that it was not yet ready for publication. The contributors? Hucklebury Squib, Bartholomew Grass, Tom Barebones-Abraham? Mr. Bentley thought he had heard the names; he might have met them in literary circles in the old days. He had the idea that Barebones-Abraham was rather below normal height, corpulent, bald — yes, Mr. Bentley was quite sure he was bald as an egg; he spoke with a stammer and dragged his left leg as he walked. Hucklebury Squib was a very tall young man — easily recognisable, for he had lost the lobe of his left ear in extraordinary circumstances when sailing before the mast; he had a front tooth missing and wore gold ear-rings.

The plain-clothes men recorded these details in shorthand. This was the sort of witness they liked, circumstantial, precise, unhesitating.

When it came to Bartholomew Grass, Mr. Bentley's invention flagged. He had never seen the man. He rather thought it might be the pseudonym for a woman.

"Thank you, Mr. Bentley," said the chief of the plain-clothes men. "I don't think we need trouble you any more. If we want you I suppose we can always find you here."

"Always," said Mr. Bentley sweetly. "I often, whimsically, refer to this little table as my grindstone. I keep my nose to it. We live in arduous times, Inspector."

A posse of police went to Ambrose's flat, where all they got was a piece of his housekeeper's mind.

"Our man's got away," they reported when they returned to their superiors.

Colonel Plum, the Inspector of Police and Basil were summoned late that afternoon to the office of the Director of Internal Security.

"I can't congratulate you," he said, "on the way this case has been handled. I'm not blaming you, Inspector, or you, Seal," and he fixed Colonel Plum with a look of detestation. "We were clearly onto a very dangerous set of men and you let four out of five slip through your fingers. I've no doubt that at this moment they are sitting in a German submarine, laughing at us."

"We've got Rampole, sir," said Colonel Plum. "I'm inclined to think he's the ringleader."

"I'm inclined to think he's an old booby."

"He has behaved in the most hostile and defiant manner throughout. He refuses to give any particulars about any of his accomplices."

"He threw a telephone directory at one of our men," said the Inspector, "and used the following expressions about them: 'nincompoops,' 'jacks-in-office . . .' "

"Yes, yes, I have the report. Rampole is obviously a violent and thoroughly unreasonable type. It won't do him any harm to cool his heels for the rest of the war. But he's not the ringleader. This fellow Barebones-Abraham is the man I want and you haven't been able to find a trace of him."

"We've got his description."

"A fat lot of good that is when he's halfway back to Germany. No, the whole thing has been grossly mismanaged. The Home Secretary takes a very poor view of it. *Somebody talked* and I mean to find out who."

When the interview, painfully protracted, came to an end, the Director told Basil to remain behind.

"Seal," he said, "I understand you were the first man to get onto this gang. Have you any idea how they were warned?"

"You put me in a very difficult position, sir."

"Come, come, my boy, this is no time for petty loyalties when your country's future is at stake."

"Well, sir, I've felt for some time that there's been too much feminine influence in our Department. Have you see Colonel Plum's secretary?"

"Hokey-pokey, eh?"

"You could call it that, sir."

"Enemy agent, eh?"

"Oh no, sir. Have a look at her."

The Director sent for Susie. When she had gone he said, "No, not an enemy agent."

"Certainly not, sir, but a frivolous, talkative girl. Colonel Plum's intimacy . . ."

"Yes, I quite understand. You did perfectly right to tell me."

"What did he want, sending for me like that and just staring?" asked Susie.

"I think I've arranged a promotion for you."

"Ooh, you are sweet."

"I'm just moving into a new flat."

"Lucky you," said Susie.

"I wish you'd come and advise me about the decorations. I'm no good at that kind of thing."

"Oh no?" said Susie in a voice she had learned at the cinema. "And what would Colonel Plum say?"

"Colonel Plum won't have anything to say. You're rising far above ADDIS."

"Ooh."

Next morning Susie received an official intimation that she was to move to the Director's office.

"Lucky you," said Basil.

She had admired all Ambrose's decorations except the Brancusi sculpture. That had been put away, out of sight, in the box-room.

At Brixton Gaol Mr. Rampole enjoyed many privileges that were not accorded to common criminals. There was a table in his cell and a tolerably comfortable chair. He was allowed, at his own expense, some additions to prison fare. He might smoke. The *Times* was delivered to him every morning and for the first time in his life he accumulated a small library. Mr. Bentley from time to time brought him papers for which his signature was required. In every way his life was much easier than it would have been in similar circumstances in any other country.

But Mr. Rampole was not content. There was an obnoxious young man next to him who, when they met at exercise, said, "Heil Mosley," and at night attempted to tap out messages of encouragement in Morse. Moreover Mr. Rampole missed his club and his home at

Hampstead. In spite of a multitude of indulgences he faced the summer without enthusiasm.

In a soft, green valley where a stream ran through close-cropped, spongy pasture and the grass grew down below the stream's edge, and merged there with the water-weed — where a road ran between grass verges and tumbled walls, and the grass merged into moss which spread upwards and over the tumbled stones of the walls, outwards over the pocked metalling and deep ruts of the road; where the ruins of a police barracks, built to command the road through the valley, burnt in the Troubles, had once been white, then black, and now were one green with the grass and the moss and the water-weed; where the smoke of burnt turf drifted down from the cabin chimneys and joined the mist that rose from the damp, green earth; where the prints of ass and pig, goose and calf and horse, mingled indifferently with those of barefoot children; where the soft, resentful voices rose and fell in the smoky cabins, merging with the music of the stream and the treading and shifting and munching of the beasts at pasture; where mist and smoke never lifted and the sun never fell direct, and evening came slowly in infinite gradations of shadow; where the priest came seldom because of the rough road and the long climb home to the head of the valley, and no one except the priest ever came from one month's end to another — there stood an inn which was frequented in bygone days by fishermen. Here in the summer nights when their sport was over, they had sat long over their whisky and their pipes — professional gentlemen from Dublin and retired military men from England. No one fished the stream now and the few trout that remained were taken by ingenious and illicit means without respect for season or ownership. No one came to stay; sometimes a couple on a walking tour, once or twice a party of motorists, paused for supper, hesitated, discussed the matter and then regretfully pushed on to the next village. Here Ambrose came, perched on an outside-car, from the railway station over the hill six miles distant.

He had discarded his clerical disguise, but there was something about his melancholy air and his precision of speech which made the landlord, who had never had contact before with an intellectual Jew, put him down as a "spoilt priest." He had heard about this inn from a garrulous fellow in the packet-boat; it was kept by a distant connection of this man's wife's, and though he had not himself visited the place, he never lost an opportunity of putting in a good word for it.

Here Ambrose settled, in the only bedroom whose windows were unbroken. Here he intended to write a book, to take up again the broken fragments of his artistic life. He spread foolscap paper on the dining-room table; and the soft, moist air settled on it and permeated it so that when, on the third day, he sat down to make a start, the ink spread and the lines ran together, leaving what might have been a brush stroke of indigo paint where there should have been a sentence of prose. Ambrose laid down the pen, and because the floor sloped where the house had settled, it rolled down the table, and down the floor-boards and under the mahogany sideboard, and lay there among napkin rings and small coins and corks and the sweepings of half a century. And Ambrose wandered out into the mist and the twilight, stepping soundlessly on the soft, green turf.

In London Basil set Susie to work. She wanted to be taken out in the evenings too often and in too expensive a style. He set her to work with needle and silk and embroidery scissors, picking off the AS from the monograms on Ambrose's crêpe-de-Chine underclothes and sub-stituting a B.

Peter Pastmaster and the absurdly youthful Colonel of the new force were drawing up a list of suitable officers in Bratt's Club.

"Most of war seems to consist of hanging about," he said. "Let's at least hang about with our own friends."

"I've a letter from a man who says he's a friend of yours. Basil Seal."

"Does he want to join?"

"Yes. Is he all right?"

"Perfect," said Peter. "A tough nut."

"Right. I'll put him down with Alastair Trumpington as your other subaltern."

"No. For God's sake don't do that. But make him liaison officer."

"You see, I know everything about you," said Angela.

"There's one thing you don't know," said Basil. "If you really want to be a widow again, we'd better marry quick. I don't think I told you. I'm joining a new racket."

"Basil, what?"

"Very secret."

"But why?"

"Well you know things haven't been quite the same at the War House lately. I don't know quite why it is, but Colonel Plum doesn't seem to love me as he did. I think he's a bit jealous about the way I pulled off the *Ivory Tower* business. We've never really been matey since. Besides, you know, that racket was all very well in the winter, when there wasn't any real war. It won't do now. There's only one serious occupation for a chap now, that's killing Germans. I have an idea I shall rather enjoy it."

"Basil's left the War Office," said Lady Seal.

"Yes," said Sir Joseph, with sinking heart. Here it was again: the old business. The news from all over the world might be highly encouraging — and, poor booby, he believed it was; we might have a great new secret weapon — and, poor booby, he thought we had; he might himself enjoy a position of great trust and dignity — poor booby, he was going, that afternoon, to address a drawing-room meeting on the subject of "Hobbies for the A.T.S." — but in spite of all this, Basil was always with him, a grim *memento mori* staring him out of countenance. "Yes," he said. "I suppose he has."

"He has joined a special *corps d'élite* that is being organised. They are going to do great things."

"He has actually joined?"

"Oh, yes."

"There's nothing I can do to help him?"

"Dear Jo, always so kind. No. Basil has arranged it all himself. I expect that his excellent record at the War Office helped. It isn't every boy who would settle to a life of official drudgery when everyone else was going out for excitement — like Emma's silly girl in the fire brigade. No, he did his duty where he found it. And now he is getting his reward. I am not quite sure what they are going to do, but I know it is very dashing and may well have a decisive effect on the war."

The grey moment was passed; Sir Joseph, who had not ceased smiling, now smiled with sincere happiness.

"There's a new spirit abroad," he said. "I see it on every side."

And, poor booby, he was bang right.

From Brideshead Revisited

A TWITCH UPON THE THREAD

A Twitch upon the Thread *is the title of the second part of* Brideshead Revisited; *it refers to "the workings of the divine purpose in a pagan world." The novel, or rather its prologue, opens during the Second World War. Captain Charles Ryder unexpectedly finds his unit transferred to Brideshead Castle, and he proceeds to tell the story of his involvement with the great Catholic family which once lived there.*

The first half of the book centers on Ryder's friendship at Oxford with Sebastian Flyte, the "magically beautiful" and eccentric younger son of the Marquis of Marchmain. To Ryder, who has been brought up by a widowed father, a self-centered and emotionally arid scholar, the relationship with Sebastian is an introduction to a world that radiates warmth and glamour. One thing baffles and irritates Ryder, at this time an agnostic contemptuous of religious "mumbo-jumbo" — the pervasive role that religion plays in the life of Sebastian's family and the trouble it appears to cause them.

The Marchmains are a house divided. The Marquis — who when he married a pious Catholic returned to the faith of his ancestors — deserted his wife after the First World War. He has settled in Venice with his Italian mistress, Cara, and is bitterly hostile to Catholicism, which is his wife's reason for refusing him a divorce. His eldest son, the Earl of Brideshead, a heavy, pompous bigot, and his youngest child, Cordelia, who hopes to become a nun when she grows up, have sided with their mother. Sebastian, like his father, feels a bit stifled by Lady Marchmain's overwhelming charm and saintly reputation. He and his older sister, Julia, though they can never forget their religious upbringing, are "half-heathen"; and in them are hot springs of anarchy. Sebastian takes to drinking heavily, and resentment at his mother's efforts to place him under supervision goads him into chronic drunkenness. The exquisite Julia, reigning debutante of her year, makes a highly unsuitable marriage to Rex Mottram, a crude, buccaneering careerist who has grown rich in dubious financial deals. At the conclusion of the first half of the novel, Lady Marchmain has just died; Sebastian is drinking himself to death in Morocco; and Ryder, after studying art in Paris, has become an architectural painter.

I

My theme is memory, that winged host that soared about me one grey morning of war-time.

These memories, which are my life — for we possess nothing certainly except the past — were always with me. Like the pigeons of St. Mark's, they were everywhere, under my feet, singly, in pairs, in little honey-voiced congregations, nodding, strutting, winking, rolling the tender feathers of their necks, perching sometimes, if I stood still, on my shoulder or pecking a broken biscuit from between my lips; until, suddenly, the noon gun boomed and in a moment, with a flutter and sweep of wings, the pavement was bare and the whole sky above dark with a tumult of fowl. Thus it was that morning.

These memories are the memorials and pledges of the vital hours of a lifetime. These hours of afflatus in the human spirit, the springs of art, are, in their mystery, akin to the epochs of history, when a race which for centuries has lived content, unknown, behind its own frontiers, digging, eating, sleeping, begetting, doing what was requisite for survival and nothing else, will, for a generation or two, stupefy the world; commit all manner of crimes, perhaps; follow the wildest chimeras, go down in the end in agony, but leave behind a record of new heights scaled and new rewards won for all mankind; the vision fades, the soul sickens, and the routine of survival starts again.

The human soul enjoys these rare, classic periods, but, apart from them, we are seldom single or unique; we keep company in this world with a hoard of abstractions and reflections and counterfeits of ourselves — the sensual man, the economic man, the man of reason, the beast, the machine and the sleep-walker, and heaven knows what besides, all in our own image, indistinguishable from ourselves to the outward eye.

We get borne along, out of sight in the press, unresisting, till we get the chance to drop behind unnoticed, or to dodge down a side street, pause, breathe freely and take our bearings, or to push ahead, outdistance our shadows, lead them a dance, so that when at length they catch up with us, they look at one another askance, knowing we have a secret we shall never share.

For nearly ten years I was thus borne along a road outwardly full of change and incident, but never during that time, except sometimes in my painting — and that at longer and longer intervals — did I come alive as I had been during the time of my friendship with Sebastian. I took it to be youth, not life, that I was losing. My work upheld me, for I had chosen to do what I could do well, did better daily, and liked doing; incidentally it was something which no one else at that time was attempting to do. I became an architectural painter. I have always loved building, holding it to be not only the highest achievement of man but one in which, at the moment of consummation, things were most clearly taken out of his hands and perfected, without his intention, by other means, and I regarded men as something much less than the buildings they made and inhabited, as mere lodgers and short-term sub-lessees of small importance in the long, fruitful life of their homes.

More even than the work of the great architects, I loved buildings that grew silently with the centuries, catching and keeping the best of each generation, while time curbed the artist's pride and the Philistine's vulgarity, and repaired the clumsiness of the dull workman. In such buildings England abounded, and in the last decade of their grandeur, Englishmen seemed for the first time to become conscious of what before was taken for granted, and to salute their achievements at the moment of extinction. Hence my prosperity, far beyond my merits; my work had nothing to recommend it except my growing technical skill, enthusiasm for my subject and independence of popular notions.

The financial slump of the period, which left many painters without employment, served to enhance my success, which was, indeed, itself a symptom of the decline. When the water-holes were dry people sought to drink at the mirage. After my first exhibition I was called to all parts of the country to make portraits of houses that were soon to be deserted or debased; indeed, my arrival seemed often to be only a few paces ahead of the auctioneers, a presage of doom.

I published three splendid folios — *Ryder's Country Seats, Ryder's English Homes,* and *Ryder's Village and Provincial Architecture,* which each sold its thousand copies at five guineas apiece. I seldom failed to please, for there was no conflict between myself and my patrons; we both wanted the same thing. But as the years passed I began to mourn the loss of something I had known in the drawing-room of Marchmain House and once or twice since, the intensity and singleness and the belief that it was not all done by hand — in a word, the inspiration.

In quest of this fading light I went abroad, in the Augustan manner, laden with the apparatus of my trade, for two years' refreshment among alien styles. I did not go to Europe; her treasures were safe, too safe, swaddled in expert care, obscured by reverence. Europe could wait. There would be a time for Europe, I thought; all too soon the days would come when I should need a man at my side to put up my easel and carry my paints; when I could not venture more than an hour's journey from a good hotel; when I should need soft breezes and mellow sunshine all day long; then I would take my old eyes to Germany and Italy. Now while I had the strength I would go to the wild lands where man had deserted his post and the jungle was creeping back to its old strongholds.

Accordingly, by slow but not easy stages, I travelled through Mexico and Central America in a world which had all I needed, and the change from parkland and hall should have quickened me and set me right with myself. I sought inspiration among gutted palaces and cloisters embowered in weed, derelict churches where the vampire-bats hung in the dome like dry seed-pods and only the ants were ceaselessly astir tunnelling in the rich stalls; cities where no road led, and mausoleums where a single, agued family of Indians sheltered from the rains. There in great labour, sickness and occasionally in some danger, I made the first drawings for *Ryder's Latin America*. Every few weeks I came to rest, finding myself once more in the zone of trade or tourism, recuperated, set up my studio, transcribed my sketches, anxiously packed the completed canvasses, despatched them to my New York agent, and then set out again, with my small retinue, into the wastes.

I was at no great pains to keep touch with England. I followed local advice for my itinerary and had no settled route, so that much of my mail never reached me, and the rest accumulated until there was more than could be read at a sitting. I used to stuff a bundle of letters into my bag and read them when I felt inclined, which was in circumstances so incongruous — swinging in my hammock under the net by the light of a storm lantern; drifting down-river, sprawled amidships in the canoe, with the boys astern of me lazily keeping our nose out of the bank, with the dark water keeping pace with us, in the green shade, with the great trees towering above us and the monkeys screeching in the sunlight, high overhead among the flowers on the roof of the forest; on the veranda of a hospitable ranch, where the ice and the dice clicked, and a tiger cat played with its chain on the mown grass — that they seemed voices so distant as to be meaningless; their matter passed clean through the mind, and out, leaving no mark, like the facts about themselves which fellow travellers distribute so freely in American railways trains.

But despite this isolation and this long sojourn in a strange world, I remained unchanged, still a small part of myself pretending to be whole. I discarded the experiences of those two years with my tropical kit and returned to New York as I had set out. I had a fine haul — eleven paintings and fifty-odd drawings — and when eventually I exhibited them in London, the art critics, many of whom hitherto had been patronising in tone as my success invited, acclaimed a new and richer note in my work.

Mr. Ryder [the most respected of them wrote] *rises like a fresh young trout to the hypodermic injection of a new culture and discloses a powerful facet in the vista of his potentialities . . . By focussing the frankly traditional battery of his elegance and erudition on the maelstrom of barbarism, Mr. Ryder has at last found himself.*

Grateful words, but, alas, not true by a long chalk. My wife, who crossed to New York to meet me, and saw the fruits of our separation displayed in my agent's office, summed the thing up better by saying: "Of course, I can see they're perfectly brilliant and really rather beautiful in a sinister way, but somehow I don't feel they are quite *you*."

In Europe my wife was sometimes taken for an American because of her dapper and jaunty way of dressing, and the curiously hygienic quality of her prettiness; in America she assumed an English softness and reticence. She arrived a day or two before me, and was on the pier when my ship docked.

"It has been a long time," she said fondly when we met.

She had not joined the expedition; she explained to our friends that the country was unsuitable and she had her son at home. There was also a daughter now, she remarked, and it came back to me that there had been talk of this before I started, as an additional reason for her staying behind. There had been some mention of it, too, in her letters.

"I don't believe you read my letters," she said that night when at last, late, after a dinner party and some hours at a cabaret, we found ourselves alone in our hotel bedroom.

"Some went astray. I remember distinctly your telling me that the daffodils in the orchard were a dream, that the nurserymaid was a jewel, that the Regency four-poster was a find, but frankly I do not remember hearing that your new baby was called Caroline. Why did you call it that?"

"After Charles, of course."

"Ah!"

"I made Bertha Van Halt godmother. I thought she was safe for a good present. What do you think she gave?"

"Bertha Van Halt is a well-known trap. What?"

"A fifteen-shilling book token. Now that Johnjohn has a companion —"

"Who?"

"Your son, darling. You haven't forgotten him, too?"

"For Christ's sake," I said, "why do you call him that?"

"It's the name he invented for himself. Don't you think it sweet? Now that Johnjohn has a companion I think we'd better not have any more for some time, don't you?"

"Just as you please."

"Johnjohn talks of you such a lot. He prays every night for your safe return."

She talked in this way while she undressed, with an effort to appear at ease; then she sat at the dressing-table, ran a comb through her hair, and with her bare back towards me, looking at herself in the glass, said, "I hope you admire my self-restraint."

"Restraint?"

"I'm not asking awkward questions. I may say I've been tormented with visions of voluptuous half-castes ever since you went away. But I determined not to ask and I haven't."

"That suits me," I said.

She left the dressing-table and crossed the room.

"Lights out?"

"As you like. I'm not sleepy."

We lay in our twin beds, a yard or two distant, smoking. I looked at my watch; it was four o'clock, but neither of us was ready to sleep, for in that city there is neurosis in the air which the inhabitants mistake for energy .

"I don't believe you've changed at all, Charles."

"No, I'm afraid not."

"D'you want to change?"

"It's the only evidence of life."

"But you might change so that you didn't love me any more."

"There is that risk."

"Charles, you haven't stopped loving me?"

"You said yourself I hadn't changed."

"Well, I'm beginning to think you have. I haven't."

"No," I said, "no; I can see that."

"Were you at all frightened at meeting me to-day?"

"Not the least."

"You didn't wonder if I should have fallen in love with someone else in the meantime?"

"No. Have you?"

"You know I haven't. Have you?"

"No. I'm not in love."

My wife seemed content with this answer. She had married me six years ago at the time of my first exhibition, and had done much since then to push our interests. People said she had "made" me, but she herself took credit only for supplying me with a congenial background; she had firm faith in my genius and in the "artistic temperament," and in the principle that things done on the sly are not really done at all.

Presently she said: "Looking forward to getting home?" (My father gave me as a wedding present the price of a house, and I bought an old rectory in my wife's part of the country.) "I've got a surprise for you."

"Yes?"

"I've turned the old tithe barn into a studio for you, so that you needn't be disturbed by the children or when we have people to stay. I got Emden to do it. Everyone thinks it a great success. There was an article on it in *Country Life*; I brought it for you to see."

She showed me the article: . . . *happy example of architectural good manners. . . . Sir Joseph Emden's tactful adaptation of traditional material to modern needs . . .* ; there were some photographs; wide oak boards now covered the earthen floor; a high, stone-mullioned bay-window had been built in the north wall, and the great timbered roof, which before had been lost in shadow, now stood out stark, well lit, with clean white plaster between the beams; it looked like a village hall. I remembered the smell of the place, which would now be lost.

"I rather liked that barn," I said.

"But you'll be able to work there, won't you?"

"After squatting in a cloud of sting-fly," I said, "under a sun which scorched the paper off the block as I drew, I could work on the top of an omnibus. I expect the vicar would like to borrow the place for whist drives."

"There's a lot of work waiting for you. I promised Lady Anchorage you would do Anchorage House as soon as you got back. That's coming down, too, you know — shops underneath and two-roomed flats above. You don't think, do you, Charles, that all this exotic work you've been doing is going to spoil you for that sort of thing?"

"Why should it?"

"Well, it's so different. Don't be cross."

"It's just another jungle closing in."

"I know just how you feel, darling. The Georgian Society made such a fuss, but we couldn't do anything. . . . Did you ever get my letter about Boy?"

"Did I? What did it say?"

(Boy Mulcaster was her brother.)

"About his engagement. It doesn't matter now because it's all off, but Father and Mother were terribly upset. She was an awful girl. They had to give her money in the end."

"No, I heard nothing of Boy."

"He and Johnjohn are tremendous friends, now. It's so sweet to see them together. Whenever he comes home the first thing he does is to drive straight to the Old Rectory. He just walks into the house, pays no attention to anyone else, and hollers out: 'Where's my chum Johnjohn?' and Johnjohn comes tumbling downstairs and off they go into the spinney together and play for hours. You'd think, to hear them talk to each other, they were the same age. It was really Johnjohn who made him see reason about that girl; seriously, you know, he's frightfully sharp. He must have heard Mother and me talking, because next time Boy came he said: 'Uncle Boy shan't marry horrid girl and leave Johnjohn,' and that was the very day he settled for two thousand pounds out of court. Johnjohn admires Boy so tremendously and imitates him in everything. It's so good for them both."

I crossed the room and tried once more, ineffectively, to moderate the heat of the radiators; I drank some iced water and opened the window, but, besides the sharp night air, music was borne in from the next room where they were playing the wireless. I shut it and turned back towards my wife.

At length she began talking again, more drowsily. . . . "The garden's come on a lot. . . . The box hedges you planted grew five inches last year. . . . I had some men down from London to put the tennis court right . . . first-class cook at the moment . . ."

As the city below us began to wake we both fell asleep, but not for long; the telephone rang and a voice of hermaphroditic gaiety said: "Savoy-Carlton-Hotel-goodmorning. It is now a quarter of eight."

"I didn't ask to be called, you know."

"Pardon me?"

"Oh, it doesn't matter."

"You're welcome."

As I was shaving, my wife from the bath said: "Just like old times. I'm not worrying any more, Charles."

"Good."

"I was so terribly afraid that two years might have made a difference. Now I know we can start again exactly where we left off."

I paused in my shaving.

"When?" I asked. "What? When we left off what?"

"When you went away, of course."

"You are not thinking of something else, a little time before?"

"Oh, Charles, that's old history. That was nothing. It was never anything. It's all over and forgotten."

"I just wanted to know," I said. "We're back as we were the day I went abroad, is that it?"

So we started that day exactly where we left off two years before, with my wife in tears.

My wife's softness and English reticence, her very white, small, regular teeth, her neat rosy finger-nails, her schoolgirl air of innocent mischief and her schoolgirl dress, her modern jewellery, which was

made at great expense to give the impression, at a distance, of having
been mass-produced, her ready, rewarding smile, her deference to me
and her zeal in my interests, her motherly heart which made her cable
daily to the nanny at home — in short, her peculiar charm — made her
popular among the Americans, and our cabin on the day of departure
was full of cellophane packages — flowers, fruit, sweets, books, toys
for the children — from friends she had known for a week. Stewards,
like sisters in a nursing home, used to judge their passengers' importance
by the number and value of these trophies; we therefore started the
voyage in high esteem.

My wife's first thought on coming aboard was of the passenger list.
"Such a lot of friends," she said. "It's going to be a lovely trip.
Let's have a cocktail party this evening."

The companion-ways were no sooner cast off than she was busy with
the telephone.

"Julia. This is Celia — Celia Ryder. It's lovely to find you on board.
What have you been up to? Come and have a cocktail this evening
and tell me all about it."

"Julia who?"

"Mottram. I haven't seen her for years."

Nor had I; not, in fact, since my wedding day, not to speak to for any
time, since the private view of my exhibition where the four canvasses
of Marchmain House, lent by Brideshead, had hung together attract-
ing much attention. Those pictures were my last contact with the
Flytes; our lives, so close for a year or two, had drawn apart. Sebastian,
I knew, was still abroad; Rex and Julia, I sometimes heard said, were
unhappy together. Rex was not prospering quite as well as had been
predicted; he remained on the fringe of the Government, prominent but
vaguely suspect. He lived among the very rich, and in his speeches
seemed to incline to revolutionary policies, flirting with Communists
and fascists. I heard the Mottrams' names in conversation; I saw their
faces now and again peeping from the *Tatler*, as I turned the pages impatiently waiting for someone to come, but they and I had fallen apart,
as one could in England and only there, into separate worlds, little
spinning planets of personal relationship; there is probably a perfect
metaphor for the process to be found in physics, from the way in which,
I dimly apprehend, particles of energy group and regroup themselves
in separate magnetic systems, a metaphor ready to hand for the man
who can speak of these things with assurance; not for me, who can only

say that England abounded in these small companies of intimate friends, so that, as in this case of Julia and myself, we could live in the same street in London, see at times, a few miles distant, the same rural horizon, could have a liking one for the other, a mild curiosity about the other's fortunes, a regret, even, that we should be separated, and the knowledge that either of us had only to pick up the telephone and speak by the other's pillow, enjoy the intimacies of the levee, coming in, as it were, with the morning orange juice and the sun, yet be restrained from doing so by the centripetal force of our own worlds, and the cold, interstellar space between them.

My wife, perched on the back of the sofa in a litter of cellophane and silk ribbons, continued telephoning, working brightly through the passenger list . . . "Yes, do of course bring him, I'm told he's sweet. . . . Yes, I've got Charles back from the wilds at last; isn't it lovely. . . . What a treat seeing your name in the list! It's made my trip . . . darling, we were at the Savoy-Carlton, too; how can we have missed you? . . ." Sometimes she turned to me and said: "I have to make sure you're still really there. I haven't got used to it yet."

I went up and out as we steamed slowly down the river to one of the great glass cases where the passengers stood to watch the land slip by. "Such a lot of friends," my wife had said. They looked a strange crowd to me; the emotions of leave-taking were just beginning to subside; some of them, who had been drinking till the last moment with those who were seeing them off, were still boisterous; others were planning where they would have their deck chairs; the band played unnoticed — all were as restless as ants.

I turned into some of the halls of the ship, which were huge without any splendour, as though they had been designed for a railway coach and preposterously magnified. I passed through vast bronze gates whose ornament was like the trade mark of a cake of soap which had been used once or twice; I trod carpets the colour of blotting paper; the painted panels of the walls were like blotting paper, too: kindergarten work in flat, drab colours; and between the walls were yards and yards of biscuit-coloured wood which no carpenter's tool had ever touched, wood that had been bent round corners, invisibly joined strip to strip, steamed and squeezed and polished; all over the blotting-paper carpet were strewn tables designed perhaps by a sanitary engineer, square blocks of stuffing, with square holes for sitting in, and, upholstered, it seemed, in blotting paper also; the light of the hall was suffused from scores of

hollows, giving an even glow, casting no shadows — the whole place
hummed from its hundred ventilators and vibrated with the turn of the
great engines below.

Here I am, I thought, back from the jungle, back from the ruins.
Here, where wealth is no longer gorgeous and power has no dignity.
Quomodo sedet sola civitas (for I had heard that great lament, which
Cordelia once quoted to me in the drawing-room of Marchmain House,
sung by a half-caste choir in Guatemala, nearly a year ago).

A steward came up to me.

"Can I get you anything, sir?"

"A whisky-and-soda, not iced."

"I'm sorry, sir, *all* the soda is iced."

"Is the water iced, too?"

"Oh yes, sir."

"Well, it doesn't matter."

He trotted off, puzzled, soundless in the pervading hum.

"Charles."

I looked behind me. Julia was sitting in a cube of blotting-paper, her
hands folded in her lap, so still that I had passed by without noticing her.

"I heard you were here. Celia telephoned to me. It's delightful."

"What are you doing?"

She opened the empty hands in her lap with a little eloquent gesture.
"Waiting. My maid's unpacking; she's been so disagreeable ever since
we left England. She's complaining now about my cabin. I can't think
why. It seems a lap to me."

The steward returned with whisky and two jugs, one of iced water,
the other of boiling water; I mixed them to the right temperature.
He watched and said: "I'll remember that's how you take it, sir."

Most passengers had fads; he was paid to fortify their self-esteem.
Julia asked for a cup of hot chocolate. I sat by her in the next cube.

"I never see you now," she said. "I never seem to see anyone I
like. I don't know why."

But she spoke as though it were a matter of weeks rather than of
years; as though, too, before our parting we had been firm friends.
It was dead contrary to the common experience of such encounters,
when time is found to have built its own defensive lines, camouflaged
vulnerable points, and laid a field of mines across all but a few well-
trodden paths, so that, more often than not, we can only signal to
one another from either side of the tangle of wire. Here she and I,

who were never friends before, met on terms of long and unbroken intimacy.

"What have you been doing in America?"

She looked up slowly from her chocolate and, her splendid, serious eyes in mine, said: "Don't you know? I'll tell you about it sometime. I've been a mug. I thought I was in love with someone, but it didn't turn out that way." And my mind went back ten years to the evening at Brideshead, when that lovely, spidery child of nineteen, as though brought in for an hour from the nursery and nettled by lack of attention from the grown-ups, had said: "I'm causing anxiety, too, you know," and I had thought at the time, though scarcely, it now seemed to me, in long trousers myself: "How important these girls make themselves with their love affairs."

Now it was different; there was nothing but humility and friendly candour in the way she spoke.

I wished I could respond to her confidence, give some token of acceptance, but there was nothing in my last, flat, eventful years that I could share with her. I began instead to talk of my time in the jungle, of the comic characters I had met and the lost places I had visited, but in this mood of old friendship the tale faltered and came to an end abruptly.

"I long to see the paintings," she said.

"Celia wanted me to unpack some and stick them round the cabin for her cocktail party. I couldn't do that."

"No. . . . Is Celia as pretty as ever? I always thought she had the most delicious looks of any girl of my year."

"She hasn't changed."

"You have, Charles. So lean and grim, not at all the pretty boy Sebastian brought home with him. Harder, too."

"And you're softer."

"Yes, I think so . . . and very patient now."

She was not yet thirty, but was approaching the zenith of her loveliness, all her rich promise abundantly fulfilled. She had lost that fashionable, spidery look; the head that I used to think Quattrocento, which had sat a little oddly on her, was now part of herself and not at all Florentine — not connected in any way with painting or the arts or with anything except herself, so that it would be idle to itemise and dissect her beauty, which was her own essence, and could only be

known in her and by her authority and in the love I was soon to have
for her.

Time had wrought another change, too; not for her the sly, complacent smile of La Gioconda; the years had been more than "the sound
of lyres and flutes," and had saddened her. She seemed to say, "Look
at me. I have done my share. I am beautiful. It is something quite
out of the ordinary, this beauty of mine. I am made for delight. But
what do *I* get out of it? Where is *my* reward?"

That was the change in her from ten years ago; that, indeed, was
her reward, this haunting, magical sadness which spoke straight to the
heart and struck silence; it was the completion of her beauty.

"Sadder, too," I said.

"Oh yes, much sadder."

My wife was in exuberant spirits when, two hours later, I returned
to the cabin.

"I've had to do everything. How does it look?"

We had been given, without paying more for it, a large suite of
rooms, one so large, in fact, that it was seldom booked except by
directors of the line, and on most voyages, the chief purser admitted,
was given to those he wished to honour. (My wife was adept in
achieving such small advantages, first impressing the impressionable
with her chic and my celebrity and, superiority once firmly established,
changing quickly to a pose of almost flirtatious affability.) In token of
her appreciation the chief purser had been asked to our party and he,
in token of his appreciation, had sent before him the life-size effigy of
a swan, moulded in ice and filled with caviar. This chilly piece of mag-
nificence now dominated the room, standing on a table in the centre,
thawing gently, dripping at the beak into its silver dish. The flowers
of the morning delivery hid as much as possible of the panelling (for
this room was a miniature of the monstrous hall above).

"You must get dressed at once. Where have you been all this time?"

"Talking to Julia Mottram."

"D'you know her? Oh, of course, you were a friend of the dipso
brother. Goodness, her glamour!"

"She greatly admires your looks, too."

"She used to be a girl friend of Boy's."

"Surely not?"

"He always said so."

"Have you considered," I asked, "how your guests are going to eat this caviar?"

"I have. It's insoluble. But there's all this" — she revealed some trays of glassy tit-bits — "and anyway, people always find ways of eating things at parties. D'you remember we once ate potted shrimps with a paper knife?"

"Did we?"

"Darling, it was the night you popped the question."

"As I remember, you popped."

"Well, the night we got engaged. But you haven't said how you like the arrangements."

The arrangements, apart from the swan and the flowers, consisted of a steward already inextricably trapped in the corner behind an improvised bar, and another steward, tray in hand, in comparative freedom.

"A cinema actor's dream," I said.

"Cinema actors," said my wife; "that's what I want to talk about."

She came with me to my dressing-room and talked while I changed. It had occurred to her that, with my interest in architecture, my true métier was designing scenery for the films, and she had asked two Hollywood magnates to the party with whom she wished to ingratiate me.

We returned to the sitting-room.

"Darling, I believe you've taken against my bird. Don't be beastly about it in front of the purser. It was sweet of him to think of it. Besides, you know, if you had read about it in a description of a sixteenth-century banquet in Venice, you would have said those were the days to live."

"In sixteenth-century Venice it would have been a somewhat different shape."

"Here *is* Father Christmas. We were just in raptures over your swan."

The chief purser came into the room and shook hands powerfully.

"Dear Lady Celia," he said, "if you'll put on your warmest clothes and come an expedition into the cold storage with me to-morrow, I can show you a whole Noah's Ark of such objects. The toast will be along in a minute. They're keeping it hot."

"Toast!" said my wife, as though this was something beyond the dreams of gluttony. "Do you hear that, Charles? *Toast.*"

Soon the guests began to arrive; there was nothing to delay them.

"Celia," they said, "what a grand cabin and what a beautiful swan!" and, for all that it was one of the largest in the ship, our room was soon painfully crowded; they began to put out their cigarettes in the little pool of ice-water which now surrounded the swan.

The purser made a sensation, as sailors like to do, by predicting a storm. "How can you be so beastly?" asked my wife, conveying the flattering suggestion that not only the cabin and the caviar, but the waves, too, were at his command. "Anyway, storms don't affect a ship like this, do they?"

"Might hold us back a bit."

"But it wouldn't make us sick?"

"Depends if you're a good sailor. I'm always sick in storms, ever since I was a boy."

"I don't believe it. He's just being sadistic. Come over here, there's something I want to show you."

It was the latest photograph of her children. "Charles hasn't even seen Caroline yet. Isn't it thrilling for him?"

There were no friends of mine there, but I knew about a third of the party, and talked away civilly enough. An elderly woman said to me, "So you're Charles. I feel I know you through and through, Celia's talked so much about you."

Through and through, I thought. Through and through is a long way, madam. Can you indeed see into those dark places where my own eyes seek in vain to guide me? Can you tell me, dear Mrs. Stuyvesant Oglander — if I am correct in thinking that is how I heard my wife speak of you — why it is that at this moment, while I talk to you, here, about my forthcoming exhibition, I am thinking all the time only of when Julia will come? Why can I talk like this to you, but not to her? Why have I already set her apart from humankind, and myself with her? What is going on in those secret places of my spirit with which you make so free? What is cooking, Mrs. Stuyvesant Oglander?

Still Julia did not come, and the noise of twenty people in that tiny room, which was so large that no one hired it, was the noise of a multitude.

Then I saw a curious thing. There was a little red-headed man whom no one seemed to know, a dowdy fellow quite unlike the general run of my wife's guests; he had been standing by the caviar for twenty minutes eating as fast as a rabbit. Now he wiped his mouth with his handkerchief and, on the impulse apparently, leaned forward and dabbed the beak of the swan, removing the drop of water that had been swelling there and would soon have fallen. Then he looked round furtively to see if he had been observed, caught my eye, and giggled nervously.

"Been wanting to do that for a long time," he said. "Bet you don't know how many drops to the minute. I do, I counted."

"I've no idea."

"Guess. Tanner if you're wrong; half a dollar if you're right. That's fair."

"Three," I said.

"Coo, you're a sharp one. Been counting 'em yourself." But he showed no inclination to pay this debt. Instead he said: "How d'you figure this out? I'm an Englishman born and bred, but this is my first time on the Atlantic."

"You flew out perhaps?"

"No, nor over it."

"Then I presume you went round the world and came across the Pacific."

"You *are* a sharp one and no mistake. I've made quite a bit getting into arguments over that one."

"What was your route?" I asked, wishing to be agreeable.

"Ah, that'd be telling. Well, I must skedaddle. So long."

"Charles," said my wife, "this is Mr. Kramm, of Interastral Films."

"So you are Mr. Charles Ryder," said Mr. Kramm.

"Yes."

"Well, well, well." He paused. I waited. "The purser here says we're heading for dirty weather. What d'you know about that?"

"Far less than the purser."

"Pardon me, Mr. Ryder, I don't quite get you."

"I mean I know less than the purser."

"Is that so? Well, well, well. I've enjoyed our talk very much. I hope that it will be the first of many."

An Englishwoman said: "Oh, that swan! Six weeks in America has given me an absolute phobia of ice. Do tell me, how did it feel meeting Celia again after two years? I know I should feel indecently bridal. But Celia's never quite got the orange blossoms out of her hair, has she?"

Another woman said: "Isn't it heaven saying good-bye and knowing we shall meet again in half an hour and go on meeting every half-hour for days?"

Our guests began to go, and each on leaving informed me of something my wife had promised to bring me to in the near future; it was the theme of the evening that we should all be seeing a lot of each other, that we had formed one of those molecular systems that physicists can illustrate. At last the swan was wheeled out, too, and I said to my wife, "Julia never came."

"No, she telephoned. I couldn't hear what she said, there was such a noise going on — something about a dress. Quite lucky really, there wasn't room for a cat. It was a lovely party, wasn't it? Did you hate it very much? You behaved beautifully and looked so distinguished. Who was your red-haired chum?"

"No chum of mine."

"How *very* peculiar! Did you say anything to Mr. Kramm about working in Hollywood?"

"Of course not."

"Oh, Charles, you are a worry to me. It's not enough just to stand about looking distinguished and a martyr for Art. Let's go to dinner. We're at the Captain's table. I don't suppose he'll dine down to-night, but it's polite to be fairly punctual."

By the time that we reached the table the rest of the party had arranged themselves. On either side of the Captain's empty chair sat Julia and Mrs. Stuyvesant Oglander; besides them there were an English diplomat and his wife, Senator Stuyvesant Oglander, and an American clergyman at present totally isolated between two pairs of empty chairs. This clergyman later described himself — redundantly it seemed —as an Episcopalian Bishop. Husbands and wives sat together here. My wife was confronted with a quick decision, and although the steward attempted to direct us otherwise, sat so that she had the Senator and I the Bishop. Julia gave us both a little dismal signal of sympathy.

"I'm miserable about the party," she said, "my beastly maid totally disappeared with every dress I have. She only turned up half an hour ago. She'd been playing ping-pong."

"I've been telling the Senator what he missed," said Mrs. Stuyvesant Oglander. "Whatever Celia is, you'll find she knows all the significant people."

"On my right," said the Bishop, "a significant couple are expected. They take all their meals in their cabin except when they have been informed in advance that the Captain will be present."

We were a gruesome circle; even my wife's high social spirit faltered. At moments I heard bits of her conversation.

". . . an extraordinary little red-haired man. Captain Foulenough in person."

"But I understood you to say, Lady Celia, that you were unacquainted with him."

"I mean he was *like* Captain Foulenough."

"I begin to comprehend. He impersonated this friend of yours in order to come to your party."

"No, no. Captain Foulenough is simply a comic character."

"There seems to have been nothing very amusing about this other man. Your friend is a comedian?"

"No, no. Captain Foulenough is an imaginary character in an English paper. You know, like your 'Popeye.' "

The Senator laid down knife and fork. "To recapitulate: an impostor came to your party and you admitted him because of a fancied resemblance to a fictitious character in a cartoon."

"Yes, I suppose that was it really."

The Senator looked at his wife as much as to say: "Significant people, huh!"

I heard Julia across the table trying to trace, for the benefit of the diplomat, the marriage-connections of her Hungarian and Italian cousins. The diamonds in her hair and on her fingers flashed with fire, but her hands were nervously rolling little balls of crumb, and her starry head drooped in despair.

The Bishop told me of the goodwill mission on which he was travelling to Barcelona . . . "a very, very valuable work of clearance had been performed, Mr. Ryder. The time has now come to rebuild on broader foundations. I have made it my aim to reconcile the so-called Anarchists and the so-called Communists, and with that in view I and my committee have digested all the available literature of the subject. Our conclusion, Mr. Ryder, is unanimous. There is *no* fundamental diversity between the two ideologies. It is a matter of personalities, Mr. Ryder, and what personalities have put asunder personalities can unite. . . ."

On the other side I heard:

"And may I make so bold as to ask what institutions sponsored your husband's expedition?"

The diplomat's wife bravely engaged the Bishop across the gulf that separated them.

"And what language will you speak when you get to Barcelona?"

"The language of Reason and Brotherhood, madam," and, turning back to me, "The speech of the coming century is in thoughts not in words. Do you not agree, Mr. Ryder?"

"Yes," I said. "Yes."

"What are words?" said the Bishop.

"What indeed?"

"Mere conventional symbols, Mr. Ryder, and this is an age rightly sceptical of conventional symbols."

My mind reeled; after the parrot-house fever of my wife's party, and the deep, unplumbed emotions of the afternoon, after all the exertions of my wife's pleasures in New York, after the months of solitude in the steaming, green shadows of the jungle, this was too much. I felt like Lear on the heath, like the Duchess of Malfi bayed by madmen. I summoned cataracts and hurricanoes, and as if by conjury the call was immediately answered.

For some time now, though whether it was a mere trick of the nerves I did not then know, I had felt a recurrent and persistently growing motion — a heave and shudder of the large dining-room as of the breast of a man in deep sleep. Now my wife turned to me and said: "Either I am a little drunk or it's getting rough," and even as she spoke we found ourselves leaning sideways in our chairs; there was a crash and tinkle of falling cutlery by the wall, and on our table the wine-glasses all together toppled and rolled over, while each of us steadied the plate and forks and looked at the others with expressions that varied between frank horror in the diplomat's wife and relief in Julia.

The gale which, unheard, unseen, unfelt, in our enclosed and in-sulated world, had for an hour been mounting over us, had now veered and fallen full on our bows.

Silence followed the crash, then a high, nervous babble of laughter. Stewards laid napkins on the pools of spilt wine. We tried to resume the conversation, but all were waiting, as the little ginger man had watched the drop swell and fall from the swan's beak, for the next great blow; it came, heavier than the last.

"This is where I say good-night to you all," said the diplomat's wife, rising.

Her husband led her to their cabin. The dining-room was emptying fast. Soon only Julia, my wife and I were left at the table, and telepathically, Julia said, "Like King Lear."

"Only each of us is all three of them."

"What can you mean?" asked my wife.

"Lear, Kent, Fool."

"Oh, dear, it's like that agonising Foulenough conversation over again. Don't try and explain."

"I doubt if I could," I said.

Another climb, another vast drop. The stewards were at work making things fast, shutting things up, hustling away unstable ornaments.

"Well, we've finished dinner and set a fine example of British phlegm," said my wife. "Let's go and see what's on."

Once on our way to the lounge we had all three to cling to a pillar; when we got there we found it almost deserted; the band played but no one danced; the tables were set for tombola but no one bought a card, and the ship's officer, who made a specialty of calling the numbers with all the patter of the lower deck — "sweet sixteen and never been kissed — key of the door, twenty-one — clickety-click, sixty-six" — was idly talking to his colleagues; there were a score of scattered novel readers, a few games of bridge, some brandy drinking in the smoking-room, but all our guests of two hours before had disappeared.

The three of us sat for a little by the empty dance floor; my wife was full of schemes by which, without impoliteness, we could move to another table in the dining-room. "It's crazy to go to the restaurant," she said, "and pay extra for exactly the same dinner. Only film people go there, anyway. I don't see why we should be made to."

Presently she said: "It's making my head ache and I'm tired, anyway. I'm going to bed."

Julia went with her. I walked round the ship, on one of the covered decks where the wind howled and the spray leaped up from the darkness and smashed white and brown against the glass screen; men were posted to keep the passengers off the open decks. Then I, too, went below.

In my dressing-room everything breakable had been stowed away, the door to the cabin was hooked open, and my wife called plaintively from within.

"I feel terrible. I didn't know a ship of this size could pitch like this," she said, and her eyes were full of consternation and resentment, like those of a woman who, at the end of her time, at length realises that however luxurious the nursing home, and however well paid the doctor, her labour is inevitable; and the lift and fall of the ship came regularly as the pains of childbirth.

I slept next door; or, rather, I lay there between dreaming and waking. In a narrow bunk, on a hard mattress, there might have been rest, but here the beds were broad and buoyant; I collected what cushions I could find and tried to wedge myself firm, but through the night I turned with each swing and twist of the ship — she was rolling now as well as pitching — and my head rang with the creak and thud which now succeeded the hum of fine weather.

Once, an hour before dawn, my wife appeared like a ghost in the doorway, supporting herself with either hand on the jambs, saying: "Are you awake? Can't you do something? Can't you get something from the doctor?"

I rang for the night steward, who had a draught ready prepared, which comforted her a little.

And all night between dreaming and waking I thought of Julia; in my brief dreams she took a hundred fantastic and terrible and obscene forms, but in my waking thoughts she returned with her sad, starry head just as I had seen her at dinner.

After first light I slept for an hour or two, then awoke clear-headed, with a joyous sense of anticipation.

The wind had dropped a little, the steward told me, but was still blowing hard and there was a very heavy swell; "which there's nothing worse than a heavy swell," he said, "for the enjoyment of the passengers. There's not many breakfasts wanted this morning."

I looked in at my wife, found her sleeping, and closed the door between us; then I ate salmon kedgeree and cold Bradenham ham and telephoned for a barber to come and shave me.

"There's a lot of stuff in the sitting-room for the lady," said the steward; "shall I leave it for the time?"

I went to see. There was a second delivery of cellophane parcels from the shops on board, some ordered by radio from friends in New York whose secretaries had failed to remind them of our departure in time, some by our guests as they left the cocktail party. It was no day for flower vases; I told him to leave them on the floor and then, struck by the thought, removed the card from Mr. Kramm's roses and sent them with my love to Julia.

She telephoned while I was being shaved.

"What a deplorable thing to do, Charles! How unlike you!"

"Don't you like them?"

"What can I do with roses on a day like this?"

"Smell them."

There was a pause and a rustle of unpacking. "They've absolutely no smell at all."

"What have you had for breakfast?"

"Muscat grapes and cantaloup."

"When shall I see you?"

"Before lunch. I'm busy till then with a masseuse."

"A masseuse?"

"Yes, isn't it peculiar. I've never had one before, except once when I hurt my shoulder hunting. What is it about being on a boat that makes everyone behave like a film star?"

"I don't."

"How about these very embarrassing roses?"

The barber did his work with extraordinary dexterity — indeed, with agility, for he stood like a swordsman in a ballet sometimes on the point of one foot, sometimes on the other, lightly flicking the lather off his blade and swooping back to my chin as the ship righted herself; I should not have dared use a safety razor on myself.

The telephone rang again.

It was my wife.

"How are you, Charles?"

"Tired."

"Aren't you coming to see me?"

"I came once. I'll be in again."

I brought her the flowers from the sitting-room; they completed the atmosphere of a maternity ward which she had managed to create in the cabin; the stewardess had the air of a midwife, standing by the bed, a pillar of starched linen and composure. My wife turned her head on the pillow and smiled wanly; she stretched out a bare arm and caressed with the tips of her fingers the cellophane and silk ribbons of the largest bouquet. "How sweet people are," she said faintly, as though the gale were a private misfortune of her own which the world in its love was condoling.

"I take it you're not getting up."

"Oh no, Mrs. Clark is being so sweet." She was always quick to get servants' names. "Don't bother. Come in sometimes and tell me what's going on."

"Now, now, dear," said the stewardess, "the less we are disturbed to-day the better."

My wife seemed to make a sacred, female rite even of seasickness.

Julia's cabin, I knew, was somewhere below ours. I waited for her by the lift on the main deck; when she came we walked once round the promenade; I held the rail, she took my other arm. It was hard going; through the streaming glass we saw a distorted world of grey sky and black water. When the ship rolled heavily I swung her round so that she could hold the rail with her other hand; the howl of the wind was subdued, but the whole ship creaked with strain. We made the circuit once; then Julia said: "It's no good. That woman beat hell out of me, and I feel limp, anyway. Let's sit down."

The great bronze doors of the lounge had torn away from their hooks and were swinging free with the roll of the ship; regularly and, it seemed, irresistibly, first one, then the other, opened and shut; they paused at the completion of each half circle, began to move slowly and finished fast with a resounding clash. There was no real risk in passing them, except of slipping and being caught by that swift, final blow; there was ample time to walk through unhurried, but there was something forbidding in the sight of that great weight of uncontrolled metal, flapping to and fro, which might have made a timid man flinch or skip through too quickly; I rejoiced to feel Julia's hand perfectly steady on my arm and know, as I walked beside her, that she was wholly undismayed.

"Bravo," said a man sitting nearby. "I confess I went round the other way. I didn't like the look of those doors somehow. They've been trying to fix them all the morning."

There were few people about that day, and that few seemed bound together by a camaraderie of reciprocal esteem; they did nothing except sit rather glumly in their armchairs, drink occasionally and exchange congratulations on not being seasick.

"You're the first lady I've seen," said the man.

"I'm very lucky."

"*We* are very lucky," he said, with a movement which began as a bow and ended as a lurch forward to his knees, as the blotting-paper floor dipped steeply between us. The roll carried us away from him, clinging together but still on our feet, and we quickly sat where our

dance led us, on the further side, in isolation; a web of life-lines had
been stretched across the lounge, and we seemed like boxers, roped
into the ring.

The steward approached. "Your usual, sir? Whisky and tepid water,
I think. And for the lady? Might I suggest a nip of champagne?"

"D'you know, the awful thing is I *would* like champagne very much?"
said Julia. "What a life of pleasure — roses, half an hour with a female
pugilist, and now champagne!"

"I wish you wouldn't go on about the roses. It wasn't my idea in
the first place. Someone sent them to Celia."

"Oh, that's quite different. It lets you out completely. But it makes
my massage worse."

"I was shaved in bed."

"I'm glad about the roses," said Julia. "Frankly, they were a shock.
They made me think we were starting the day on quite the wrong
footing."

I knew what she meant, and in that moment felt as though I had
shaken off some of the dust and grit of ten dry years; then and always,
however she spoke to me — in half sentences, single words, stock phrases
of contemporary jargon, in scarcely perceptible movements of eyes or
lips or hands — however inexpressible her thought, however deep and
far it had glanced from the matter in hand, however deep it had
plunged, as it often did, straight from the surface to the depths, I
knew; even that day when I still stood on the extreme verge of love,
I knew what she meant.

We drank our wine and soon our new friend came lurching towards
us down the life-line.

"Mind if I join you? Nothing like a bit of rough weather for bringing people together. This is my tenth crossing, and I've never seen
anything like it. I can see you are an experienced sailor, young lady."

"No. As a matter of fact, I've never been at sea before except coming to New York and, of course, crossing the Channel. I don't feel
sick, thank God, but I feel tired. I thought at first it was only the
massage, but I'm coming to the conclusion it's the ship."

"My wife's in a terrible way. She's an experienced sailor. Only shows,
doesn't it?"

He joined us at luncheon, and I did not mind his being there; he
had clearly taken a fancy to Julia, and he thought we were man and
wife; this misconception and his gallantry seemed in some way to bring

her and me closer together. "Saw you two last night at the Captain's table," he said, "with all the nobs."

"Very dull nobs."

"If you ask me, nobs always are. When you get a storm like this you find out what people are really made of."

"You have a predilection for good sailors?"

"Well, put like that I don't know that I do — what I mean is, it makes for getting together."

"Yes."

"Take us for example. But for this we might never have met. I've had some very romantic encounters at sea in my time. If the lady will excuse me, I'd like to tell you about a little adventure I had in the Gulf of Lyons when I was younger than I am now."

We were both weary; lack of sleep, the incessant din and the strain every movement required, wore us down. We spent that afternoon apart in our cabins. I slept, and when I awoke the sea was as high as ever, inky clouds swept over us and the glass streamed still with water, but I had grown used to the storm in my sleep, had made its rhythm mine, had become part of it, so that I arose strongly and confidently and found Julia already up and in the same temper.

"What d'you think?" she said. "That man's giving a little 'get-together party' to-night in the smoking-room for all the good sailors. He asked me to bring my husband."

"Are we going?"

"Of course. . . . I wonder if I ought to feel like the lady our friend met on the way to Barcelona. I don't, Charles, not a bit."

There were eighteen people at the "get-together party"; we had nothing in common except immunity from seasickness. We drank champagne, and presently our host said: "Tell you what, I've got a roulette wheel. Trouble is we can't go to my cabin on account of the wife, and we aren't allowed to play in public."

So the party adjourned to my sitting-room and we played for low stakes until late into the night, when Julia left and our host had drunk too much wine to be surprised that she and I were not in the same quarters. When all but he had gone he fell asleep in his chair, and I left him there. It was the last I saw of him, for later, so the steward told me when he came from returning the roulette things to the man's cabin, he broke his collar-bone, falling in the corridor, and was taken to the ship's hospital.

All next day Julia and I spent together without interruption; talking, scarcely moving, held in our chairs by the swell of the sea. After luncheon the last hardy passengers went to rest and we were alone as though the place had been cleared for us, as though tact on a Titanic scale had sent everyone tiptoeing out to leave us to one another.

The bronze doors of the lounge had been fixed, but not before two seamen had been injured and removed to the sick-bay. They had tried various devices, lashing with ropes and, later, when these failed, with steel hawsers, but there was nothing to which they could be made fast; finally, they drove wooden wedges under them, catching them in the brief moment of repose when they were full open, and these held them.

When, before dinner, she went to her cabin to get ready (no one dressed that night) and I came with her, uninvited, unopposed, expected, and behind closed doors took her in my arms and first kissed her, there was no alteration from the mood of the afternoon. Later, turning it over in my mind, as I turned in my bed with the rise and fall of the ship, through the long, lonely, drowsy night, I recalled the courtships of the past, dead, ten years; how, knotting my tie before setting out, putting the gardenia in my buttonhole, I would plan my evening and think, At such and such a time, at such and such an opportunity, I shall cross the start-line and open my attack for better or worse; this phase of the battle has gone on long enough, I would think; a decision must be reached. With Julia there were no phases, no start-line, no tactics at all.

But later that night when she went to bed and I followed her to her door she stopped me.

"No, Charles, not yet. Perhaps never. I don't know. I don't know if I want love."

Then something, some surviving ghost from those dead ten years — for one cannot die, even for a little, without some loss — made me say, "Love? I'm not asking for love."

"Oh yes, Charles, you are," she said, and putting up her hand gently stroked my cheek; then shut her door.

And I reeled back, first on one wall, then on the other, of the long, softly lighted, empty corridor; for the storm, it appeared, had the form of a ring. All day we had been sailing through its still centre; now we were once more in the full fury of the wind — and that night was to be rougher than the one before.

Ten hours of talking: what had we to say? Plain fact mostly, the record of our two lives, so long widely separate, now being knit to one. Through all that storm-tossed night I rehearsed what she had told me; she was no longer the alternate succubus and starry vision of the night before; she had given all that was transferable of her past into my keeping. She told me, as I have already retold, of her courtship and marriage; she told me, as though fondly turning the pages of an old nursery-book, of her childhood; and I lived long, sunny days with her in the meadows, with Nanny Hawkins on her camp stool and Cordelia asleep in the pram, slept quiet nights under the dome with the religious pictures fading round the cot as the nightlight burned low and the embers settled in the grate. She told me of her life with Rex and of the secret, vicious, disastrous escapade that had taken her to New York. She, too, had had her dead years. She told me of her long struggle with Rex as to whether she should have a child; at first she wanted one, but learned after a year that an operation was needed to make it possible; by that time Rex and she were out of love, but he still wanted his child, and when at last she consented, it was born dead.

"Rex has never been unkind to me intentionally," she said. "It's just that he isn't a real person at all; he's just a few faculties of a man highly developed; the rest simply isn't there. He couldn't imagine why it hurt me to find, two months after we came back to London from our honeymoon, that he was still keeping up with Brenda Champion."

"I was glad when I found Celia was unfaithful," I said. "I felt it was all right for me to dislike her."

"Is she? Do you? I'm glad. I don't like her either. Why did you marry her?"

"Physical attraction. Ambition. Everyone agrees she's the ideal wife for a painter. Loneliness, missing Sebastian."

"You loved him, didn't you?"

"Oh yes. He was the forerunner."

Julia understood.

The ship creaked and shuddered, rose and fell. My wife called to me from the next room: "Charles, are you there?"

"Yes."

"I've been asleep such a long while. What time is it?"

"Half-past three."

"It's no better, is it?"

"Worse."

"I feel a little better, though. D'you think they'd bring me some tea or something if I rang the bell?"

I got her some tea and biscuits from the night steward.

"Did you have an amusing evening?"

"Everyone's seasick."

"Poor Charles. It was going to have been such a lovely trip, too. It may be better to-morrow."

I turned out the light and shut the door between us.

Waking and dreaming, through the strain and creak and heave of the long night, flat on my back with my arms and legs spread wide to check the roll, and my eyes open to the darkness, I lay thinking of Julia.

". . . We thought Papa might come back to England after Mummy died, or that he might marry again, but he lives just as he did. Rex and I often go to see him now. I've grown fond of him. . . . Sebastian's disappeared completely . . . Cordelia's in Spain with an ambulance . . . Bridey leads his own extraordinary life. He wanted to shut Brideshead after Mummy died, but Papa wouldn't have it for some reason, so Rex and I live there now, and Bridey has two rooms up in the dome, next to Nanny Hawkins, part of the old nurseries. He's like a character from Chekhov. One meets him sometimes coming out of the library or on the stairs — I never know when he's at home — and now and then he suddenly comes in to dinner like a ghost quite unexpectedly.

". . . Oh, Rex's parties! Politics and money. They can't do anything except for money; if they walk round the lake they have to make bets about how many swans they see . . . sitting up till two, amusing Rex's girls, hearing them gossip, rattling away endlessly on the backgammon board while the men play cards and smoke cigars. The cigar smoke . . . I can smell it in my hair when I wake up in the morning; it's in my clothes when I dress at night. Do I smell of it now? D'you think that woman who rubbed me felt it in my skin?

". . . At first I used to stay away with Rex in his friends' houses. He doesn't make me any more. He was ashamed of me when he found I didn't cut the kind of figure he wanted, ashamed of himself for having been taken in. I wasn't at all the article he'd bargained for. He can't see the point of me, but whenever he's made up his mind there isn't a point and he's begun to feel comfortable, he gets a surprise — some man, or even woman, he respects takes a fancy to me and he suddenly sees that there is a whole world of things we understand and he doesn't. . . . He was upset when I went away. He'll be delighted to have me back. I was faithful to him until this last thing came along. There's nothing like a good upbringing. Do you know last year, when I thought I was going to have a child, I'd decided to have it brought up a Catholic? I hadn't thought about religion before; I haven't since; but just at that time, when I was waiting for the birth, I thought, 'That's one thing I can give her. It doesn't seem to have done me much good, but my child shall have it.' It was odd, wanting to give something one had lost oneself. Then, in the end, I couldn't even give that: I couldn't even give her life. I never saw her; I was too ill to know what was going on, and afterwards for a long time, until now, I didn't want to speak about her — she was a daughter, so Rex didn't so much mind her being dead.

"I've been punished a little for marrying Rex. You see, I can't get all that sort of thing out of my mind, quite — Death, Judgment, Heaven, Hell, Nanny Hawkins, and the Catechism. It becomes part of oneself, if they give it one early enough. And yet I wanted my child to have it. . . . Now I suppose I shall be punished for what I've just done. Perhaps that is why you and I are here together like this . . . part of a plan."

That was almost the last thing she said to me — "part of a plan" — before we went below and parted at her cabin door.

Next day the wind had again dropped, and again we were wallowing in the swell. The talk was less of seasickness now than of broken bones; people had been thrown about in the night, and there had been many nasty accidents on bathroom floors.

That day, because we had talked so much the day before and because what we had to say needed few words, we spoke little. We had books; Julia found a game she liked. When after long silences we spoke, our thoughts, we found, had kept pace together side by side.

Once I said, "You are standing guard over your sadness."

"It's all I have earned. You said yesterday. My wages."

"An I.O.U. from life. A promise to pay on demand."

Rain ceased at midday; at evening the clouds dispersed and the sun, astern of us, suddenly broke into the lounge where we sat, putting all the lights to shame.

"Sunset," said Julia, "the end of our day."

She rose and, though the roll and pitch of the ship seemed unabated, led me up to the boat-deck. She put her arm through mine and her hand into mine, in my great-coat pocket. The deck was dry and empty, swept only by the wind of the ship's speed. As we made our halting, laborious way forward, away from the flying smuts of the smoke-stack, we were alternately jostled together, then strained, nearly sundered, arms and fingers interlocked as I held the rail and Julia clung to me, thrust together again, drawn apart; then, in a plunge deeper than the rest, I found myself flung across her, pressing her against the rail, warding myself off her with the arms that held her prisoner on either side, and as the ship paused at the end of its drop as though gathering strength for the ascent, we stood thus embraced, in the open, cheek against cheek, her hair blowing across my eyes; the dark horizon of tumbling water, flashing now with gold, stood still above us, then came sweeping down till I was staring through Julia's dark hair into a wide and golden sky, and she was thrown forward on my heart, held up by my hands on the rail, her face still pressed to mine.

In that minute, with her lips to my ear and her breath warm in the salt wind, Julia said, though I had not spoken, "Yes, now," and as the ship righted herself and for the moment ran into calmer waters, Julia led me below.

So at sunset I took formal possession of her as her lover. It was no time for the sweets of luxury; they would come, in their season, with the swallow and the lime-flowers. Now on the rough water, as I was made free of her narrow loins and, it seemed now, in assuaging that fierce appetite, cast a burden which I had borne all my life, toiled under, not knowing its nature — now, while the waves still broke and thundered on the prow, the act of possession was a symbol, a rite of ancient origin and solemn meaning.

We dined that night high up in the ship, in the restaurant, and saw through the bow windows the stars come out and sweep across the sky as once, I remembered, I had seen them sweep above the towers and gables of Oxford. The stewards promised that to-morrow night the band would play again and the place be full. We had better book now, they said, if we wanted a good table.

"Oh dear," said Julia, "where can we hide in fair weather, we orphans of the storm?"

I could not leave her that night, but early next morning, as once again I made my way back along the corridor, I found I could walk without difficulty; the ship rode easily on a smooth sea, and I knew that our solitude was broken.

My wife called joyously from her cabin: "Charles, Charles, I feel so well. What do you think I am having for breakfast?"

I went to see. She was eating a beef-steak.

"I've fixed up for a visit to the hairdresser — do you know they couldn't take me till four o'clock this afternoon, they're so busy suddenly? So I shan't appear till the evening, but lots of people are coming in to see us this morning, and I've asked Miles and Janet to lunch with us in our sitting-room. I'm afraid I've been a worthless wife to you the last two days. What have you been up to?"

"One gay evening," I said, "we played roulette till two o'clock, next door in the sitting-room, and our host passed out."

"Goodness. It sounds very disreputable. Have you been behaving, Charles? You haven't been picking up sirens?"

"There was scarcely a woman about. I spent most of the time with Julia."

"Oh, good. I always wanted to bring you together. She's one of my friends I knew you'd like. I expect you were a godsend to her. She's had rather a gloomy time lately. I don't expect she mentioned it, but . . ." my wife proceeded to relate a current version of Julia's journey to New York. "I'll ask her to cocktails this morning," she concluded.

Julia came, and it was happiness enough, now, merely to be near her.

"I hear you've been looking after my husband for me," my wife said.

"Yes, we've become very matey. He and I and a man whose name we don't know."

"Mr. Kramm, what have you done to your arm?"

"It was the bathroom floor," said Mr. Kramm, and explained at length how he had fallen.

That night the Captain dined at his table and the circle was complete, for claimants came to the chairs on the Bishop's right, two Japanese who expressed deep interest in his projects for world-brotherhood. The Captain was full of chaff at Julia's endurance in the storm, offering to engage her as a seaman; years of sea-going had given him jokes for every occasion. My wife, fresh from the beauty parlour, was unravaged by her three days of distress, and in the eyes of many seemed to outshine Julia, whose sadness had gone and been replaced by an incommunicable content and tranquillity; incommunicable save to me; she and I, separated by the crowd, sat alone together close enwrapped, as we had lain in each other's arms the night before.

There was a gala spirit in the ship that night. Though it meant rising at dawn to pack, everyone was determined that for this one night he would enjoy the luxury the storm had denied him. There was no solitude. Every corner of the ship was thronged; dance music and high, excited chatter, stewards darting everywhere with trays of glasses, the voice of the officer in charge of tombola: "Kelly's eye — number one; legs, eleven; and we'll Shake the Bag" — Mrs. Stuyvesant Oglander in a paper cap, Mr. Kramm and his bandages, the two Japanese decorously throwing paper streamers and hissing like geese.

I did not speak to Julia, alone, all that evening. We met for a minute next day on the starboard side of the ship while everyone else crowded to port to see the officials come aboard and to gaze at the green coastline of Devon.

"What are your plans?"

"London for a bit," she said.

"Celia's going straight home. She wants to see the children."

"You, too?"

"No."

"In London then."

"Charles, the little red-haired man — Foulenough. Did you see? Two plain-clothes police have taken him off."

"I missed it. There was such a crowd on that side of the ship."

"I found out the trains and sent a telegram. We shall be home by dinner. The children will be asleep. Perhaps we might wake John-john up, just for once."

"You go down," I said. "I shall have to stay in London."

"Oh, but Charles, you *must* come. You haven't seen Caroline."

"Will she change much in a week or two?"

"Darling, she changes every day."

"Then what's the point of seeing her now? I'm sorry, my dear, but I must get the pictures unpacked and see how they've travelled. I must fix up for the exhibition right away."

"Must you?" she said, but I knew that her resistance ended when I appealed to the mysteries of my trade. "It's very disappointing. Besides, I don't know if Andrew and Cynthia will be out of the flat. They took it till the end of the month."

"I can go to a hotel."

"But that's so grim. I can't bear you to be alone your first night home. I'll stay and go down to-morrow."

"You mustn't disapoint the children."

"No." Her children, my art, the two mysteries of our trades . . .

"Will you come for the week-end?"

"If I can."

"All British passports to the smoking-room, please," said a steward.

"I've arranged with that sweet Foreign Office man at our table to get us off early with him," said my wife.

II

It was my wife's idea to hold the private view on Friday.

"We are out to catch the critics this time," she said. "It's high time they began to take you seriously, and they know it. This is their chance. If you open on Monday they'll most of them have just come up from the country, and they'll dash off a few paragraphs before dinner — I'm only worrying about the weeklies of course. If we give them the week-end to think about it, we shall have them in an urbane Sunday-in-the-country mood. They'll settle down after a good luncheon, tuck up their cuffs, and turn out a nice, leisurely, full-length essay, which they'll reprint later in a nice little book. Nothing less will do this time."

She was up and down from the Old Rectory several times during the month of preparation, revising the list of invitations and helping with the hanging.

On the morning of the private view I telephoned to Julia and said: "I'm sick of the pictures already and never want to see them again, but I suppose I shall have to put in an appearance."

"D'you want me to come?"

"I'd much rather you didn't."

"Celia sent a card with 'Bring everyone' written across it in green ink. When do we meet?"

"In the train. You might pick up my luggage."

"If you'll have it packed soon I'll pick you up, too, and drop you at the gallery. I've got a fitting next door at twelve."

When I reached the gallery my wife was standing looking through the window to the street. Behind her half a dozen unknown picture-lovers were moving from canvas to canvas, catalogue in hand: they were people who had once bought a wood-cut and were consequently on the gallery's list of patrons.

"No one has come yet," said my wife. "I've been here since ten and it's been very dull. Whose car was that you came in?"

"Julia's."

"Julia's? Why didn't you bring her in? Oddly enough, I've just been talking about Brideshead to a funny little man who seemed to know us very well. He said he was called Mr. Samgrass. Apparently he's one of Lord Copper's middle-aged young men on the *Daily Beast*. I tried to feed him some paragraphs, but he seemed to know more about you than I do. He said he'd met me years ago at Brideshead. I wish Julia had come in; then we could have asked her about him."

"I remember him well. He's a crook."

"Yes, that stuck out a mile. He's been talking all about what he calls 'the Brideshead set.' Apparently Rex Mottram had made the place a nest of party mutiny. Did you know? What would Teresa Marchmain have thought?"

"I'm going there to-night."

"Not to-night, Charles; you can't go there *to-night*. You're expected at home. You promised, as soon as the exhibition was ready, you'd come home. Johnjohn and Nanny have made a banner with 'Welcome' on it. And you haven't seen Caroline yet."

"I'm sorry, it's all settled."

"Besides, Daddy will think it so odd. And Boy is home for Sunday. And you haven't seen the new studio. You can't go to-night. Did they ask me?"

"Of course; but I knew you wouldn't be able to come."

"I can't now. I could have if you'd let me know earlier. I should adore to see the 'Brideshead set' at home. I do think you're perfectly beastly, but this is no time for a family rumpus. The Clarences promised to come in before luncheon; they may be here any minute."

We were interrupted, however, not by royalty, but by a woman reporter from one of the dailies, whom the manager of the gallery now led up to us. She had not come to see the pictures but to get a "human story" of the dangers of my journey. I left her to my wife, and next day read in her paper: —

CHARLES "STATELY HOMES" RYDER STEPS OFF THE MAP

That the snakes and vampires of the jungle have nothing on Mayfair is the opinion of socialite artist Ryder, who has abandoned the houses of the great for the ruins of equatorial Africa. . . .

The rooms began to fill and I was soon busy being civil. My wife was everywhere, greeting people, introducing people, deftly transforming the crowd into a party. I saw her lead friends forward one after another to the subscription list that had been opened for the book of *Ryder's Latin America*; I heard her say: "No, darling, I'm not at all surprised, but you wouldn't expect *me* to be, would you? You see Charles lives for one thing — Beauty. I think he got bored with finding it ready-made in England; he had to go and create it for himself. He wanted new worlds to conquer. After all, he has said the last word about country houses, hasn't he? Not, I mean, that he's given that up altogether. I'm sure he'll always do one or two more for *friends*."

A photographer brought us together, flashed a lamp in our faces, and let us part.

Presently there was the slight hush and edging away which follows the entry of a royal party. I saw my wife curtsey and heard her say: "Oh, sir, you are sweet"; then I was led into the clearing and the Duke of Clarence said: "Pretty hot out there I should think."

"It was, sir."

"Awfully clever the way you've hit off the impression of heat. Makes me feel quite uncomfortable in my great-coat."

"Ha, ha."

When they had gone my wife said: "Goodness, we're late for lunch. Margot's giving a party in your honour," and in the taxi she said: "I've just thought of something. Why don't you write and ask the Duchess's permission to dedicate *Latin America* to her?"

"Why should I?"

"She'd love it so."

"I wasn't thinking of dedicating it to anyone."

"There you are; that's typical of you, Charles. Why miss an opportunity to give pleasure?"

There were a dozen at luncheon, and though it pleased my hostess and my wife to say that they were there in my honour, it was plain to me that half of them did not know of my exhibition and had come because they had been invited and had no other engagement. Throughout luncheon they talked without stopping of Mrs. Simpson, but they all, or nearly all, came back with us to the gallery.

The hour after luncheon was the busiest time. There were representatives of the Tate Gallery, the Chantrey Bequest, the National Art Collections Fund, who all promised to return shortly with colleagues

and, in the meantime, reserved certain pictures for further consideration. The most influential critic, who in the past had dismissed me with
a few wounding commendations, peered out at me from between his
slouch hat and woollen muffler, gripped my arm, and said: "I knew
you had it. I saw it there. I've been waiting for it."

From fashionable and unfashionable lips alike I heard fragments of
praise. "If you'd asked me to guess," I overheard, "Ryder's is the last
name would have occurred to me. They're so virile, so passionate."

They all thought they had found something new. It had not been
thus at my last exhibition in these same rooms, shortly before my going
abroad. Then there had been an unmistakable note of weariness. Then
the talk had been less of me than of the houses, anecdotes of their
owners. That same woman, it came back to me, who now applauded
my virility and passion, had stood quite near me, before a painfully
laboured canvas, and said, "So facile."

I remembered the exhibition, too, for another reason; it was the week
I detected my wife in adultery. Then, as now, she was a tireless hostess,
and I heard her say: "Whenever I see anything lovely nowadays — a
building or a piece of scenery — I think to myself, 'That's by Charles.'
I see everything through his eyes. He *is* England to me."

I heard her say that; it was the sort of thing she had the habit of
saying. Throughout our married life, again and again, I had felt my
bowels shrivel within me at the things she said. But that day, in this
gallery, I heard her unmoved, and suddenly realized that she was
powerless to hurt me any more; I was a free man; she had given me
my manumission in that brief, sly lapse of hers; my cuckold's horns made
me lord of the forest.

At the end of the day my wife said: "Darling, I must go. It's been
a terrific success, hasn't it? I'll think of something to tell them at
home, but I wish it hadn't got to happen quite this way."

So she knows, I thought. She's a sharp one. She's had her nose down
since luncheon and picked up the scent.

I let her get clear of the place and was about to follow — the rooms
were nearly empty — when I heard a voice at the turnstile I had not
heard for many years, an unforgettable self-taught stammer, a sharp
cadence of remonstration.

"No. I have *not* brought a card of invitation. I do not even know
whether I received one. I have not come to a social function; I do not
seek to scrape acquaintance with Lady Celia; I do not want my

photograph in the *Tatler;* I have not come to exhibit myself. I have come to see the *pictures.* Perhaps you are unaware that there are any pictures here. I happen to have a personal interest in the *artist* — if that word has any meaning for you."

"Antoine," I said. "Come in."

"My dear, there is a g-g-gorgon here who thinks I am g-g-gate-crashing. I only arrived in London yesterday, and heard quite by chance at luncheon that you were having an exhibition, so of course I dashed impetuously to the shrine to pay homage. Have I changed? Would you recognise me? Where are the pictures? Let me explain them to you."

Anthony Blanche had not changed from when I last saw him; not, indeed, from when I first saw him. He swept lightly across the room to the most prominent canvas — a jungle landscape — paused a moment, his head cocked like a knowing terrier, and asked: "Where, my dear Charles, did you find this sumptuous greenery? The corner of a hot-house at T-t-trent or T-t-tring? What gorgeous usurer nurtured these fronds for your pleasure?"

Then he made a tour of the two rooms; once or twice he sighed deeply, otherwise he kept silence. When he came to the end he sighed once more, more deeply than ever, and said: "But they tell me, my dear, you are happy in love. That is everything, is it not, or nearly everything?"

"Are they as bad as that?"

Anthony dropped his voice to a piercing whisper: "My dear, let us not expose your little imposture before these good, plain people" — he gave a conspiratorial glance to the last remnants of the crowd — "let us not spoil their innocent pleasure. We know, you and I, that this is all t-t-terrible t-t-tripe. Let us go, before we offend the connoisseurs. I know of a *louche* little bar quite near here. Let us go there and talk of your other c-c-conquests."

It needed this voice from the past to recall me; the indiscriminate chatter of praise all that crowded day had worked on me like a succession of advertisement hoardings on a long road, kilometre after kilometre between the poplars, commanding one to stay at some new hotel, so that when at the end of the drive, stiff and dusty, one arrives at the destination, it seems inevitable to turn into the yard under the name that had first bored, then angered one, and finally become an inseparable part of one's fatigue.

Anthony led me from the gallery and down a side street to a door between a disreputable news agent and a disreputable chemist, painted with the words BLUE GROTTO CLUB. *Members Only.*

"Not quite your milieu, my dear, but mine, I assure you. After all, you have been in your milieu all day."

He led me downstairs, from a smell of cats to a smell of gin and cigarette-ends and the sound of a wireless.

"I was given the address by a dirty old man in the Boeuf sur le Toit. I am most grateful to him. I have been out of England so long, and really sympathetic little joints like this change so fast. I presented myself here for the first time yesterday evening, and already I feel *quite* at home. Good evening, Cyril."

" 'Lo, Toni, back again?" said the youth behind the bar.

"We will take our drinks and sit in a corner. You must remember, my dear, that *here* you are just as conspicuous and, may I say, abnormal, my dear, as I should be in B-b-bratt's."

The place was painted cobalt; there was cobalt linoleum on the floor. Fishes of silver and gold paper had been pasted haphazard on ceiling and walls. Half a dozen youths were drinking and playing with the slot-machines; an older, natty, crapulous-looking man seemed to be in control; there was some sniggering round the fruit-gum machine; then one of the youths came up to us and said, "Would your friend care to rumba?"

"No, Tom, he would *not,* and I'm not going to give a drink; not yet, anyway. . . . That's a very impudent boy, a regular little gold-digger, my dear."

"Well," I said, affecting an ease I was far from feeling in that den, "what have you been up to all these years?"

"My dear, it is what *you* have been up to that we are here to talk about. I've been watching you, my dear. I'm a faithful old body and I've kept my eye on you." As he spoke the bar and the bar-tender, the blue wicker furniture, the gambling-machines, the wireless, the couple of youths dancing on the oilcloth, the youths sniggering round the slots, the purple-veined, stiffly dressed elderly man drinking in the corner opposite us, the whole drab and furtive joint, seemed to fade, and I was back in Oxford looking out over Christ Church meadow through a window of Ruskin Gothic. "I went to your first exhibition," said Anthony; "I found it — charming. There was an interior of Marchmain House, very English, very correct, but quite delicious. 'Charles has done something,' I said; 'not all he will do, not all he can do, but something.'

"Even then, my dear, I wondered a little. It seemed to me that there was something a little *gentlemanly* about your painting. You must remember I am not English; I cannot understand this keen zest to be well-bred. English snobbery is more macabre to me even than English morals. However, I said, 'Charles has done something delicious. What will he do next?'

"The next thing I saw was your very handsome volume — *Village and Provincial Architecture*, was it called? Quite a tome, my dear, and what did I find? Charm again. 'Not quite my cup of tea,' I thought; 'this is too English.' I have the fancy for rather spicy things, you know, not for the shade of the cedar tree, the cucumber sandwich, the silver cream-jug, the English girl dressed in whatever English girls do wear for tennis — not that, not Jane Austen, *not* M-m-miss M-m-mitford. Then, to be frank, dear Charles, I despaired of you. 'I am a degenerate old d-d-dago,' I said, 'and Charles — I speak of your art, my dear — is a dean's daughter in flowered muslin.'

"Imagine then my excitement at luncheon to-day. Everyone was talking about you. My hostess was a friend of my mother's, a Mrs. Stuyvesant Oglander; a friend of yours, too, my dear. Such a frump! Not at all the society I imagined you to keep. However, they had all been to your exhibition, but it was *you* they talked of, how you had broken away, my dear, gone to the tropics, become a Gauguin, a Rimbaud. You can imagine how my old heart leaped.

" 'Poor Celia,' they said, 'after all she's done for him.' 'He owes everything to her. It's too bad.' 'And with Julia,' they said, 'after the way she behaved in America.' 'Just as she was going back to Rex.'

" 'But the pictures,' I said; 'tell me about *them*.'

" 'Oh, the pictures,' they said; 'they're most peculiar.' 'Not at all what he usually does.' 'Very forceful.' 'Quite barbaric.' 'I call them downright unhealthy,' said Mrs. Stuyvesant Oglander.

"My dear, I could hardly keep still in my chair. I wanted to dash out of the house and leap in a taxi and say, 'Take me to Charles's unhealthy pictures.' Well, I went, but the gallery after luncheon was so full of absurd women in the sort of hats they should be made to *eat*, that I rested a little — I rested here with Cyril and Tom and these saucy boys. Then I came back at the unfashionable time of five o'clock, all

agog, my dear; and what did I find? I found, my dear, a very naughty
and very successful practical joke. It reminded me of dear Sebastian
when he liked so much to dress up in false whiskers. It was charm
again, my dear, simple, creamy English charm, playing tigers."

"You're quite right," I said.

"My dear, of course I'm right. I was right years ago — more years,
I am happy to say, than either of us shows — when I *warned* you. I
took you out to dinner to warn you of charm. I warned you expressly
and in great detail of the Flyte family. Charm is the great English
blight. It does not exist outside these damp islands. It spots and kills
anything it touches. It kills love; it kills art; I greatly fear, my dear
Charles, it has killed *you*."

The youth called Tom approached us again. "Don't be a tease, Toni;
buy me a drink." I remembered my train and left Anthony with him.

As I stood on the platform by the restaurant-car I saw my luggage and
Julia's go past with Julia's sour-faced maid strutting beside the porter.
They had begun shutting the carriage-doors when Julia arrived, unhurried, and took her place in front of me. I had a table for two.
This was a very convenient train; there was half an hour before
dinner and half an hour after it; then, instead of changing to the
branch line, as had been the rule in Lady Marchmain's day, we were
met at the junction. It was night as we drew out of Paddington, and
the glow of the town gave place first to the scattered lights of the suburbs,
then to the darkness of the fields.

"It seems days since I saw you," I said.

"Six hours; and we were together all yesterday. You look worn out."

"It's been a day of nightmare — crowds, critics, the Clarences, a
luncheon party at Margot's, ending up with half an hour's well-reasoned
abuse of my pictures in a pansy bar. . . .I think Celia knows about us."

"Well, she had to know sometime."

"Everyone seems to know. My pansy friend had not been in London
twenty-four hours before he'd heard."

"Damn everybody."

"What about Rex?"

"Rex isn't anybody at all," said Julia; "he just doesn't exist."

The knives and forks jingled on the tables as we sped through the
darkness; the little circle of gin and vermouth in the glasses lengthened
to oval, contracted again, with the sway of the carriage, touched the lip,
lapped back again, never spilt; I was leaving the day behind me. Julia

pulled off her hat and tossed it into the rack above her, and shook her night-dark hair with a little sigh of ease — a sigh fit for the pillow, the sinking firelight and a bedrom window open to the stars and the whisper of bare trees.

"It's great to have you back, Charles; like the old days."
Like the old days? I thought.
Rex, in his early forties, had grown heavy and ruddy; he had lost his Canadian accent and acquired instead the hoarse, loud tone that was common to all his freinds, as though their voices were perpetually strained to make themselves heard above a crowd, as though, with youth forsaking them, there was no time to wait the opportunity to speak, no time to listen, no time to reply; time for a laugh — a throaty mirthless laugh, the base currency of goodwill.

There were half a dozen of these friends in the Tapestry Hall: politicians, "young conservatives" in the early forties, with sparse hair and high blood-pressure; a socialist from the coal mines who had already caught their clear accents, whose cigars came to pieces in his lips, whose hand shook when he poured himself out a drink; a lovesick columnist, who alone was silent, gloating sombrely on the only woman of the party; a financier older than the rest, and, one might guess from the way they treated him, richer; a woman they called "Grizel," a knowing rake whom, in their hearts, they all feared a little.

They all feared Julia, too, Grizel included. She greeted them and apologised for not being there to welcome them, with a formality which hushed them for a minute; then she came and sat with me near the fire, and the storm of talk arose once more and whirled about our ears.

"Of course, he can marry her and make her queen to-morrow."
"We had our chance in October. Why didn't we send the Italian fleet to the bottom of Mare Nostrum? Why didn't we blow Spezia to blazes. Why didn't we land on Pantelleria?"
"Franco's simply a German agent. They tried to put him in to prepare air bases to bomb France. That bluff has been called, anyway."
"It would make the monarchy stronger than it's been since Tudor times. The people are with him."
"The press are with him."
"I'm with him."
"Who cares about divorce now except a few old maids who aren't married, anyway?"

"If he has a showdown with the old gang, they'll just disappear like, like . . ."

"Why didn't we close the Canal? Why didn't we bomb Rome?"

"It wouldn't have been necessary. One firm note . . ."

"One firm speech."

"One showdown."

"Anyway, Franco will soon be skipping back to Morocco. Chap I saw to-day just come from Barcelona . . ."

". . . Chap just come from Fort Belvedere . . ."

". . . Chap just come from the Palazzo Venezia . . ."

"All we want is a showdown."

"A showdown with Baldwin."

"A showdown with Hitler."

"A showdown with the Old Gang."

". . . That I should live to see my country, the land of Clive and Nelson . . ."

". . . *My* country of Hawkins and Drake."

". . . *My* country of Palmerston . . ."

"Would you very much mind not doing that?" said Grizel to the columnist, who had been attempting in a maudlin manner to twist her wrist. "I don't happen to enjoy it."

"I wonder which is the more horrible," I said, "Celia's Art and Fashion or Rex's Politics and Money."

"Why worry about them?"

"Oh, my darling, why is it that love makes me hate the world? It's supposed to have quite the opposite effect. I feel as though all mankind, and God, too, were in a conspiracy against us."

"They are, they are."

"But we've got our happiness in spite of them; here and now, we've taken possession of it. They can't hurt us, can they?"

"Not to-night; not now."

"Not for how many nights?"

III

"Do you remember," said Julia, in the tranquil, lime-scented evening, "do you remember the storm?"

"The bronze doors banging."

"The roses in cellophane."

"The man who gave the 'get-together' party and was never seen again."

"Do you remember how the sun came out on our last evening just as it has done to-day?"

It had been an afternoon of low cloud and summer squalls, so overcast that at times I had stopped work and roused Julia from the light trance in which she sat — she had sat so often; I never tired of painting her, forever finding in her new wealth and delicacy — until at length we had gone early to our baths, and on coming down, dressed for dinner, in the last half-hour of the day, we found the world transformed; the sun had emerged; the wind had fallen to a soft breeze which gently stirred the blossom in the limes and carried its fragrance, fresh from the late rains, to merge with the sweet breath of box and the drying stone. The shadow of the obelisk spanned the terrace.

I had carried two garden cushions from the shelter of the colonnade and put them on the rim of the fountain. There Julia sat, in a tight little gold tunic and a white gown, one hand in the water idly turning an emerald ring to catch the fire of the sunset; the carved animals mounted over her dark head in a cumulus of green moss and glowing stone and dense shadow, and the waters round them flashed and bubbled and broke into scattered beads of flame.

". . . So much to remember," she said. "How many days have there been since then, when we haven't seen each other; a hundred, do you think?"

"Not so many."

"Two Christmases" — those bleak, annual excursions into propriety. Boughton, home of my family, home of my cousin Jasper, with what glum memories of childhood I revisited its pitch-pine corridors and dripping walls! How querulously my father and I, seated side by side in my uncle's Humber, approached the avenue of Wellingtonias knowing that at the end of the drive we should find my uncle, my aunt, my aunt Philippa, my cousin Jasper and, of recent years, Jasper's wife and children; and besides them, perhaps already arrived, perhaps every moment expected, my wife and my children. This annual sacrifice united us; here among the holly and mistletoe and the cut spruce, the parlour games ritually performed, the brandy-butter and the Carlsbad plums, the village choir in the pitch-pine minstrels' gallery, gold twine and sprigged wrapping-paper, she and I were accepted, whatever ugly rumours had been afloat in the past year, as man and wife. "We must keep it up, whatever it costs us, for the sake of the children," my wife said.

"Yes, two Christmases. . . . And the three days of good taste before I followed you to Capri."

"Our first summer."

"Do you remember how I hung about Naples, then followed, how we met by arrangement on the hill path and how flat it fell?"

"I went back to the villa and said, 'Papa, who do you think has arrived at the hotel?' and he said, 'Charles Ryder, I suppose.' I said, 'Why did you think of him?' and Papa replied, 'Cara came back from Paris with the news that you and he were inseparable. He seems to have a penchant for my children. However, bring him here. I think we have the room.'"

"There was the time you had jaundice and wouldn't let me see you."

"And when I had flu and you were afraid to come."

"Countless visits to Rex's constituency."

"And Coronation Week, when you ran away from London. Your goodwill mission to your father-in-law. The time you went to Oxford to paint the picture they didn't like. Oh, yes, quite a hundred days."

"A hundred days wasted out of two years and a bit . . . not a day when you were not in my heart; not a day's coldness or mistrust or disappointment."

"Never that."

We fell silent; only the birds spoke in a multitude of small, clear voices in the lime-trees; only the waters spoke among their carved stones.

Julia took the handkerchief from my breast pocket and dried her hand; then lit a cigarette. I feared to break the spell of memories, but for once our thoughts had not kept pace together, for when at length Julia spoke, she said sadly: "How many more? Another hundred?"

"A lifetime."

"I want to marry you, Charles."

"One day; why now?"

"War," she said, "this year, next year, sometime soon. I want a day or two with you of real peace."

"Isn't this peace?"

The sun had sunk now to the line of woodland beyond the valley; all the opposing slope was already in twilight, but the lakes below us were aflame; the light grew in strength and splendour as it neared death, spreading long shadows across the pasture, falling full on the rich stone spaces of the house, firing the panes in the windows, glowing on cornices and colonnade and dome, drawing out all the hidden sweetness of colour and scent from earth and stone and leaf, glorifying the head and golden shoulders of the woman beside me.

"What do you mean by 'peace'; if not this?"

"So much more"; and then in a chill, matter-of-fact tone she continued: "Marriage isn't a thing we can take when the impulse moves us. There must be a divorce — two divorces. We must make plans."

"Plans, divorce, war— on an evening like this."

"Sometimes," said Julia, "I feel the past and the future pressing so hard on either side that there's no room for the present at all."

Then Wilcox came down the steps into the sunset to tell us that dinner was ready.

Shutters were up, curtains drawn, candles lit, in the Painted Parlour.

"Hullo, it's laid for three."

"Lord Brideshead arrived half an hour ago, my lady. He sent a message would you please not wait dinner for him as he may be a little late."

"It seems months since he was here last," said Julia. "What *does* he do in London?"

It was often a matter for speculation between us — giving birth to many fantasies, for Bridey was a mystery; a creature from under ground; a hard-snouted, burrowing, hibernating animal who shunned the light. He had been completely without action in all his years of adult life; the talk of his going into the army, and into Parliament, and into a monastery, had all come to nothing. All that he was known with certainty to have done — and this because in a season of scant news it had formed the subject of a newspaper article entitled PEER's UNUSUAL HOBBY — was to form a collection of match-boxes; he kept them mounted on boards, card-indexed, yearly occupying a larger and larger space in his small house in Westminster. At first he was bashful about the notoriety which the newspaper caused, but later greatly pleased, for he found it the means of getting into touch with other collectors in all parts of the world with whom he now corresponded and swapped duplicates. Other than this he was not known to have any interests. He remained Joint-Master of the Marchmain and hunted with them dutifully on their two days a week when he was at home; he never hunted with the neighbouring pack, who had the better country. He had no real zest for sport, and had not been out a dozen times that season; he had few friends; he visited his aunts; he went to public dinners held in the Catholic interest. At Brideshead he performed all unavoidable local duties, bringing with him to platform and fête and committee room his own thin mist of clumsiness and aloofness.

"There was a girl found strangled with a piece of barbed wire at Wandsworth last week," I said, reviving an old fantasy.

"That must be Bridey. He is naughty."

When we had been a quarter of an hour at the table he joined us, coming ponderously into the room in the bottle-green velvet smoking suit which he kept at Brideshead and always wore when he was there. At thirty-eight he had grown heavy and bald, and might have been taken for forty-five.

"Well," he said, "well, only you two; I hoped to find Rex here."

I often wondered what he made of me and of my continual presence; he seemed to accept me, without curiosity, as one of the household. Twice in the past two years he had surprised me by what seemed to be acts of friendship; last Christmas he sent me a photograph of himself in the robes of a Knight of Malta, and shortly afterwards he asked me to go with him to a dining club. Both acts had an explanation: he had had more copies of his portrait printed than he knew what to do with; he was proud of his club. It was a surprising association of men quite eminent in their professions who met once a month for an evening of ceremonious buffoonery; each had his sobriquet — Bridey was called "Brother Grandee" — and a specially designed jewel worn like an order of chivalry, symbolizing it; they had club buttons for their waistcoats and an elaborate ritual for the introduction of guests; after dinner a paper was read and facetious speeches made. There was plainly some competition to bring guests of distinction, and since Bridey had few friends, and since I was tolerably well-known, I was invited. Even on that convivial evening I could feel my host emanating little magnetic waves of social uneasiness, creating, rather, a pool of general embarrassment about himself in which he floated with log-like calm.

He sat down opposite me and bowed his sparse, pink head over his plate.

"Well, Bridey. What's the news?"

"As a matter of fact," he said, "I have some news. But it can wait."

"Tell us now."

He made a grimace which I took to mean "not in front of the servants," and said, "How is the painting, Charles?"

"Which painting?"

"Whatever you have on the stocks."

"I began a sketch of Julia, but the light was tricky all to-day."

"Julia? I thought you'd done her before. I suppose it's a change from architecture, and much more difficult."

His conversation abounded in long pauses during which his mind seemed to remain motionless; he always brought one back with a start to the exact point where he had stopped. Now after more than a minute he said: "The world is full of different subjects."

"Very true, Bridey."

"If I were a painter," he said, "I should choose an entirely different subject every time; subjects with plenty of action in them like . . ." Another pause. What, I wondered, was coming? "The *Flying Scotsman*"? "The Charge of the Light Brigade"? "Henley Regatta"? Then surprisingly he said: ". . . like 'Macbeth.'" There was something supremely preposterous in the idea of Bridey as a painter of action pictures; he was usually preposterous yet seldom quite absurd. He achieved dignity by his remoteness and agelessness; he was still half-child, already half-veteran; there seemed no spark of contemporary life in him; he had a kind of massive rectitude and impermeability, an indifference to the world, which compelled respect. Though we often laughed at him, he was never wholly ridiculous; at times he was even formidable.

We talked of the news from Central Europe until, suddenly cutting across this barren topic, Bridey asked: "Where are Mummy's jewels?"

"This was hers," said Julia, "and this. Cordelia and I had all her own things. The family jewels went to the bank."

"It's so long since I've seen them — I don't know that I ever saw them all. What is there? Aren't there some rather famous rubies, someone was telling me?"

"Yes, a necklace. Mummy used often to wear it, don't you remember? And there are the pearls — she always had those out. But most of it stayed in the bank year after year. There are some hideous diamond fenders, I remember, and a Victorian diamond collar no one could wear now. There's a mass of good stones. Why?"

"I'd like to have a look at them some day."

"I say, Papa isn't going to pop them, is he? He hasn't got into debt again?"

"No, no, nothing like that."

Bridey was a slow and copious eater. Julia and I watched him between the candles. Presently he said: "If I was Rex . . ." His mind seemed full of such suppositions: "If I was Archbishop of Westminster," "If I was head of the Great Western Railway," "If I was an actress" — as though it were a mere trick of fate that he was none of these things, and he might awake any morning to find the matter adjusted. "If I was Rex I should want to live in my constituency."

"Rex says it saves four days' work a week not to."

"I'm sorry he's not here. I have a little announcement to make."

"Bridey, don't be so mysterious. Out with it."

He made the grimace which seemed to mean "not before the servants."

Later, when port was on the table and we three were alone, Julia said: "I'm not going till I hear the announcement."

"Well," said Bridey sitting back in his chair and gazing fixedly at his glass. "You have only to wait until Monday to see it in black and white in the newspapers. I am engaged to be married. I hope you are pleased."

"Bridey. How . . . how very exciting! Who to?"

"Oh, no one you know."

"Is she pretty?"

"I don't think you would exactly call her pretty; 'comely' is the word I think of in her connection. She is a big woman."

"Fat?"

"No, big. She is called Mrs. Muspratt; her Christian name is Beryl. I have known her for a long time, but until last year she had a husband; now she is a widow. Why do you laugh?"

"I'm sorry. It isn't the least funny. It's just so unexpected. Is she . . . is she about your own age?"

"Just about, I believe. She has three children, the eldest boy has just gone to Ampleforth. She is not at all well off."

"But Bridey, where did you find her?"

"Her late husband, Admiral Muspratt, collected match-boxes," he said with complete gravity.

Julia trembled on the verge of laughter, recovered her self-possession and asked: "You're not marrying her for her match-boxes?"

"No, no; the whole collection was left to the Falmouth Town Library.

I have a great affection for her. In spite of all her difficulties she is a very cheerful woman, very fond of acting. She is connected with the Catholic Players' Guild."

"Does Papa know?"

"I had a letter from him this morning giving me his approval. He has been urging me to marry for some time."

It occurred to both Julia and myself simultaneously that we were allowing curiosity and surprise to predominate; now we congratulated him in gentler tones from which mockery was almost excluded.

"Thank you," he said, "thank you. I think I am very fortunate."

"But when are we going to meet her? I do think you might have brought her down with you."

He said nothing, sipped and gazed.

"Bridey," said Julia. "You sly, smug old brute, why haven't you brought her here?"

"Oh I couldn't do that, you know."

"Why couldn't you? I'm dying to meet her. Let's ring her up now and invite her. She'll think us most peculiar leaving her alone at a time like this."

"She has the children," said Brideshead. "Besides, you *are* peculiar, aren't you?"

"What can you mean?"

Brideshead raised his head and looked solemnly at his sister, and continued in the same simple way, as though he were saying nothing particularly different from what had gone before, "I couldn't ask her here, as things are. It wouldn't be suitable. After all, I am a lodger here. This is Rex's house at the moment, as far as it's anybody's. What goes on here is his business. But I couldn't bring Beryl here."

"I simply don't understand," said Julia rather sharply. I looked at her. All the gentle mockery had gone; she was alert, almost scared, it seemed. "Of course, Rex and I want her to come."

"Oh yes, I don't doubt that. The difficulty is quite otherwise." He finished his port, refilled his glass, and pushed the decanter towards me. "You must understand that Beryl is a woman of strict Catholic principle fortified by the prejudices of the middle class. I couldn't possibly bring her here. It is a matter of indifference whether you choose to live in sin with Rex or Charles or both — I have always avoided enquiry into the details of your ménage — but in no case would Beryl consent to be your guest."

Julia rose. "Why, you pompous ass . . ." she said, stopped, and turned towards the door.

At first I thought she was overcome by laughter; then, as I opened the door to her, I saw with consternation that she was in tears. I hesitated. She slipped past me without a glance.

"I may have given the impression that this was a marriage of convenience," Brideshead continued placidly. "I cannot speak for Beryl; no doubt the security of my position has some influence on her. Indeed, she has said as much. But for myself, let me emphasise, I am ardently attracted."

"Bridey, what a bloody offensive thing to say to Julia!"

"There was nothing she should object to. I was merely stating a fact well known to her."

She was not in the library; I mounted to her room, but she was not there. I paused by her laden dressing-table wondering if she would come. Then through the open window, as the light streamed out across the terrace, into the dusk, to the fountain which in that house seemed always to draw us to itself for comfort and refreshment, I caught the glimpse of a white skirt against the stones. It was nearly night. I found her in the darkest refuge, on a wooden seat, in a bay of the clipped box which encircled the basin. I took her in my arms and she pressed her face to my heart.

"Aren't you cold out here?"

She did not answer, only clung closer to me and shook with sobs.

"My darling, what is it? Why do you mind? What does it matter what that old booby says?"

"I don't; it doesn't. It's just the shock. Don't laugh at me."

In the two years of our love, which seemed a lifetime, I had not seen her so moved or felt so powerless to help.

"How dare he speak to you like that?" I said. "The cold-blooded old humbug . . ." But I was failing her in sympathy.

"No," she said, "it's not that. He's quite right. They know all about it, Bridey and his widow; they've got it in black and white; they bought it for a penny at the church door. You can get anything there for a penny, in black and white, and nobody to see that you pay; only an old woman with a broom at the other end, rattling round the confessionals, and a young woman lighting a candle at the Seven

Dolours. Put a penny in the box, or not, just as you like; take your tract. There you've got it, in black and white.

"All in one word, too, one little, flat, deadly word that covers a lifetime.

" 'Living in sin'; not just doing wrong, as I did when I went to America; doing wrong, knowing it's wrong, stopping doing it, forgetting. That's not what they mean. That's not Bridey's pennyworth. He means just what it says in black and white.

"*Living in sin*, with sin, by sin, for sin, every hour, every day, year in, year out. Waking up with sin in the morning, seeing the curtains drawn on sin, bathing it, dressing it, clipping diamonds to it, feeding it, showing it round, giving it a good time, putting it to sleep at night with a tablet of Dial if it's fretful.

"Always the same, like an idiot child carefully nursed, guarded from the world. 'Poor Julia,' they say, 'she can't go out. She's got to take care of her little sin. A pity it ever lived,' they say, 'but it's so strong. Children like that always are. Julia's so good to her little, mad sin.' "

An hour ago, I thought, under the sunset, she sat turning her ring in the water and counting the days of happiness; now under the first stars and the last grey whisper of day, all this mysterious tumult of sorrow! What had happened to us in the Painted Parlour? What shadow had fallen in the candlelight? Two rough sentences and a trite phrase. She was beside herself; her voice, now muffled in my breast, now clear and anguished, came to me in single words and broken sentences, which may be strung together thus:

"Past and future; the years when I was trying to be a good wife, in the cigar smoke, while time crept on and the counters clicked on the backgammon board, and the man who was 'dummy' at the men's table filled the glasses; when I was trying to bear his child, torn in pieces by something already dead; putting him away, forgetting him, finding you, the past two years with you, all the future with you, all the future with or without you, war coming, world ending — sin.

"A word from so long ago, from Nanny Hawkins stitching by the hearth and the nightlight burning before the Sacred Heart. Cordelia and me with the catechism, in Mummy's room, before luncheon on Sundays. Mummy carrying my sin with her to church, bowed under it and the black lace veil, in the chapel; slipping out with it in London before the fires were lit; taking it with her through the empty streets where the milkman's ponies stood with their forefeet on the pavement;

Mummy dying with my sin eating at her, more cruelly than her own deadly illness.

"Mummy dying with it; Christ dying with it, nailed hand and foot; hanging over the bed in the night-nursery; hanging year after year in the dark little study at Farm Street with the shining oilcloth; hanging in the dark church where only the old charwoman raises the dust and one candle burns; hanging at noon, high among the crowds and the soldiers; no comfort except a sponge of vinegar and the kind words of a thief; hanging for ever; never the cool sepulchre and the grave clothes spread on the stone slab, never the oil and spices in the dark cave; always the midday sun and the dice clicking for the seamless coat.

"Never the shelter of the cave or of the castle walls. Outcast in the desolate spaces where the hyenas roam at night and the rubbish heaps smoke in the daylight. No way back; the gates barred; all the saints and angels posted along the walls. Nothing but bare stone and dust and the smouldering dumps. Thrown away, scrapped, rotting down; the old man with lupus and the forked stick who limps out at nightfall to turn the rubbish, hoping for something to put in his sack, something marketable, turns away with disgust.

"Nameless and dead, like the baby they wrapped up and took away before I had seen her."

Between her tears she talked herself into silence. I could do nothing; I was adrift in a strange sea; my hands on the metal-spun threads of her tunic were cold and stiff, my eyes dry; I was as far from her in spirit, as she clung to me in the darkness, as when years ago I had lit her cigarette on the way from the station; as far as when she was out of mind, in the dry, empty years at the Old Rectory and in the jungle.

Tears spring from speech; presently in the silence her weeping stopped. She sat up, away from me, took my handkerchief, shivered, rose to her feet.

"Well," she said, in a voice much like normal. "Bridey is one for bombshells, isn't he?"

I followed her into the house and to her room; she sat at her looking-glass. "Considering that I've just recovered from a fit of hysteria," she said, "I don't call that at all bad." Her eyes seemed unnaturally large and bright, her cheeks pale with two spots of high colour, where, as a girl, she used to put a dab of rouge. "Most hysterical women look as if they had a bad cold. You'd better change your shirt before going down; it's all tears and lipstick."

"Are we going down?"

"Of course, we mustn't leave poor Bridey on his engagement night."

When I came back to her she said: "I'm sorry for that appalling scene, Charles. I can't explain."

Brideshead was in the library, smoking his pipe, placidly reading a detective story.

"Was it nice out? If I'd known you were going I'd have come, too."

"Rather cold."

"I hope it's not going to be inconvenient for Rex moving out of here. You see, Barton Street is much too small for us and the three children. Besides, Beryl likes the country. In his letter Papa proposed making over the whole estate right away."

I remembered how Rex had greeted me on my first arrival at Brideshead as Julia's guest. "A very happy arrangement," he had said. "Suits me down to the ground. The old boy keeps the place up; Bridey does all the feudal stuff with the tenants; I have the run of the house rent-free. All it costs me is the food and the wages of the indoor servants. Couldn't ask fairer than that, could you?"

"I should think he'll be sorry to go," I said.

"Oh, he'll find another bargain somewhere," said Julia; "trust him."

"Beryl's got some furniture of her own she's very attached to. I don't know that it would go very well here. You know, oak dressers and coffin stools and things. I thought she could put it in Mummy's old room."

"Yes, that would be the place."

So brother and sister sat and talked about the arrangement of the house until bed-time. An hour ago, I thought, in the black refuge in the box hedge, she wept her heart out for the death of her God; now she is discussing whether Beryl's children shall take the old smoking-room or the schoolroom for their own. I was all at sea.

"Julia," I said later, when Brideshead had gone upstairs, "have you ever seen a picture of Holman Hunt's called 'The Awakened Conscience'?"

"No."

I had seen a copy of *Pre-Raphaelitism* in the library some days before; I found it again and read her Ruskin's description. She laughed quite happily.

"You're perfectly right. That's exactly what I did feel."

"But, darling, I can't believe that all that tempest of emotion came just from a few words of Bridey's. You must have been thinking about it before."

"Hardly at all; now and then; more, lately, with the Last Trump so near."

"Of course it's a thing psychologists could explain; a pre-conditioning from childhood; feelings of guilt from the nonsense you were taught in the nursery. You do know at heart that it's all bosh, don't you?"

"How I wish it was!"

"Sebastian once said almost the same thing to me."

"He's gone back to the Church, you know. Of course, he never left it as definitely as I did. I've gone too far; there's no turning back now; I know that, if that's what you mean by thinking it all bosh. All I can hope to do **is to** put my life in some sort of order in a human way, before all human order comes to an end. That's why I want to marry you. I should like to have a child. That's one thing I can do. . . . Let's go out again. The moon should be up by now."

The moon was full and high. We walked round the house; under the limes Julia paused and idly snapped off one of the long shoots, last year's growth, that fringed their boles, and stripped it as she walked, making a switch, as children do, but with petulant movements that were not a child's, snatching nervously at the leaves and crumpling them between her fingers; she began peeling the bark, scratching it with her nails.

Once more we stood by the fountain.

"It's like the setting of a comedy," I said. "Scene: a baroque fountain in a nobleman's grounds. Act One, Sunset; Act Two, Dusk; Act Three, Moonlight. The characters keep assembling at the fountain for no very clear reason."

"Comedy?"

"Drama. Tragedy. Farce. What you will. This is the reconciliation scene."

"Was there a quarrel?"

"Estrangement and misunderstanding in Act Two."

"Oh, don't talk in that damned bounderish way. Why must you see everything secondhand? Why must this be a play? Why must my conscience be a Pre-Raphaelite picture?"

"It's a way I have."

"I hate it."

Her anger was as unexpected as every change on this evening of swift veering moods. Suddenly she cut me across the face with her switch, a vicious, stinging little blow as hard as she could strike.

"Now do you see how I hate it?"

She hit me again.

"All right," I said, "go on."

Then, though her hand was raised, she stopped and threw the half-peeled wand into the water, where it floated white and black in the moonlight.

"Did that hurt?"

"Yes."

"Did it? . . . Did I?"

In the instant her rage was gone; her tears, newly flowing, were on my cheek. I held her at arm's length and she put down her head, stroking my hand on her shoulder with her face, cat-like, but, unlike a cat, leaving a tear there.

"Cat on the roof-top," I said.

"Beast!"

She bit at my hand, but when I did not move it and her teeth touched me, she changed the bite to a kiss, the kiss to a lick of her tongue.

"Cat in the moonlight."

This was the mood I knew. We turned towards the house. When we came to the lighted hall she said: "Your poor face," touching the weals with her fingers. "Will there be a mark to-morrow?"

"I expect so."

"Charles, am I going crazy? What's happened to-night? I'm so tired."

She yawned; a fit of yawning took her. She sat at her dressing-table, head bowed, hair over her face, yawning helplessly; when she looked up I saw over her shoulder in the glass a face that was dazed with weariness like a retreating soldier's, and beside it my own, streaked with two crimson lines.

"So tired," she repeated, taking off her gold tunic and letting it fall to the floor, "tired and crazy and good for nothing."

I saw her to bed; the blue lids fell over her eyes; her pale lips moved on the pillow, but whether to wish me good-night or to murmur a prayer — a jingle of the nursery that came to her now in the twilit world between sorrow and sleep; some ancient pious rhyme that had come down to Nanny Hawkins from centuries of bedtime whispering, through all the changes of language, from the days of pack-horses on the Pilgrim's Way — I did not know.

Next night Rex and his political associates were with us.

"They won't fight."

"They can't fight. They haven't the money; they haven't the oil."

"They haven't the wolfram; they haven't the men."

"They haven't the guts."

"They're afraid."

"Scared of the French; scared of the Czechs; scared of the Slovaks; scared of us."

"It's a bluff."

"Of course it's a bluff. Where's their tungsten? Where's their manganese?"

"Where's their chrome?"

"I'll tell you a thing . . ."

"Listen to this; it'll be good; Rex will tell you a thing."

". . . Friend of mine motoring in the Black Forest, only the other day, just came back and told me about it while we played a round of golf. Well, this friend driving along, turned down a lane into the high road. What should he find but a military convoy? Couldn't stop, drove right into it, smack into a tank, broadside-on. Gave himself up for dead. . . . Hold on, this is the funny part."

"This is the funny part."

"Drove clean through it, didn't scratch his paint. What do you think? It was made of canvas — a bamboo frame and painted canvas."

"They haven't the steel."

"They haven't the tools. They haven't the labour. They're half starving. They haven't the fats. The children have rickets."

"The women are barren."

"The men are impotent."

"They haven't the doctors."

"The doctors were Jewish."

"Now they've got consumption."

"Now they've got syphilis."

"Goering told a friend of mine . . ."

"Goebbels told a friend of mine . . ."

"Ribbentrop told me that the army just kept Hitler in power so long as he was able to get things for nothing. The moment anyone stands up to him, he's finished. The army will shoot him."

"The liberals will hang him."

"The Communists will tear him limb from limb."

"He'll scupper himself."

"He'd do it now if it wasn't for Chamberlain."

"If it wasn't for Halifax."

"If it wasn't for Sir Samuel Hoare."

"And the 1920 Committee."

"Peace Pledge."

"Foreign Office."

"New York banks."

"All that's wanted is a good strong line."

"A line from Rex."

"And a line from me."

"We'll give Europe a good strong line. Europe is waiting for a speech from Rex."

"And a speech from me."

"And a speech from me. Rally the freedom-loving peoples of the world. Germany will rise; Austria will rise. The Czechs and the Slovaks are bound to rise."

"To a speech from Rex and a speech from me."

"What about a rubber? How about a whisky? Which of you chaps will have a big cigar? Hullo, you two going out?"

"Yes, Rex," said Julia. "Charles and I are going into the moonlight."

We shut the windows behind us and the voices ceased; the moonlight lay like hoar-frost on the terrace and the music of the fountain crept in our ears; the stone balustrade of the terrace might have been the Trojan walls, and in the silent park might have stood the Grecian tents where Cressid lay that night.

"A few days, a few months."

"No time to be lost."

"A lifetime between the rising of the moon and its setting. Then the dark."

IV

"AND of course Celia will have custody of the children."

"Of course."

"Then what about the Old Rectory? I don't imagine you'll want to settle down with Julia bang at our gates. The children look on it as their home, you know. Robin's got no place of his own till his uncle dies. After all, you never used the studio, did you? Robin was saying only the other day what a good playroom it would make — big enough for badminton."

"Robin can have the Old Rectory."

"Now with regard to money, Celia and Robin naturally don't want to accept anything for themselves, but there's the question of the children's education."

"That will be all right. I'll see the lawyers about it."

"Well, I think that's everything," said Mulcaster. "You know, I've seen a few divorces in my time, and I've never known one work out so happily for all concerned. Almost always, however matey people are at the start, bad blood crops up when they get down to detail. Mind you, I don't mind saying there have been times in the last two years when I thought you were treating Celia a bit rough. It's hard to tell with one's own sister, but I've always thought her a jolly attractive girl, the sort of girl any chap would be glad to have — artistic, too, just down your street. But I must admit you're a good picker. I've always had a soft spot for Julia. Anyway, as things have turned out everyone seems satisfied. Robin's been mad about Celia for a year or more. D'you know him?"

"Vaguely. A half-baked, pimply youth as I remember him."

"Oh, I wouldn't quite say that. He's rather young, of course, but the great thing is that Johnjohn and Caroline adore him. You've got two grand kids there, Charles. Remember me to Julia; wish her all the best for old time's sake."

"So you're being divorced," said my father. "Isn't that rather unnecessary, after you've been happy together all these years?"

"We weren't particularly happy, you know."

"Weren't you? Were you not? I distinctly remember last Christmas seeing you together and thinking how happy you looked, and wondering why. You'll find it very disturbing, you know, starting off again. How old are you — thirty-four? That's no age to be starting. You ought to be settling down. Have you made any plans?"

"Yes. I'm marrying again as soon as the divorce is through."

"Well, I do call that a lot of nonsense. I can understand a man wishing he hadn't married and trying to get out of it — though I never felt anything of the kind myself — but to get rid of one wife and take up with another immediately is beyond all reason. Celia was always perfectly civil to me. I had quite a liking for her, in a way. If you couldn't be happy with her, why on earth should you expect to be happy with anyone else? Take my advice, my boy, and give up the whole idea."

"Why bring Julia and me into this?" asked Rex. "If Celia wants to marry again, well and good; let her. That's your business and hers. But I should have thought Julia and I were quite happy as we are. You can't say I've been difficult. Lots of chaps would have cut up nasty. I hope I'm a man of the world. I've had my own fish to fry, too. But a divorce is a different thing altogether; I've never known a divorce do anyone any good."

"That's your affair and Julia's."

"Oh, Julia's set on it. What I hoped was, you might be able to talk her round. I've tried to keep out of the way as much as I could; if I've been around too much, just tell me, I shan't mind. But there's too much going on altogether at the moment, what with Bridey wanting me to clear out of the house; it's disturbing, and I've got a lot on my mind."

Rex's public life was approaching a climacteric. Things had not gone as smoothly with him as he had planned. I knew nothing of finance, but I heard it said that his dealings were badly looked on by orthodox conservatives; even his good qualities of geniality and impetuosity counted against him, for his parties at Brideshead got talked about. There was always too much about him in the papers; he was one with the press lords and their sad-eyed, smiling hangers-on; in his speeches he said the sort of thing which "made a story" in Fleet Street, and that did him no good with his party chiefs; only war could put Rex's fortunes right and carry him into power. A divorce would do him no harm with these cronies; it was rather that with a big bank running he could not look up from the table.

"If Julia insists on a divorce, I suppose she must have it," he said. "But she couldn't have chosen a worse time. Tell her to hang on a bit, Charles, there's a good fellow."

"Bridey's widow said: 'So you're divorcing one divorced man and marrying another. It sounds rather complicated, but my dear' — she called me 'my dear' about twenty times — 'I've usually found every Catholic family has one lapsed member, and it's often the nicest.' "

Julia had just returned from a luncheon party given by Lady Rosscommon in honour of Brideshead's engagement.

"What's she like?"

"Majestic and voluptuous; common, of course; might be Irish or Jewish or both; husky voice, big mouth, small eyes, dyed hair — I'll tell you one thing, she's lied to Bridey about her age. She's a good forty-five. I don't see her providing an heir. Bridey can't take his eyes off her. He was gloating on her in the most revolting way all through luncheon."

"Friendly?"

"Goodness, yes, in a condescending way. You see, I imagine she's been used to bossing things rather in naval circles, with flag-lieutenants trotting round and young officers-on-the-make sucking up to her. Well, she clearly couldn't do a great deal of bossing at Aunt Fanny's, so it put her rather at ease to have me there as the black sheep. She concentrated on me, in fact; asked my advice about shops and things; said, rather pointedly, she hoped to see me often *in London*. I think Bridey's scruples only extend to her sleeping under the same roof with me. Apparently I can do her no serious harm in a hat-shop or hairdresser's or lunching at the Ritz. The scruples are all on Bridey's part, anyway; the widow is madly tough."

"Does she boss him?"

"Not yet, much. He's in an amorous stupor, poor beast, and doesn't quite know where he is. She's just a good-hearted woman who wants a good home for her children and isn't going to let anything get in her way. She's playing up the religious stuff at the moment for all it's worth. I daresay she'll ease up a bit when she's settled."

The divorces were much talked of among our friends; even in that summer of general alarm there were still corners where private affairs commanded first attention. My wife was able to put it across that the business was a matter of congratulation for her and reproach for me; that she had behaved wonderfully, had stood it longer than anyone but she would have done; Robin was seven years younger and a little immature for his age, they whispered in their private corners, but he was absolutely devoted to poor Celia, and really she deserved it after all she had been through. As for Julia and me, that was an old story. "To put it crudely," said my cousin Jasper, as though he had ever in his life put anything otherwise: "I don't see why you bother to marry."

Summer passed; delirious crowds cheered Neville Chamberlain's return from Munich; Rex made a rabid speech in the House of Com-

mons which sealed his fate one way or the other; sealed it, as is sometimes done with naval orders, to be opened later at sea. Julia's family
lawyers, whose black, tin boxes, painted MARQUIS OF MARCHMAIN,
seemed to fill a room, began the slow process of her divorce; my own,
brisker firm, two doors down, were weeks ahead with my affairs. It was
necessary for Rex and Julia to separate formally, and since, for the time
being, Brideshead was still her home, she remained there and Rex
removed his trunks and valet to their house in London. Evidence was
taken against Julia and me in my flat. A date was fixed for Brideshead's
wedding, early in the Christmas holidays, so that his future step-
children might take part.

One afternoon in November Julia and I stood at a window in the
drawing-room watching the wind at work stripping the lime-trees,
sweeping down the yellow leaves, sweeping them up and round and
along the terrace and lawns, trailing them through puddles and over the
wet grass, pasting them on walls and window-panes, leaving them at
length in sodden piles against the stonework.

"We shan't see them in spring," said Julia; "perhaps never again."

"Once before," I said, "I went away, thinking I should never return."

"Perhaps years later, to what's left of it, with what's left of us . . ."

A door opened and shut in the darkling room behind us. Wilcox
approached through the firelight into the dusk about the long windows.

"A telephone message, my lady, from Lady Cordelia."

"Lady Cordelia! Where was she?"

"In London, my lady."

"Wilcox, how lovely! Is she coming home?"

"She was just starting for the station. She will be here after dinner."

"I haven't seen her for twelve years," I said — not since the evening
when we dined together and she spoke of being a nun; the evening
when I painted the drawing-room at Marchmain House. "She was an
enchanting child."

"She's had an odd life. First, the convent; then, when that was no
good, the war in Spain. I've not seen her since then. The other girls
who went with the ambulance came back to their homes, helping in the
prison camps. An odd girl. She's grown up quite plain, you know."

"Does she know about us?"

"Yes, she wrote me a sweet letter."

It hurt to think of Cordelia growing up quite plain; to think of all
that burning love spending itself on serum injections and delousing

powder. When she arrived, tired from her journey, rather shabby, moving in the manner of one who has no interest in pleasing, I thought her an ugly woman. It was odd, I thought, how the same ingredients, differently dispensed, could produce Brideshead, Sebastian, Julia and her. She was unmistakably their sister, without any of Julia's or Sebastian's grace, without Brideshead's gravity. She seemed brisk and matter-of-fact, steeped in the atmosphere of camp and dressing station, so accustomed to gross suffering as to lose the finer shades of pleasure. She looked more than her twenty-six years; hard living had roughened her; constant intercourse in a foreign tongue had worn away the nuances of speech; she straddled a little as she sat by the fire, and when she said, "It's wonderful to be home," it sounded to my ears like the grunt of an animal returning to its basket.

Those were the impressions of the first half-hour, sharpened by the contrast with Julia's white skin and silk and jewelled hair and with my memories of her as a child.

"My job's over in Spain," she said; "the authorities were very polite, thanked me for all I'd done, gave me a medal and sent me packing. It looks as though there'll be plenty of the same sort of work over here soon."

Then she said: "Is it too late to see Nanny?"

"No, she sits up to all hours with her wireless." We went up, all three together, to the old nursery. Julia and I always spent part of our day there. Nanny Hawkins and my father were two people who seemed impervious to change; neither an hour older than when I first knew them. A wireless set had now been added to Nanny Hawkins's small assembly of pleasures — the rosary, the *Peerage* with its neat brown-paper wrapping protecting the red and gold covers, the photographs and holiday souvenirs — on her table. When we broke it to her that Julia and I were to be married, she said, "Well, dear, I hope it's all for the best," for it was not part of her religion to question the propriety of Julia's actions.

Brideshead had never been a favourite with her; she greeted the news of his engagement with "He's certainly taken long enough to make up his mind," and, when the search through Debrett afforded no information about Mrs. Muspratt's connections: "She's caught him, I daresay."

We found her, as always in the evening, at the fireside with her teapot, and the wool rug she was making.

"I knew you'd be up," she said. "Mr. Wilcox sent to tell me you were coming."

"I brought you some lace."

"Well, dear, that is nice. Just like her poor Ladyship used to wear at mass. Though why they made it black I never did understand, seeing lace is white naturally. That is very welcome, I'm sure."

"May I turn off the wireless, Nanny?"

"Why, of course; I didn't notice it was still on, in the pleasure of seeing you. What have you done to your hair?"

"I know it's terrible. I must get all that put right now I'm back. Darling Nanny."

As we sat there talking, and I saw Cordelia's fond eyes on all of us, I began to realize that she, too, had a beauty of her own.

"I saw Sebastian last month."

"What a time he's been gone! Was he quite well?"

"Not very. That's why I went. It's quite near you know from Spain to Tunis. He's with the monks there."

"I hope they look after him properly. I expect they find him a regular handful. He always sends to me at Christmas, but it's not the same as having him home. Why you must all always be going abroad I never did understand. Just like his Lordship. When there was that talk about going to war with Munich, I said to myself, there's Cordelia and Sebastian and his Lordship all abroad; that'll be very awkward for them."

"I wanted him to come home with me, but he wouldn't. He's got a beard now, you know, and he's very religious."

"That I won't believe, not even if I see it. He was always a little heathen. Brideshead was one for church, not Sebastian. And a beard, only fancy; such a nice fair skin as he had; always looked clean though he'd not been near water all day, while Brideshead there was no doing anything with scrub as you might."

"It's frightening," Julia once said, "to think how completely you have forgotten Sebastian."

"He was the forerunner."

"That's what you said in the storm. I've thought since: perhaps I am only a forerunner, too."

Perhaps, I thought, while her words still hung in the air between us like a wisp of tobacco smoke — a thought to fade and vanish like smoke without a trace — perhaps all our loves are merely hints and symbols; a hill of many invisible crests; doors that open as in a dream to reveal only a further stretch of carpet and another door; perhaps you and I are types and this sadness which sometimes falls between us springs from disappointment in our search, each straining through and beyond the other, snatching a glimpse now and then of the shadow which turns the corner always a pace or two ahead of us.

I had not forgotten Sebastian. He was with me daily in Julia; or rather it was Julia I had known in him, in those distant, Arcadian days.

"That's cold comfort for a girl," she said when I tried to explain. "How do I know I shan't suddenly turn out to be somebody else? It's an easy way to chuck."

I had not forgotten Sebastian; every stone of the house had a memory of him, and when I heard him spoken of by Cordelia as someone she had seen a month ago, my lost friend filled my thoughts. When we left the nursery, I said, "I want to hear all about Sebastian."

"To-morrow. It's a long story."

And next day, walking through the wind-swept park, she told me:

"I heard he was dying," she said. "A journalist in Burgos told me, who'd just arrived from North Africa. A down-and-out called Flyte, who people said was an English lord, whom the fathers had found starving and taken in at a monastery near Carthage. That was how the story reached me. I knew it couldn't be quite true — however little we did for Sebastian, he at least got his money sent him — but I started off at once.

"It was all quite easy. I went to the consulate first and they knew all about him; he was in the infirmary of the head house of some missionary fathers. The consul's story was that Sebastian had turned up in Tunis one day, some weeks before, in a motor bus from Algiers, and had applied to be taken on as a missionary lay brother. The fathers took one look at him and turned him down. Then he started drinking. He lived in a little hotel on the edge of the Arab quarter. I went to see the place later; it was a bar with a few rooms over it, kept by a Greek, smelling of hot oil and garlic and stale wine and old clothes, a place where the small Greek traders came and played draughts and listened to the wireless. He stayed there a month drinking Greek absinthe, occasionally wandering out, they didn't know where, coming back and drinking again. They were afraid he would come to harm and followed him sometimes, but he only went to the church or took a car to the monastery outside the town. They loved him there. He's still loved, you see, wherever he goes, whatever condition he's in. It's a thing about him he'll never lose. You should have heard the proprietor and his family talk of him, tears running down their cheeks; they'd clearly robbed him right and left, but they'd looked after him and tried to make him eat his meals. That was the thing that shocked them about him: that he wouldn't eat; there he was with all that money, so thin. Some of the clients of the place came in while we were talking in very peculiar French; they all had the same story: such a *good* man, they said, it made them unhappy to see him so low. They thought very ill of his family for leaving him like that; it couldn't happen with their people, they said, and I daresay they're right.

"Anyway, that was later; after the consulate I went straight to the monastery and saw the Superior. He was a grim old Dutchman who had spent fifty years in Central Africa. He told me his part of the story; how Sebastian had turned up, just as the consul said, with his beard and a suitcase, and asked to be admitted as a lay brother. 'He was very earnest,' the Superior said" — Cordelia imitated his guttural tones; she had had an aptitude for mimicry, I remembered, in the school-room — " 'please do not think there is any doubt of that — he is quite sane and quite in earnest.' He wanted to go to the bush, as far away as he could get, among the simplest people, to the cannibals. The Superior said: 'We have no cannibals in our missions.' He said, well, pygmies would do, or just a primitive village somewhere on a river; or lepers — lepers would do best of anything. The Superior said: 'We have plenty of lepers, but they live in our settlements with doctors and nuns. It is all very orderly.' He thought again, and said perhaps lepers were not what he wanted, was there not some small church by a river — he always wanted a river you see — which he could look after when the priest was away. The Superior said: 'Yes, there are such churches. Now tell me about yourself.' 'Oh, I'm nothing,' he said. 'We see some queer fish' " — Cordelia lapsed again into mimicry; " 'he was a queer fish, but he was very earnest.' The Superior told him about the novitiate and the training and said: 'You are not a young man. You do not seem strong to me.' He said: 'No, I don't want to be trained. I don't want to do things that need training.' The Superior said: 'My friend, you need a missionary for yourself,' and he said: 'Yes, of course.' Then he sent him away.

"Next day he came back again. He had been drinking. He said he had decided to become a novice and be trained. 'Well,' said the Superior, 'there are certain things that are impossible for a man in the bush. One of them is drinking. It is not the worst thing, but it is nevertheless quite fatal. I sent him away.' Then he kept coming two or three times a week, always drunk, until the Superior gave orders that the porter was to keep him out. I said, 'Oh dear, I'm afraid he was a terrible nuisance to you,' but of course that's a thing they don't understand in a place like that. The Superior simply said, 'I did not think there was anything I could do to help him except pray.' He was a very holy old man and recognised it in others."

"Holiness?"

"Oh yes, Charles, that's what you've got to understand about Sebastian.

"Well, finally one day they found Sebastian lying outside the main gate unconscious; he had walked out — usually he took a car — and fallen down and lain there all night. At first they thought he was merely drunk again; then they realised he was very ill, so they put him in the infirmary, where he's been ever since.

"I stayed a fortnight with him till he was over the worst of his illness. He looked terrible, any age, rather bald with a straggling beard, but he had his old sweet manner. They'd given him a room to himself; it was barely more than a monk's cell with a bed and a crucifix and white walls. At first he couldn't talk much and was not at all surprised to see me; then he was surprised and wouldn't talk much, until just before I was going, when he told me all that had been happening to him. It was mostly about Kurt, his German friend. Well, you met him, so you know all about that. He sounds gruesome, but as long as Sebastian had him to look after, he was happy. He told me he'd practically given up drinking at one time while he and Kurt lived together. Kurt was ill and had a wound that wouldn't heal. Sebastian saw him through that. Then they went to Greece when Kurt got well. You know how Germans sometimes seem to discover a sense of decency when they get to a classical country. It seems to have worked with Kurt. Sebastian says he became quite human in Athens. Then he got sent to prison; I couldn't quite make out why; apparently it wasn't particularly his fault — some brawl with an official. Once he was locked up the German authorities got at him. It was the time when they were rounding up all their nationals from all parts of the world to make them into Nazis. Kurt didn't at all want to leave Greece. But the Greeks didn't want him, and he was marched straight from prison with a lot of other toughs into a German boat and shipped home.

"Sebastian went after him, and for a year could find no trace. Then in the end he ran him to earth dressed as a storm trooper in a provincial town. At first he wouldn't have anything to do with Sebastian; spouted all the official jargon about the rebirth of his country, and his belonging to his country and finding self-realisation in the life of the race. But it was only skin-deep with him. Six years of Sebastian had taught him more than a year of Hitler; eventually he chucked it, admitted he hated Germany, and wanted to get out. I don't know how much it was simply the call of the easy life, sponging on Sebastian, bathing in the Mediterranean, sitting about in cafés, having his shoes polished. Sebastian says it wasn't entirely that; Kurt had just begun to grow up in Athens. It may be he's right. Anyway, he decided to try and get out. But it didn't work. He always got into trouble whatever he did, Sebastian said. They caught him and put him in a concentration camp. Sebastian couldn't get near him or hear a word of him; he couldn't even find what camp he was in; he hung about for nearly a year in Germany, drinking again, until one day in his cups he took up with a man who was just out of the camp where Kurt had been, and learned that he had hanged himself in his hut the first week.

"So that was the end of Europe for Sebastian. He went back to Morocco, where he had been happy, and gradually drifted down the coast, from place to place, until one day when he had sobered up — his drinking goes in pretty regular bouts now — he conceived the idea of escaping to the savages. And there he was.

"I didn't suggest his coming home. I knew he wouldn't, and he was too weak still to argue it out. He seemed quite happy by the time I left. He'll never be able to go into the bush, of course, or join the order, but the Father Superior is going to take charge of him. They had the idea of making him a sort of under-porter; there are usually a few odd hangers-on in a religious house, you know; people who can't quite fit in either to the world or the monastic rule. I suppose I'm something of the sort myself. But as I don't happen to drink, I'm more employable."

We had reached the turn in our walk, the stone bridge at the foot of the last and smallest lake, under which the swollen waters fell in a cataract to the stream below; beyond the path doubled back towards the house. We paused at the parapet looking down into the dark water.

"I once had a governess who jumped off this bridge and drowned herself."

"Yes, I know."

"How could you know?"

"It was the first thing I ever heard about you — before I ever met you."

"How very odd. . . ."

"Have you told Julia this about Sebastian?"

"The substance of it; not quite as I told you. She never loved him, you know, as we do."

"*Do.*" The word reproached me; there was no past tense in Cordelia's verb "to love."

"Poor Sebastian!" I said. "It's too pitiful. How will it end?"

"I think I can tell you exactly, Charles. I've seen others like him, and I believe they are very near and dear to God. He'll live on, half in, half out of the community, a familiar figure pottering round with his broom and his bunch of keys. He'll be a great favourite with the old fathers, something of a joke to the novices. Everyone will know about his drinking; he'll disappear for two or three days every month or so, and they'll all nod and smile and say in their various accents, 'Old Sebastian's on the spree again,' and then he'll come back dishevelled and shamefaced and be more devout for a day or two in the chapel. He'll probably have little hiding places about the garden where he keeps a bottle and takes a swig now and then on the sly. They'll bring him forward to act as guide, whenever they have an English-speaking visitor; and he will be completely charming, so that before they go they'll ask about him and perhaps be given a hint that he has high connections at home. If he lives long enough, generations of missionaries in all kinds of remote places will think of him as a queer old character who was somehow part of the Hope of their student days, and remember him in their masses. He'll develop little eccentricities of devotion, intense personal cults of his own; he'll be found in the chapel at odd times and missed when he's expected. Then one morning, after one of his drinking bouts, he'll be picked up at the gate dying, and show by a mere flicker of the eyelid that he is conscious when they give him the last sacraments. It's not such a bad way of getting through one's life."

I thought of the joyful youth with the Teddy-bear under the flowering chestnuts. "It's not what one would have foretold," I said. "I suppose he doesn't suffer?"

"Oh, yes, I think he does. One can have no idea what the suffering may be, to be maimed as he is — no dignity, no power of will. No one is ever holy without suffering. It's taken that form with him. . . . I've seen so much suffering in the last few years; there's so much coming for everybody soon. It's the spring of love . . ." And then in condescension to my paganism, she added: "He's in a very beautiful place, you know, by the sea — white cloisters, a bell tower, rows of green vegetables, and a monk watering them when the sun is low."

I laughed. "You knew I wouldn't understand?"

"You and Julia . . ." she said. And then, as we moved on towards the house, "When you met me last night did you think, 'Poor Cordelia, such an engaging child, grown up a plain and pious spinster, full of good works'? Did you think 'thwarted'?"

It was no time for prevarication. "Yes," I said, "I did; I don't now, so much."

"It's funny," she said, "that's exactly the word I thought of for you and Julia. When we were up in the nursery with Nanny. 'Thwarted passion,' I thought."

She spoke with that gentle, infinitesimal inflection of mockery which descended to her from her mother, but later that evening the words came back to me poignantly.

Julia wore the embroidered Chinese robe which she often used when we were dining alone at Brideshead; it was a robe whose weight and stiff folds stressed her repose; her neck rose exquisitely from the plain gold circle at her throat; her hands lay still among the dragons in her lap. It was thus that I had rejoiced to see her nights without number, and that night, watching her as she sat between the firelight and the shaded lamp, unable to look away for love of her beauty, I suddenly thought, When else have I seen her like this? Why am I reminded of another moment of vision? And it came back to me that this was how she had sat in the liner, before the storm; this was how she had looked; and I realised that she had regained what I thought she had lost for ever, the magical sadness which had drawn me to her, the thwarted look that had seemed to say, "Surely I was made for some other purpose than this?"

That night I woke in the darkness and lay awake turning over in my mind the conversation with Cordelia. How I had said, "You knew I would not understand?" How often, it seemed to me, I was brought up short, like a horse in full stride suddenly refusing an obstacle, backing from the spurs, too shy even to put his nose at it and look at the thing.

And another image came to me, of an arctic hut and a trapper alone with his furs and oil lamp and log fire; the remains of supper on the table, a few books, skis in the corner; everything dry and neat and warm inside, and outside the last blizzard of winter raging and the snow piling up against the door. Quite silently a great weight forming against the timber; the bolt straining in its socket; minute by minute in the darkness outside the white heap sealing the door, until quite soon, when the wind dropped and the sun came out on the ice slopes and the thaw set in, a block would move, slide and tumble, high above, gather way, gather weight, till the whole hillside seemed to be falling, and the little lighted place would crash open and splinter and disappear, rolling with the avalanche into the ravine.

V

My divorce case, or rather my wife's, was due to be heard at about the same time as Brideshead was to be married. Julia's would not come up till the following term; meanwhile the game of General Post — moving my property from the Old Rectory to my flat, my wife's from my flat to the Old Rectory, Julia's from Rex's house and from Brideshead to my flat, Rex's from Brideshead to his house, and Mrs. Muspratt's from Falmouth to Brideshead — was in full swing and we were all, in varying degrees, homeless, when a halt was called and Lord Marchmain, with a taste for the dramatically inopportune which was plainly the prototype of his elder son's, declared his intention, in view of the international situation, of returning to England and passing his declining years in his old home.

The only member of the family to whom this change promised any benefit was Cordelia, who had been sadly abandoned in the turmoil. Brideshead, indeed, had made a formal request to her to consider his house her home for as long as it suited her, but when she learned that her sister-in-law proposed to install her children there for the holidays immediately after the wedding, in the charge of a sister of hers and the sister's friend, Cordelia had decided to move, too, and was talking of setting up alone in London. She now found herself, Cinderella-like, promoted chatelaine, while her brother and his wife, who had till that

moment expected to find themselves, within a matter of days, absolute
owners of the entire property, were without a roof; the deeds of con-
veyance, engrossed and ready for signing, were rolled up, tied and put
away in one of the black tin boxes in Lincoln's Inn. It was bitter for
Mrs. Muspratt; she was not an ambitious woman; something very much
less grand than Brideshead would have contented her heartily; but she
did aspire to finding some shelter for her children over Christmas. The
house at Falmouth was stripped and up for sale; moreover, Mrs. Muspratt
had taken leave of the place with some justifiably rather large talk of
her new establishment; they could not return there. She was obliged
in a hurry to move her furniture from Lady Marchmain's room to a
disused coachhouse and to take a furnished villa at Torquay. She was
not, as I have said, a woman of high ambition, but, having had her
expectations so much raised, it was disconcerting to be brought so low
so suddenly. In the village the working party who had been preparing
the decorations for the bridal entry began unpicking the B's on the
bunting and substituting M's, obliterating the Earl's points and stencil-
ling balls and strawberry leaves on the painted coronets, in preparation
for Lord Marchmain's return.

News of his intentions came first to the solicitors, then to Cordelia,
then to Julia and me, in a rapid succession of contradictory cables. Lord
Marchmain would arrive in time for the wedding; he would arrive after
the wedding, having seen Lord and Lady Brideshead on their way
through Paris; he would see them in Rome. He was not well enough
to travel at all; he was just starting; he had unhappy memories of winter
at Brideshead and would not come until spring was well advanced and
the heating apparatus overhauled; he was coming alone; he was bringing
his Italian household; he wished his return to be unannounced and
to lead a life of complete seclusion; he would give a ball. At last a date
in January was chosen which proved to be the correct one.

Plender preceded him by some days; there was a difficulty here.
Plender was not an original member of the Brideshead household; he
had been Lord Marchmain's servant in the yeomanry, and had only once
met Wilcox, on the painful occasion of the removal of his master's luggage when it was decided not to return from the war; then Plender
had been valet, as, officially, he still was, but he had in the past years
introduced a kind of curate, a Swiss body-servant, to attend to the wardrobe and also, when occasion arose, lend a hand with less dignified tasks
about the house, and had in effect become major-domo of that fluctuat-

ing and mobile household; sometimes he even referred to himself on the telephone as the "secretary." There was an acre of thin ice between him and Wilcox.

Fortunately the two men took a liking to one another, and the thing was solved in a series of three-cornered discussions with Cordelia. Plender and Wilcox became Joint Grooms of the Chambers, like Blues and Life Guards with equal precedence, Plender having as his particular province his Lordship's own apartments, and Wilcox a sphere of influence in the public rooms; the senior footman was given a black coat and promoted butler, the nondescript Swiss, on arrival, was to have full valet's status; there was a general increase in wages to meet the new dignities, and all were content.

Julia and I, who had left Brideshead a month before, thinking we should not return, moved back for the reception. When the day came, Cordelia went to the station and we remained to greet him at home. It was a bleak and gusty day. Cottages and lodges were decorated; plans for a bonfire that night and for the village silver band to play on the terrace were put down, but the house flag that had not flown for twenty-five years was hoisted over the pediment, and flapped sharply against the leaden sky. Whatever harsh voices might be bawling into the microphones of Central Europe, and whatever lathes spinning in the armament factories, the return of Lord Marchmain was a matter of first importance in his own neighbourhood.

He was due at three o'clock. Julia and I waited in the drawing-room until Wilcox, who had arranged with the station-master to be kept informed, announced "The train is signalled," and a minute later, "The train is in; his Lordshp is on the way." Then we went to the front portico and waited there with the upper servants. Soon the Rolls appeared at the turn in the drive, followed at some distance by the two vans. It drew up; first Cordelia got out, then Cara; there was a pause, a rug was handed to the chauffeur, a stick to the footman; then a leg was cautiously thrust forward. Plender was by now at the car door; another servant — the Swiss valet — had emerged from a van; together they lifted Lord Marchmain out and set him on his feet; he felt for his stick, grasped it, and stood for a minute collecting his strength for the few low steps which led to the front door.

Julia gave a little sigh of surprise and touched my hand. We had seen him nine months ago at Monte Carlo, when he had been an upright and stately figure, little changed from when I first met him in

Venice. Now he was an old man. Plender had told us his master had been unwell lately; he had not prepared us for this.

Lord Marchmain stood bowed and shrunken, weighed down by his great-coat, a white muffler fluttering untidily at his throat, a cloth cap pulled low on his forehead, his face white and lined, his nose coloured by the cold; the tears which gathered in his eyes came not from emotion but from the east wind; he breathed heavily. Cara tucked in the end of his muffler and whispered something to him. He raised a gloved hand — a schoolboy's glove of grey wool — and made a small, weary gesture of greeting to the group at the door; then, very slowly, with his eyes on the ground before him, he made his way into the house.

They took off his coat and cap and muffler and the kind of leather jerkin which he wore under them; thus stripped he seemed more than ever wasted but more elegant; he had cast the shabbiness of extreme fatigue. Cara straightened his tie; he wiped his eyes with a bandanna handkerchief and shuffled with his stick to the hall fire.

There was a little heraldic chair by the chimney-piece, one of a set which stood against the walls, a little, inhospitable, flat-seated thing, a mere excuse for the elaborate armorial painting on its back, on which, perhaps, no one, not even a weary footman, had ever sat since it was made; there Lord Marchmain sat and wiped his eyes.

"It's the cold," he said. "I'd forgotten how cold it is in England. Quite bowled me over."

"Can't I get you anything, my lord?"

"Nothing, thank you. Cara, where are those confounded pills?"

"Alex, the doctor said not more than three times a day."

"Damn the doctor. I feel quite bowled-over."

Cara produced a blue bottle from her bag and Lord Marchmain took a pill. Whatever was in it seemed to revive him. He remained seated, his long legs stuck out before him, his cane between them, his chin on its ivory handle, but he began to take notice of us all, to greet us and to give orders.

"I'm afraid I'm not at all the thing to-day; the journey's taken it out of me. Ought to have waited a night at Dover. Wilcox, what rooms have you prepared for me?"

"Your old ones, my lord."

"Won't do; not till I'm fit again. Too many stairs; must be on the ground floor. Plender, get a bed made up for me downstairs."

Plender and Wilcox exchanged an anxious glance.

"Very good, my lord. Which room shall we put it in?"

Lord Marchmain thought for a moment. "The Chinese drawing-room; and, Wilcox, the 'Queen's bed.'"

"The Chinese drawing-room, my lord, the 'Queen's bed'?"

"Yes, yes. I may be spending some time there in the next few weeks."

The Chinese drawing-room was one I had never seen used; in fact one could not normally go further into it than a small roped area round the door, where sight-seers were corralled on the days the house was open to the public; it was a splendid, uninhabitable museum of Chippendale carving and porcelain and lacquer and painted hangings; the "Queen's bed," too, was an exhibition piece, a vast velvet tent like the Baldachino at St. Peter's. Had Lord Marchmain planned his lying-in-state for himself, I wondered, before he left the sunshine of Italy? Had he thought of it during the scudding rain of his long, fretful journey? Had it come to him at that moment, an awakened memory of childhood, a dream in the nursery — "When I'm grown up I'll sleep in the Queen's bed in the Chinese drawing-room" — the apotheosis of adult grandeur?

Few things, certainly, could have caused more stir in the house. What had been foreseen as a day of formality became one of fierce exertion; housemaids began making a fire, removing covers, unfolding linen; men in aprons, never normally seen, shifted furniture; the estate carpenters were collected to dismantle the bed. It came down the main staircase in pieces, at intervals during the afternoon; huge sections of rococo, velvet-covered cornice; the twisted gilt and velvet columns which formed its posts; beams of unpolished wood, made not to be seen, which performed invisible, structural functions below the draperies; plumes of dyed feathers, which sprang from gold-mounted ostrich eggs and crowned the canopy; finally, the mattresses with four toiling men to each. Lord Marchmain seemed to derive comfort from the consequences of his whim; he sat by the fire watching the bustle, while we stood in a half-circle — Cara, Cordelia, Julia and I — and talked to him.

Colour came back to his cheeks and light to his eyes. "Brideshead and his wife dined with me in Rome," he said. "Since we are all members of the family" — and his eye moved ironically from Cara to me — "I can speak without reserve. I found her deplorable. Her former consort, I understand, was a seafaring man and, presumably, the less exacting, but how my son, at the ripe age of thirty-eight, with unless things have changed very much, a very free choice among the women of England, can have settled on — I suppose I must call her so — *Beryl* . . ." He left the sentence eloquently unfinished.

Lord Marchmain showed no inclination to move, so presently we drew up chairs — the little heraldic chairs, for everything else in the hall was ponderous — and sat round him.

"I daresay I shall not be really fit again until summer comes," he said. "I look to you four to amuse me."

There seemed little we could do at the moment to lighten the rather sombre mood; he, indeed, was the most cheerful of us. "Tell me," he said, "the circumstances of Brideshead's courtship."

We told him what we knew.

"Match-boxes," he said. "Match-boxes. I think she's past child-bearing."

Tea was brought us at the hall fireplace.

"In Italy," he said, "no one believes there will be a war. They think it will all be 'arranged.' I suppose, Julia, you no longer have access to political information? Cara, here, is fortunately a British subject by marriage. It is not a thing she customarily mentions, but it may prove valuable. She is legally Mrs. Hicks, are you not, my dear? We know little of Hicks, but we shall be grateful to him, none the less, if it comes to war. And you," he said, turning the attack to me, "you will no doubt become an official artist?"

"No. As a matter of fact I am negotiating now for a commission in the Special Reserve."

"Oh, but you should be an artist. I had one with my squadron during the last war, for weeks — until we went up to the line."

This waspishness was new. I had always been aware of a frame of malevolence under his urbanity, now it protruded like his own sharp bones through the sunken skin.

It was dark before the bed was finished; we went to see it, Lord Marchmain stepping quite briskly now through the intervening rooms.

"I congratulate you. It really looks remarkably well. Wilcox, I seem to remember a silver basin and ewer — they stood in a room we called 'the Cardinal's dressing-room,' I think — suppose we had them here on the console. Then if you will send Plender and Gaston to me, the luggage can wait till to-morrow — simply the dressing-case and what I need for the night. Plender will know. If you will leave me with Plender and Gaston, I will go to bed. We will meet later; you will dine here and keep me amused."

We turned to go; as I was at the door he called me back.

"It looks very well, does it not?"

"Very well."

"You might paint it, eh — and call it 'The Death Bed'?"

"Yes," said Cara, "he has come home to die."

"But when he first arrived he was talking so confidently of recovery."

"That was because he was so ill. When he is himself, he knows he is dying and accepts it. His sickness is up and down; one day, sometimes for several days on end, he is strong and lively and then he is ready for death, then he is down and afraid. I do not know how it will be when he is more and more down. That must come in good time. The doctors in Rome gave him less than a year. There is someone coming from London, I think to-morrow, who will tell us more."

"What is it?"

"His heart; some long word at the heart. He is dying of a long word."

That evening Lord Marchmain was in good spirits; the room had a Hogarthian aspect, with the dinner-table set for the four of us by the grotesque, chinoiserie chimney-piece, and the old man propped among his pillows, sipping champagne, tasting, praising, and failing to eat the succession of dishes which had been prepared for his homecoming. Wilcox had brought out for the occasion the gold plate, which I had not before seen in use; that and the gilt mirrors and the lacquer and the drapery of the great bed and Julia's mandarin coat gave the scene an air of pantomime, of Aladdin's cave.

Just at the end, when the time came for us to go, his spirits flagged. "I shall not sleep," he said. "Who is going to sit with me? Cara, *carissima*, you are fatigued. Cordelia, will you watch for an hour in this Gethsemane?"

Next morning I asked her how the night had passed.

"He went to sleep almost at once. I came in to see him at two to make up the fire; the lights were on, but he was asleep again. He must have woken up and turned them on; he had to get out of bed to do that. I think perhaps he is afraid of the dark."

It was natural, with her hospital experience, that Cordelia should take charge of her father. When the doctors came that day they gave their instructions to her, instinctively.

"Until he gets worse," she said, "I and the valet can look after him. We don't want nurses in the house before they are needed."

At this stage the doctors had nothing to recommend except to keep him comfortable and administer certain drugs when his attacks came on.

"How long will it be?"

"Lady Cordelia, there are men walking about in hearty old age whom their doctors gave a week to live. I have learned one thing in medicine: never prophesy."

These two men had made a long journey to tell her this; the local doctor was there to accept the same advice in technical phrases.

That night Lord Marchmain reverted to the topic of his new daughter-in-law; it had never been long out of his mind, finding expression in various sly hints throughout the day; now he lay back in his pillows and talked of her at length.

"I have never been much moved by family piety until now," he said, "but I am frankly appalled at the prospect of — of Beryl taking what was once my mother's place in this house. Why should that uncouth pair sit here childless while the place crumbles about their ears? I will not disguise from you that I have taken a dislike to Beryl.

"Perhaps it was unfortunate that we met in Rome. Anywhere else might have been more sympathetic. And yet, if one comes to consider it where could I have met her without repugnance? We dined at Ranieri's; it is a quiet little restaurant I have frequented for years — no doubt you know it. Beryl seemed to fill the place. I, of course, was host, though to hear Beryl press my son with food, you might have thought otherwise. Brideshead was always a greedy boy; a wife who has his best interests at heart should seek to restrain him. However, that is a matter of small importance.

"She had no doubt heard of me as a man of irregular life. I can only describe her manner to me as roguish. A naughty old man, that's what she thought I was. I suppose she had met naughty old admirals and knew how they should be humoured; a stage-door chappie, a bit of a lad . . . I could not attempt to reproduce her conversation. I will give you one example.

"They had been to an audience at the Vatican that morning; a blessing for their marriage — I did not follow attentively —something of the kind had happened before I gathered, some previous husband, some previous Pope. She described, rather vivaciously, how on this earlier occasion she had gone with a whole body of newly married couples, mostly Italians of all ranks, some of the simpler girls in their wedding dresses, and how each had appraised the other, the bridegrooms looking the brides over, comparing their own with one another's, and so forth. Then she said, 'This time, of course, we were in private, but do you know, Lord Marchmain, I felt as though it was I who was leading in the bride.'

"It was said with great indelicacy. I have not yet quite fathomed her meaning. Was she making a play on my son's name, or was she, do you think, referring to his undoubted virginity? I fancy the latter. Anyway, it was with pleasantries of that kind that we passed the evening.

"I don't think she would be quite in her proper element here, do you? Who shall I leave it to? The entail ended with me, you know. Sebastian, alas, is out of the question. Who wants it? *Quis?* Would you like it, Cara? No, of course you would not. Cordelia? I think I shall leave it to Julia and Charles."

"Of course not, Papa, it's Bridey's."

"And . . . Beryl's? I will have Gregson down one day soon and go over the matter. It is time I brought my will up to date; it is full of anomalies and anachronisms. . . . I have rather a fancy for the idea of installing Julia here; so beautiful this evening, my dear; so beautiful always; much, much more suitable."

Shortly after this he sent to London for his solicitor, but on the day he came, Lord Marchmain was suffering from an attack and would not see him. "Plenty of time," he said, between painful gasps for breath, "another day, when I am stronger," but the choice of his heir was constantly in his mind, and he referred often to the time when Julia and I should be married and in possession.

"Do you think he really means to leave it to us?" I asked Julia.

"Yes, I think he does."

"But it's monstrous for Bridey."

"Is it? I don't think he cares much for the place. I do, you know. He and Beryl would be much more content in some little house somewhere."

"You mean to accept it?"

"Certainly. It's Papa's to leave as he likes. I think you and I could be very happy here."

It opened a prospect; the prospect one gained at the turn of the avenue, as I had first seen it with Sebastian, of the secluded valley, the lakes falling away one below the other, the old house in the foreground, the rest of the world abandoned and forgotten; a world of its own of peace and love and beauty; a soldier's dream in a foreign bivouac; such a prospect perhaps as a high pinnacle of the temple afforded after the hungry days in the desert and the jackal-haunted nights. Need I reproach myself if sometimes I was rapt in the vision?

The weeks of illness wore on and the life of the house kept pace with the faltering strength of the sick man. There were days when Lord Marchmain was dressed, when he stood at the window or moved on his valet's arm from fire to fire through the rooms of the ground floor, when visitors came and went — neighbours and people from the estate, men of business from London — parcels of new books were opened and discussed, a piano moved into the Chinese drawing-room; once at the end of February, on a single, unexpected day of brilliant sunshine, he called for a car and got as far as the hall, had on his fur coat and reached the front door. Then suddenly he lost interest in the drive, said, "Not now. Later. One day in the summer," took his man's arm again and was led back to his chair. Once he had the humour of changing his room and gave detailed orders for a move to the Painted Parlour; the chinoiserie, he said, disturbed his rest — he kept the lights full on at night — but again lost heart, countermanded everything, and kept his room.

On other days the house was hushed as he sat high in bed, propped by pillows, with labouring breath; even then he wanted to have us round him; night or day he could not bear to be alone; when he could not speak his eyes followed us, and if anyone left the room he would look distressed, and Cara, sitting often for hours at a time by his side against the pillows with an arm in his, would say, "It's all right, Alex, she's coming back."

Brideshead and his wife returned from their honeymoon and stayed a few nights; it was one of the bad times, and Lord Marchmain refused to have them near him. It was Beryl's first visit, and she would have been unnatural if she had shown no curiosity about what had nearly been, and now again promised soon to be, her home. Beryl was natural enough, and surveyed the place fairly thoroughly in the days she was there. In the strange disorder caused by Lord Marchmain's illness, it must have seemed capable of much improvement; she referred once or twice to the way in which establishments of similar size had been managed at various Government Houses she had visited. Brideshead took her visiting among the tenants by day, and in the evenings she talked to me of painting, or to Cordelia of hospitals, or to Julia of clothes, with cheerful assurance. The shadow of betrayal, the knowledge of how precarious were their just expectations, was all one-sided. I was not easy with them; but that was no new thing to Brideshead; in the little circle of shyness in which he was used to move, my guilt passed unseen.

Eventually it became clear that Lord Marchmain did not intend to see more of them. Brideshead was admitted alone for a minute's leave-taking; then they left.

"There's nothing we can do here," said Brideshead, "and it's very distressing for Beryl. We'll come back if things get worse."

The bad spells became longer and more frequent; a nurse was engaged. "I never saw such a room," she said, "nothing like it anywhere; no conveniences of any sort." She tried to have her patient moved upstairs, where there was running water, a dressing-room for herself, a "sensible" narrow bed she could "get round" — what she was used to — but Lord Marchmain would not budge. Soon, as days and nights became indistinguishable to him, a second nurse was installed; the specialists came again from London; they recommended a new and rather daring treatment, but his body seemed weary of all drugs and did not respond. Presently there were no good spells, merely brief fluctuations in the speed of his decline.

Brideshead was called. It was the Easter holidays and Beryl was busy with her children. He came alone, and having stood silently for some minutes beside his father, who sat silently looking at him, he left the room and, joining the rest of us who were in the library, said, "Papa must see a priest."

It was not the first time the topic had come us. In the early days, when Lord Marchmain first arrived, the parish priest — since the chapel was shut there was a new church and presbytery in Melstead — had come to call as a matter of politeness. Cordelia had put him off with apologies and excuses, but when he was gone she said: "Not yet. Papa doesn't want him yet."

Julia, Cara and I were there at the time; we each had something to say, began to speak, and thought better of it. It was never mentioned between the four of us, but Julia, alone with me, said, "Charles, I see great Church trouble ahead."

"Can't they even let him die in peace?"

"They mean something so different by 'peace.'"

"It would be an outrage. No one could have made it clearer, all his life, what he thought of religion. They'll come now, when his mind's wandering and he hasn't the strength to resist, and claim him as a death-bed penitent. I've had a certain respect for their Church up till now. If they do a thing like that I shall know everything stupid people say about them is quite true — that it's all superstition and trickery." Julia said nothing. "Don't you agree?" Still Julia said nothing. "Don't you agree?"

"I don't know, Charles. I simply don't know."

And, though none of us spoke of it, I felt the question ever present, growing through all the weeks of Lord Marchmain's illness; I saw it when Cordelia drove off early in the mornings to mass; I saw it as Cara took to going with her; this little cloud, the size of a man's hand, that was going to swell into a storm among us.

Now Brideshead, in his heavy, ruthless way, planted the problem down before us.

"Oh, Bridey, do you think he would?" asked Cordelia.

"I shall see that he does," said Brideshead. "I shall take Father Mackay in to him to-morrow."

Still the clouds gathered and did not break; none of us spoke. Cara and Cordelia went back to the sick-room; Brideshead looked for a book, found one, and left us.

"Julia," I said, "how can we stop this tomfoolery?"

She did not answer for some time; then: "Why should we?"

"You know as well as I do. It's just — just an unseemly incident."

"Who am I to object to unseemly incidents?" she asked sadly. "Anyway, what harm can it do? Let's ask the doctor."

We asked the doctor, who said: "It's hard to say. It might alarm him of course; on the other hand, I have known cases where it has had a wonderfully soothing effect on a patient; I've even known it act as a positive stimulant. It certainly is usually a great comfort to the relations. Really I think it's a thing for Lord Brideshead to decide. Mind you, there is no need for immediate anxiety. Lord Marchmain is very weak to-day; to-morrow he may be quite strong again. Is it not usual to wait a little?"

"Well, he wasn't much help," I said to Julia, when we left him.

"Help? I really can't quite see why you've taken it so much at heart that my father shall not have the last sacraments."

"It's such a lot of witchcraft and hypocrisy."

"Is it? Anyway, it's been going on for nearly two thousand years. I don't know why you should suddenly get in a rage now." Her voice rose; she was swift to anger of late months. "For Christ's sake, write to *The Times*; get up and make a speech in Hyde Park; start a 'No Popery' riot — but don't bore me about it. What's it got to do with you or me whether my father sees his parish priest?"

I knew these fierce moods of Julia's, such as had overtaken her at the fountain in moonlight, and dimly surmised their origin; I knew they could not be assuaged by words. Nor could I have spoken, for the answer to her question was still unformed, but lay in a pocket of my mind, like sea-mist in a dip of the sand-dunes; the cloudy sense that the fate of more souls than one was at issue; that the snow was beginning to shift on the high slopes.

Brideshead and I breakfasted together next morning with the night-nurse, who had just come off duty.

"He's much brighter to-day," she said. "He slept very nicely for nearly three hours. When Gaston came to shave him he was quite chatty."

"Good," said Brideshead. "Cordelia went to mass. She's driving Father Mackay back here to breakfast."

I had met Father Mackay several times; he was a stocky, middle-aged, genial Glasgow-Irishman who, when we met, was apt to ask me such questions as, "Would you say now, Mr. Ryder, that the painter Titian was more truly artistic than the painter Raphael?" and, more disconcertingly still, to remember my answers: "To revert, Mr. Ryder, to what you said when last I had the pleasure to meet you, would it be right now to say that the painter Titian . . ." usually ending with some such reflection as: "Ah, it's a grand resource for a man to have the talent you have, Mr. Ryder, and the time to indulge it." Cordelia could imitate him brilliantly.

This morning he made a hearty breakfast, glanced at the headlines of the paper, and then said with professional briskness: "And now, Lord Brideshead, would the poor soul be ready to see me, do you think?"

Brideshead led him out; Cordelia followed and I was left alone among the breakfast things. In less than a minute I heard the voices of all three outside the door.

". . . can only apologize."

". . . poor soul. Mark you, it was seeing a strange face; depend upon it, it was that — an unexpected stranger. I will understand it."

". . . Father, I am sorry . . . bringing you all this way . . ."

"Don't think about it at all, Lady Cordelia. Why, I've had bottles thrown at me in the Gorbals. . . . Give him time. I've known worse cases make beautiful deaths. Pray for him . . . I'll come again . . . and now if you'll excuse me I'll just pay a little visit to Mrs. Hawkins. Yes, indeed, I know the way well."

Then Cordelia and Brideshead came into the room.

"I gather the visit was not a success."

"It was not. Cordelia, will you drive Father Mackay home when he comes down from Nanny? I'm going to telephone to Beryl and see when she needs me home."

"Bridey, it was horrible. What are we to do?"

"We've done everything we can at the moment." He left the room.

Cordelia's face was grave; she took a piece of bacon from the dish, dipped it in mustard and ate it. "Damn Bridey," she said, "I knew it wouldn't work."

"What happened?"

"Would you like to know? We walked in there in a line; Cara was reading the paper aloud to Papa. Bridey said, 'I've brought Father Mackay to see you'; Papa said, 'Father Mackay, I am afraid you have been brought here under a misapprehension. I am not *in extremis,* and I have not been a practising member of your Church for twenty-five years. Brideshead, show Father Mackay the way out.' Then we all turned about and walked away, and I heard Cara start reading the paper again, and that, Charles, was that."

I carried the news to Julia, who lay with her bed-table amid a litter of newspapers and envelopes. "Mumbo-jumbo is off," I said, "the witch-doctor has gone."

"Poor Papa."

"It's great sucks to Bridey."

I felt triumphant. I had been right, everyone else had been wrong, truth had prevailed; the threat that I had felt hanging over Julia and me ever since that evening at the fountain had been averted, perhaps dispelled for ever; and there was also — I can now confess it — another unexpressed, inexpressible, indecent little victory that I was furtively celebrating. I guessed that that morning's business had put Brideshead some considerable way further from his rightful inheritance.

In that I was correct; a man was sent for from the solicitors in London;

and in a day or two he came and it was known throughout the house that Lord Marchmain had made a new will. But I was wrong in thinking that the religious controversy was quashed; it flamed up again after dinner on Brideshead's last evening.

". . . What Papa said was, 'I am not *in extremis*; I have not been a practising member of the Church for twenty-five years.'"

"Not '*the* Church,' 'your Church.'"

"I don't see the difference."

"There's every difference."

"Bridey, it's quite plain what he meant."

"I presume he meant what he said. He meant that he had not been accustomed regularly to receive the sacraments, and since he was not at the moment dying, he did not mean to change his ways — *yet*."

"That's simply a quibble."

"Why do people always think that one is quibbling when one tries to be precise? His plain meaning was that he did not want to see a priest that day, but that he would when he was *in extremis*."

"I wish someone would explain to me," I said, "quite what the significance of these sacraments is. Do you mean that if he dies alone he goes to hell, and that if a priest puts oil on him —"

"Oh, it's not the oil," said Cordelia, "that's to heal him."

"Odder still — well, whatever it is the priest does — that he then goes to heaven? Is that what you believe?"

Cara then interposed: "I think my nurse told me, someone did anyway, that if the priest got there before the body was cold it was all right. That's so, isn't it?"

The others turned on her.

"No, Cara, it's not."

"Of course not."

"You've got it all wrong, Cara."

"Well, I remember when Alphonse de Grenet died, Madame de Grenet had a priest hidden outside the door — he couldn't bear the sight of a priest — and brought him in *before the body was cold;* she told me herself, and they had a full requiem for him, and I went to it."

"Having a requiem doesn't mean you go to heaven necessarily."

"Madame de Grenet thought it did."

"Well, she was wrong."

"Do any of you Catholics know what good you think this priest can do?" I asked. "Do you simply want to arrange it so that your father

can have Christian burial? Do you want to keep him out of hell?
I only want to be told."

Brideshead told me at some length, and when he had finished Cara
slightly marred the unity of the Catholic front by saying in simple
wonder, "I never heard that before."

"Let's get this clear," I said; "he has to make an act of will; he has
to be contrite and wish to be reconciled; is that right? But only God
knows whether he has really made an act of will; the priest can't tell;
and if there isn't a priest there, and he makes the act of will alone,
that's as good as if there were a priest. And it's quite possible that the
will may still be working when a man is too weak to make any outward
sign of it; is that right? He may be lying as though for dead, and willing
all the time, and being reconciled, and God understands that; is
that right?"

"More or less," said Brideshead.

"Well, for heaven's sake," I said, "what is the priest for?"

There was a pause in which Julia sighed and Brideshead drew breath
as though to start further subdividing the propositions. In the silence
Cara said, "All I know is that I shall take very good care to have a priest."

"Bless you," said Cordelia, "I believe that's the best answer."

And we let the argument drop, each for different reasons, thinking
it had been inconclusive.

Later Julia said: "I wish you wouldn't start these religious arguments."

"I didn't start it."

"You don't convince anyone else and you don't really convince
yourself."

"I only want to know what these people believe. They say it's all
based on logic."

"If you'd let Bridey finish, he would have made it all quite logical."

"There were four of you," I said. "Cara didn't know the first thing
it was about, and may or may not have believed it; you knew a bit and
didn't believe a word; Cordelia knew about as much and believed it
madly; only poor Bridey knew and believed, and I thought he made
a pretty poor show when it came to explaining. And people go round
saying, 'At least Catholics know what they believe,' We had a fair
cross-section to-night — "

"Oh, Charles, don't rant. I shall begin to think you're getting
doubts yourself."

The weeks passed and still Lord Marchmain lived on. In June my divorce was made absolute and my former wife married for the second time. Julia would be free in September. The nearer our marriage got, the more wistfully, I noticed, Julia spoke of it; war was growing nearer, too — we neither of us doubted that — but Julia's tender, remote, it sometimes seemed desperate longing did not come from any uncertainty outside herself; it suddenly darkened too, into brief accesses of hate when she seemed to throw herself against the restraints of her love for me like a caged animal against the bars.

I was summoned to the War Office, interviewed and put on a list in case of emergency; Cordelia also, on another list; lists were becoming part of our lives once more, as they had been at school — those strips of paper on the green baize notice boards which defined success and failure. No one in that dark office spoke the word "war"; it was taboo; we should be called for if there was "an emergency" — not in case of strife, an act of human will; nothing so clear and simple as wrath or retribution; an emergency; something coming out of the waters, a monster with sightless face and thrashing tail thrown up from the depths.

Lord Marchmain took little interest in events outside his own room; we took him the papers daily and made the attempt to read to him, but he turned his head on the pillows and with his eyes followed the intricate patterns about him. "Shall I go on?" "Please do if it's not boring you." But he was not listening; occasionally at a familiar name he would whisper: "Irwin . . . I knew him — a mediocre fellow"; occasionally some remote comment: "Czechs make good coachmen; nothing else"; but his mind was far from world affairs; it was there, on the spot, turned in on himself; he had no strength for any other war than his own solitary struggle to keep alive.

I said to the doctor, who was with us daily: "He's got a wonderful will to live, hasn't he?"

"Would you put it like that? I should say a great fear of death."

"Is there a difference?"

"Oh dear, yes. He doesn't derive any strength from his fear, you know. It's wearing him out."

Next to death, perhaps because they are like death, he feared darkness and loneliness. He liked to have us in his room and the lights burnt all night among the gilt figures; he did not wish us to speak much, but he talked himself, so quietly that we could often not hear him; he talked, I think, because his was the only voice he could trust, when it assured him that he was still alive; what he said was not for us, nor for any ears but his own.

"Better to-day. Better to-day. I can see now, in the corner of the fireplace, where the mandarin is holding his gold bell and the crooked tree is in flower below his feet, where yesterday I was confused and took the little tower for another man. Soon I shall see the bridge and the three storks and know where the path leads over the hill.

"Better to-morrow. We live long in our family and marry late. Seventy-three is no age. Aunt Julia, my father's aunt, lived to be eighty-eight, born and died here, never married, saw the fire on beacon hill for the battle of Trafalgar, always called it 'the New House'; that was the name they had for it in the nursery and in the fields when un-lettered men had long memories. You can see where the old house stood near the village church; they call the field 'Castle Hill,' Horlick's field where the ground's uneven and half of it is waste, nettle and brier in hollows too deep for ploughing. They dug to the foundations to carry the stone for the new house; the house that was a century old when Aunt Julia was born. Those were our roots in the waste hollows of Castle Hill, in the brier and nettle; among the tombs in the old church and the chantrey where no clerk sings.

"Aunt Julia knew the tombs, cross-legged knight and doubleted earl, marquis like a Roman senator, limestone, alabaster, and Italian marble; tapped the escutcheons with her ebony cane, made the casque ring over old Sir Roger. We were knights then, barons since Agincourt; the larger honours came with the Georges. They came the last and they'll go the first; the barony descends in the female line; when Brideshead is buried — he married late — Julia's son will be called by the name his fathers bore before the fat days; the days of wool shearing and the wide corn lands, the days of growth and building, when the marshes were drained and the waste land brought under the plough, when one built the house, his son added the dome, his son spread the wings and dammed the river. Aunt Julia watched them build the fountain; it was old before it came here, weathered two hundred years by the suns of Naples, brought by man-o'-war in the days of Nelson. Soon the fountain will be dry till the rain fills it, setting the fallen leaves afloat in the basin and over the lakes the reeds will spread and close. Better to-day.

"Better to-day. I have lived carefully, sheltered myself from the cold winds, eaten moderately of what was in season, drunk fine claret, slept in my own sheets; I shall live long. I was fifty when they dismounted us and sent us into the line; old men stay at the base, the orders said, but Walter Venables, my commanding officer, my nearest neighbour, said: 'You're as fit as the youngest of them, Alex.' So I was; so I am now, if I could only breathe.

"No air; no wind stirring under the velvet canopy; no one has opened the door for a thousand years in Aladdin's treasury, deep underground where the jinns burrow like moles and no wind stirs. When the summer comes," said Lord Marchmain, oblivious of the deep corn and swelling fruit and the surfeited bees who slowly sought their hives in the heavy afternoon sunlight outside his windows, "when the summer comes I shall leave my bed and sit in the open air and breathe more easily.

"Better to-morrow, when the wind comes down the valley and a man can turn to meet it and fill himself with air like a beast at water. Who would have thought that all these little gold men, gentlemen in their own country, could live so long without breathing? Like toads in the coal, down a deep mine, untroubled. God take it, why have they dug a hole for me? Must a man stifle to death in his own cellars? Plender, Gaston, open the windows."

"The windows are all wide open, my lord."

"I know them. I was born in this house. They open from a cellar into a tunnel. It can only be done by gunpowder; bore the rock, cram it with powder, trace the fuse, crouch under cover round the corner while we touch it off; we'll blast our way to daylight."

A cylinder of oxygen was placed beside his bed, with a long tube, a facepiece, and a little stop-cock he could work himself. Often he said: "It's empty; look, nurse, there's nothing comes out."

"No, Lord Marchmain, it's quite full; the bubble here in the glass bulb shows that; it's at full pressure; listen, don't you hear it hiss? Try and breathe slowly, Lord Marchmain; quite gently, then you get the benefit."

"Free as air; that's what they say — 'free as air.' I was free once. I committed a crime in the name of freedom. Now they bring me my air in an iron barrel."

Once he said: "Cordelia, what became of the chapel?"

"They locked it up, Papa, when Mummy died."

"It was hers, I gave it to her. We've always been builders in our family. I built it for her; pulled down the pavilion that stood there; rebuilt with the old stones; it was the last of the new house to come, the first to go. There used to be a chaplain until the war. Do you remember him?"

"I was too young."

"Then I went away — left her in the chapel praying. It was hers. It was the place for her. I never came back to disturb her prayers. They said we were fighting for freedom; I had my own victory. Was it a crime?"

"I think it was, Papa."

"Crying to heaven for vengeance? Is that why they've locked me in this cave, do you think, with a black tube of air and the little yellow men along the walls, who live without breathing? Do you think that, child? But the wind will come soon, to-morrow perhaps, and we'll breathe again. The ill wind that will blow me good. Better to-morrow."

Thus, till mid-July, Lord Marchmain lay dying, wearing himself down in the struggle to live. Then, since there was no reason to expect an immediate change, Cordelia went to London to see her women's organization about the coming "emergency." That day Lord Marchmain's condition became suddenly worse. He lay silent and quite still, breathing laboriously; only his open eyes, which sometimes moved about the room, gave any sign of consciousness.

"Is this the end?" Julia asked.

"It is impossible to say," the doctor answered; "when he does die it will probably be like this. He may recover from the present attack. The only thing is not to disturb him. The least shock would be fatal."

"I'm going for Father Mackay," she said.

I was not surprised. I had seen it in her mind all the summer. When she had gone I said to the doctor, "We must stop this nonsense."

He said: "My business is with the body. It's not my business to argue whether people are better alive or dead, or what happens to them after death. I only try to keep them alive."

"And you said just now any shock would kill him. What could be worse for a man who fears death, as he does, than to have a priest brought to him — a priest he turned out when he had the strength?"

"I think it may kill him."

"Then will you forbid it?"

"I've no authority to forbid anything. I can only give my opinion."

"Cara, what do you think?"

"I don't want him made unhappy. That is all there is to hope for now; that he'll die without knowing it. But I should like the priest there, all the same."

"Will you try and persuade Julia to keep him away — until the end? After that he can do no harm."

"I will ask her to leave Alex happy, yes."

In half an hour Julia was back with Father Mackay. We all met in the library.

"I've telegraphed for Bridey and Cordelia," I said. "I hope you agree that nothing must be done till they arrive."

"I wish they were here," said Julia.

"You can't take the responsibility alone," I said; "everyone else is against you. Doctor, tell her what you said to me just now."

"I said that the shock of seeing a priest might well kill him; without that he may survive this attack. As a medical man I must protest against anything being done to disturb him."

"Cara?"

"Julia, dear, I know you are thinking for the best, but, you know, Alex was not a religious man. He scoffed always. We mustn't take advantage of him, now he's weak, to comfort our own consciences. If Father Mackay comes to him when he is unconscious, then he can be buried in the proper way, can he not, Father?"

"I'll go and see how he is," said the doctor, leaving us.

"Father Mackay," I said. "You know how Lord Marchmain greeted you last time you came; do you think it possible he can have changed now?"

"Thank God, by His grace it is possible."

"Perhaps," said Cara, "you could slip in while he is sleeping, say the words of absolution over him; he would never know."

"I have seen so many men and women die," said the priest; "I never knew them sorry to have me there at the end."

"But they were Catholics; Lord Marchmain has never been one except in name — at any rate, not for years. He was a scoffer, Cara said so."

"Christ came to call, not the righteous, but sinners to repentance."

The doctor returned. "There's no change," he said.

"Now, Doctor," said the priest, "how would I be a shock to anyone?" He turned his bland, innocent, matter-of-fact face first on the doctor, then upon the rest of us. "Do you know what I want to do? It is something so small, no show about it. I don't wear special clothes, you know. I go just as I am. He knows the look of me now. There's nothing alarming. I just want to ask him if he is sorry for his sins. I want him to make some little sign of assent; I want him, anyway, not to refuse me; then I want to give him God's pardon. Then, though that's not essential, I want to anoint him. It is nothing, a touch of the fingers, just some oil from this little box, look, it is pure oil, nothing to hurt him."

"Oh, Julia," said Cara, "what are we to say? Let me speak to him."

She went to the Chinese drawing-room; we waited in silence; there was a wall of fire between Julia and me. Presently Cara returned.

"I don't think he heard," she said. "I thought I knew how to put it to him. I said: 'Alex, you remember the priest from Melstead. You were very naughty when he came to see you. You hurt his feelings very much. Now he's here again. I want you to see him just for my sake, to make friends.' But he didn't answer. If he's unconscious, it couldn't make him unhappy to see the priest, could it, Doctor?"

Julia, who had been standing still and silent, suddenly moved.

"Thank you for your advice, Doctor," she said. "I take full responsibility for whatever happens. Father Mackay, will you please come and see my father now," and without looking at me, led him to the door.

We all followed. Lord Marchmain was lying as I had seen him that morning, but his eyes were now shut; his hands lay, palm-upwards, above the bed-clothes; the nurse had her fingers on the pulse of one of them. "Come in," she said brightly, "you won't disturb him now."

"D'you mean . . .?"

"No, no, but he's past noticing anything."

She held the oxygen apparatus to his face and the hiss of escaping gas was the only sound at the bedside.

The priest bent over Lord Marchmain and blessed him. Julia and Cara knelt at the foot of the bed. The doctor, the nurse and I stood behind them.

"Now," said the priest, "I know you are sorry for all the sins of your life, aren't you? Make a sign, if you can. You're sorry, aren't you?" But there was no sign. "Try and remember your sins; tell God you are sorry. I am going to give you absolution. While I am giving it, tell God you are sorry you have offended Him." He began to speak in Latin. I recognized the words *Ego te absolvo in nomine Patris* . . . and saw the priest make the sign of the cross. Then I knelt, too, and prayed: "O God, if there is a God, forgive him his sins, if there is such a thing as sin," and the man on the bed opened his eyes and gave a sigh, the sort of sigh I had imagined people made at the moment of death, but his eyes moved so that we knew there was still life in him.

I suddenly felt the longing for a sign, if only of courtesy, if only for the sake of the woman I loved, who knelt in front of me, praying, I knew, for a sign. It seemed so small a thing that was asked, the bare acknowledgment of a present, a nod in the crowd. All over the world people were on their knees before innumerable crosses, and here the drama was being played again by two men — by one man, rather, and he nearer death than life; the universal drama in which there is only one actor.

The priest took the little silver box from his pocket and spoke again in Latin, touching the dying man with an oily wad; he finished what he had to do, put away the box and gave the final blessing. Suddenly Lord Marchmain moved his hand to his forehead; I thought he had felt the touch of the chrism and was wiping it away. "O God," I prayed, "don't let him do that." But there was no need for fear; the hand moved slowly down his breast, then to his shoulder, and Lord Marchmain made the sign of the cross. Then I knew that the sign I had asked for was not a little thing, not a passing nod of recognition, and a phrase came back to me from my childhood of the veil of the temple being rent from top to bottom.

It was over; we stood up; the nurse went back to the oxygen cylinder; the doctor bent over his patient.

Julia whispered to me: "Will you see Father MacKay out? I'm staying here for a little."

Outside the door Father Mackay became the simple, genial man I had known before. "Well, now, and that was a beautiful thing to see. I've known it happen that way again and again. The devil resists to the last moment and then the Grace of God is too much for him. You're not a Catholic, I think, Mr. Ryder, but at least you'll be glad for the ladies to have the comfort of it."

As we were waiting for the chauffeur, it occurred to me that Father Mackay should be paid for his services. I asked him awkwardly. "Why, don't think about it, Mr. Ryder. It was a pleasure," he said, "but anything you care to give is useful in a parish like mine." I found I had three pounds in my note-case and gave them to him. "Why, indeed, that's more than generous. God bless you, Mr. Ryder. I'll call again, but I don't think the poor soul has long for this world."

Julia remained in the Chinese drawing-room until, at five o'clock that evening, her father died, proving both sides right in the dispute, priest and doctor.

Thus I come to the broken sentences which were the last words spoken between Julia and me, the last memories.

When her father died Julia remained some minutes with his body; the nurse came to the next room to announce the news and I had a glimpse of her, through the open door, kneeling at the foot of the bed, and of Cara sitting by her. Presently the two women came out together, and Julia said to me: "Not now; I'm just taking Cara up to her room; later."

While she was still upstairs Brideshead and Cordelia arrived from London; when at last we met alone it was by stealth, like young lovers.

Julia said: "Here in the shadow, in the corner of the stair — a minute to say good-bye."

"So long to say so little."

"You knew?"

"Since this morning; since before this morning; all this year."

"I didn't know till to-day. Oh, my dear, if you could only understand. Then I could bear to part, or bear it better. I should say my heart was breaking, if I believed in broken hearts. I can't marry you, Charles; I can't be with you ever again."

"I know."

"How can you know?"

"What will you do?"

"Just go on — alone. How can I tell what I shall do? You know the whole of me. You know I'm not one for a life of mourning. I've always been bad. Probably I shall be bad again, punished again. But the worse I am, the more I need God. I can't shut myself out from His mercy. That is what it would mean; starting a life with you, without Him. One can only hope to see one step ahead. But I saw to-day there was one thing unforgivable — like things in the schoolroom, so bad they are unpunishable, that only Mummy could deal with — the bad thing I was on the point of doing, that I'm not quite bad enough to do; to set up a rival good to God's. Why should I be allowed to understand that, and not you, Charles? It may be because of Mummy, Nanny, Cordelia, Sebastian — perhaps Bridey and Mrs. Muspratt — keeping my name in their prayers; or it may be a private bargain between me and God, that if I give up this one thing I want so much, however bad I am, He won't quite despair of me in the end.

"Now we shall both be alone, and I shall have no way of making you understand."

"I don't want to make it easier for you," I said; "I hope your heart may break; but I do understand."

The avalanche was down, the hillside swept bare behind it; the last echoes died on the white slopes; the new mound glittered and lay still in the silent valley.

The Loved One

A Warning

This is a purely fanciful tale, a little nightmare produced by the unaccustomed high living of a brief visit to Hollywood. Readers whose pleasure in fiction derives from identifying the characters and scenes with real people and real places will be disappointed. If in the vast variety of life in America there is anyone at all like any one of the characters I have invented, I can only remind that person that we never met, and assure him or her that, had we done so, I would not have attempted to portray a living individual in a book where all the incidents are entirely imaginary.

As I have said, this is a nightmare and in parts, perhaps, somewhat gruesome. The squeamish should return their copies to the library or the bookstore unread.

I

ALL day the head had been barely supportable but at evening a breeze arose in the West, blowing from the heart of the setting sun and from the ocean, which lay unseen, unheard behind the scrubby foothills. It shook the rusty fringes of palm-leaf and swelled the dry sounds of summer, the frog-voices, the grating cicadas, and the ever present pulse of music from the neighbouring native huts.

In that kindly light the stained and blistered paint of the bungalow and the plot of weeds between the veranda and the dry water-hole lost their extreme shabbiness, and the two Englishmen, each in his rocking-chair, each with his whisky and soda and his outdated magazine, the counterparts of numberless fellow-countrymen exiled in the barbarous regions of the world, shared in the brief illusory rehabilitation.

"Ambrose Abercrombie will be here shortly," said the elder. "I don't know why. He left a message he would come. Find another glass, Dennis, if you can." Then he added more petulantly: "Kierkegaard,

Kafka, Connolly, Compton Burnet, Sartre, 'Scottie' Wilson. Who are they? What do they want?"

"I've heard of some of them. They were being talked about in London at the time I left."

"They talked of 'Scottie' Wilson?"

"No. I don't think so. Not of him."

"That's 'Scottie' Wilson. Those drawings there. Do they make any sense to you?"

"No."

"No."

Sir Francis Hinsley's momentary animation subsided. He let fall his copy of *Horizon* and gazed towards the patch of deepening shadow which had once been a pool. His was a weak, sensitive, intelligent face, blurred somewhat by soft living and long boredom. "It was Hopkins once," he said; "Joyce and Freud and Gertrude Stein. I couldn't make any sense of *them* either. I never was much good at anything new. 'Arnold Bennett's debt to Zola'; 'Flecker's debt to Henley.' That was the nearest I went to the moderns. My best subjects were 'The English Parson in English Prose' or 'Cavalry Actions with the Poets' — that kind of thing. People seemed to like them once. Then they lost interest. I did too. I was always the most defatigable of hacks. I needed a change. I've never regretted coming away. The climate suits me. They are a very decent, generous lot of people out here and *they don't expect you to listen*. Always remember that, dear boy. It's the secret of social ease in this country. They talk entirely for their own pleasure. Nothing they say is designed to be heard."

"Here comes Ambrose Abercrombie," said the young man.

"Evening, Frank. Evening, Barlow," said Sir Ambrose Abercrombie coming up the steps. "It's been another scorcher, eh? Mind if I take a pew? When," he added aside to the young man who helped him to whisky. "Right up with soda, please."

Sir Ambrose wore dark grey flannels, an Eton Rambler tie, an I Zingari ribbon in his boater hat. This was his invariable dress on sunny days; whenever the weather allowed it he wore a deerstalker-cap and an Inverness cape. He was still on what Lady Abercrombie fatuously called the "right" side of sixty but after many years of painfully attempting to look youthful, he now aspired to the honours of age. It was his latest quite vain wish that people should say of him: "Grand old boy."

"Been meaning to look you up for a long time. Trouble about a place like this one's so darn busy, one gets in a groove and loses touch. Doesn't do to lose touch. We limeys have to stick together. You shouldn't hide yourself away, Frank, you old hermit."

"I remember a time when you lived not so far away."

"Did I? 'Pon my soul I believe you're right. That takes one back a bit. It was before we went to Beverly Hills. Now, as of course you know, we're in Bel Air. But to tell you the truth I'm getting a bit restless there. I've got a bit of land out on Pacific Palisades. Just waiting for building costs to drop. Where was it I used to live? Just across the street, wasn't it?"

Just across the street, twenty years or more ago, when this neglected district was the centre of fashion, Sir Francis, in prime middle-age, was then the only knight in Hollywood, the doyen of English society, chief script-writer in Megalopolitan Pictures and President of the Cricket Club. Then the young, or youngish, Ambrose Abercrombie used to bounce about the lots in his famous series of fatiguing roles, acrobatic heroic historic, and come almost nightly to Sir Francis for refreshment. English titles abounded now in Hollywood, several of them authentic, and Sir Ambrose had been known to speak slightingly of Sir Francis as a "Lloyd George creation." The seven league boots of failure had carried the old and the ageing man far apart. Sir Francis had descended to the Publicity Department and now held rank, one of a dozen, as Vice-President of the Cricket Club. His swimming pool which had once flashed like an aquarium with the limbs of long-departed beauties was empty now and cracked and over-grown with weed.

Yet there was a chivalric bond between the two.

"How are things at Megalo?" asked Sir Ambrose.

"Greatly disturbed. We are having trouble with Juanita del Pablo."

" 'Luscious, languid and lustful'?"

"Those are not the correct epithets. She is — or rather was — 'surly, lustrous and sadistic.' I should know because I composed the phrase myself. It was a 'smash-hit,' as they say, and set a new note in personal publicity.

"Miss del Pablo has been a particular protégée of mine from the first. I remember the day she arrived. Poor Leo bought her for her eyes. She was called Baby Aaronson then — splendid eyes and a fine head of black hair. So Leo made her Spanish. He had most of her

nose cut off and sent her to Mexico for six weeks to learn flamenco
singing. Then he handed her over to me. *I* named her. *I* made her an
anti-Fascist refugee. *I* said she hated men because of her treatment by
Franco's Moors. That was a new angle then. It caught on. And she
was really quite good in her way, you know — with a truly horrifying
natural scowl. Her legs were never *photogénique* but we kept her in
long skirts and used an understudy for the lower half in scenes of
violence. I was proud of her and she was good for another ten years'
work at least.

"And now there's been a change of policy at the top. We are only
making healthy films this year to please the Catholic League of Decency.
So poor Juanita has to start at the beginning again as an Irish colleen.
They've bleached her hair and dyed it vermilion. I told them colleens
were dark but the technicolor men insisted. She's working ten hours
a day learning the brogue and to make it harder for the poor girl they've
pulled all her teeth out. She never had to smile before and her own
set was good enough for a snarl. Now she'll have to laugh roguishly
all the time. That means dentures.

"I've spent three days trying to find a name to please her. She's
turned everything down. Maureen — there are two here already;
Deirdre — no one could pronounce it; Oonagh — sounds Chinese;
Bridget — too common. The truth is she's in a thoroughly nasty temper."

Sir Ambrose, in accordance with local custom, had refrained from
listening.

"Ah," he said, "healthy films. All for 'em. I said to the Knife and
Fork Club, 'I've always had two principles throughout all my life in
motion-pictures: never do before the camera what you would not do
at home and never do at home what you would not do before the
camera.' "

He enlarged this theme while Sir Francis, in his turn, sequestered his
thoughts. Thus the two knights sat for nearly an hour, side by side
in their rocking-chairs, alternately eloquent and abstracted, gazing into
the gloaming through their monocles while the young man from time
to time refilled their glasses and his own.

The time was apt for reminiscence and in his silent periods Sir
Francis strayed back a quarter of a century and more to foggy London
streets lately set free for all eternity from fear of the Zeppelin; to
Harold Monro reading aloud at the Poetry Bookshop; Blunden's latest in
the *London Mercury*; Robin de la Condamine at the Phoenix matinées;

luncheon with Maud in Grosvenor Square, tea with Gosse in Hanover Terrace; eleven neurotic ballad-mongers in a Fleet Street pub just off for a day's cricket in Metroland, the boy with the galley-proofs plucking at his sleeve; numberless toasts at numberless banquets to numberless Immortal Memories . . .

Sir Ambrose had a more adventurous past but he lived existentially. He thought of himself as he was at that moment, brooded fondly on each several excellence and rejoiced.

"Well," he said at length, "I should be toddling. Mustn't keep the missus waiting"; but he made no move and turned instead to the young man. "And how are things with you, Barlow? We haven't seen you on the cricket field lately. Very busy at Megalo, I suppose?"

"No. As a matter of fact my contract ran out three weeks ago."

"I say, did it? Well, I expect you're glad of a rest. I know I should be." The young man did not answer. "If you'll take my advice, just sit easy for a time until something attractive turns up. Don't jump at the first thing. These fellows out here respect a man who knows his own value. Most important to keep the respect of these fellows.

"We limeys have a peculiar position to keep up, you know, Barlow. They may laugh at us a bit — the way we talk and the way we dress; our monocles — they may think us cliquey and stand-offish, but, by God, they respect us. Your five-to-two is a judge of quality. He knows what he's buying and it's only the finest type of Englishman that you meet out here. I often feel like an ambassador, Barlow. It's a responsibility, I can tell you, and in various degrees every Englishman out here shares it. We can't all be at the top of the tree but we are all men of responsibility. You never find an Englishman among the under-dogs — except in England, of course. That's understood out here, thanks to the example we've set. There are jobs that an Englishman just doesn't take.

"We had an unfortunate case some years ago of a very decent young fellow who came out as a scene designer. Clever chap but he went completely native — wore ready-made shoes, and a belt instead of braces, went about without a tie, ate at drug-stores. Then, if you'll believe it, he left the studio and opened a restaurant with an Italian partner. Got cheated, of course, and the next thing he was behind a bar shaking cocktails. Appalling business. We raised a subscription at the Cricket Club to send him home, but the blighter wouldn't go. Said he liked the place, if you please. That man did irreparable harm, Barlow. He was nothing less than a deserter. Luckily the war came. He went home then all right and got himself killed in Norway. He atoned, but I always think how much better not to have anything to atone for, eh?

"Now you're a man of reputation in your own line, Barlow. If you weren't you wouldn't be here. I don't say poets are much in demand but they're bound to want one again sooner or later and when they do, they'll come to you cap in hand — if you haven't done anything in the meantime to lose their respect. See what I mean?

"Well, here I am talking like a Dutch uncle while the missus is waiting for her dinner. I must toddle. So long, Frank, I've enjoyed our talk. Wish we saw you more often at the Cricket Club. Good-bye, young man, and just remember what I've been saying. I may look like an old buffer but I know what I'm talking about. Don't move, either of you. I can find my way."

It was quite dark now. The head-lamps of the waiting car spread a brilliant fan of light behind the palm trees, swept across the front of the bungalow and receded towards Hollywood Boulevard.

"What do you make of that?" said Dennis Barlow.

"He's heard something. That was what brought him here."

"It was bound to come out."

"Certainly. If exclusion from British society can be counted as martyr-dom, prepare for the palm and the halo. You have not been to your place of business to-day?"

"I'm on the night shift. I actually managed to write to-day. Thirty lines. Would you like to see them?"

"No," said Sir Francis. "It is one of the numberless compensations of my exile that I need never read unpublished verses — or, for that matter, verses in any condition. Take them away, dear boy, prune and polish at your leisure. They would only distress me. I should not under-stand them and I might be led to question the value of a sacrifice which I now applaud. You are a young man of genius, the hope of English poetry. I have heard it said and I devoutly believe it. I have served the cause of art enough by conniving at your escape from a bondage to which I myself have been long happily reconciled.

"Did they ever, when you were a child, take you to a Christmas play called *Where the Rainbow Ends* — a very silly piece? Saint George and a midshipman flew off on a carpet to rescue some lost children from a Dragon's country. It always seemed to me a gross interference. The children were perfectly happy. They paid tribute, I remember, of their letters from home, unopened. Your verses are my letters from home — like Kierkegaard and Kafka and 'Scottie' Wilson. I pay without protest or resentment. Fill my glass, dear boy. I am your *memento mori*. I am deep in thrall to the Dragon King. Hollywood is my life.

"Did you see the photograph some time ago in one of the magazines of a dog's head severed from its body, which the Russians are keeping alive for some obscene Muscovite purpose by pumping blood into it from a bottle? It dribbles at the tongue when it smells a cat. That's what all of us are, you know, out here. The studios keep us going with a pump. We are still just capable of a few crude reactions — nothing more. If we ever got disconnected from our bottle, we should simply crumble. I like to think that it was the example of myself before your eyes day after day for more than a year that inspired your heroic resolution to set up in an independent trade. You have had example and perhaps now and then precept. I may have counselled you in so many words to leave the studio while you could still do so."

"You did. A thousand times."

"Surely not so often? Once or twice when I was in liquor. Not a thousand times. And my advice, I think, was to return to Europe. I never suggested anything so violently macabre, so Elizabethan, as the work you chose. Tell me, do you give your new employer satisfaction, do you think?"

"My manner is congenial. He told me so yesterday. The man they had before caused offence by his gusto. They find me reverent. It is my combination of melancholy with the English accent. Several of our clientele have commented favourably upon it."

"But our fellow expatriates? We cannot expect sympathy from them. What did our late visitor say? 'There are jobs that an Englishman just doesn't take.' Yours, dear boy, is pre-eminently one of those."

Dennis Barlow went to work after dinner. He drove towards Burbank, past luminous motels, past the golden gates and flood-lit temples of Whispering Glades Memorial Park, almost to the extremity of the city, to his place of business. His colleague, Miss Myra Poski, was waiting for relief, hatted and freshly painted.

"I hope I'm not late."

"You're sweet. I've a date at the Planetarium or I'd stay and fix you some coffee. There's been nothing to do all day except mail a few remembrance cards. Oh, and Mr. Schultz says if anything comes

in put it straight on the ice this hot weather. Good-bye"; and she was
gone leaving Dennis in sole charge of the business.

The office was furnished in sombre good taste that was relieved by
a pair of bronze puppies on the chimney-piece. A low trolley of steel
and white enamel alone distinguished the place from a hundred thousand modern American reception-rooms; that and the clinical smell.
A bowl of roses stood beside the telephone; their scent contended with
the carbolic, but did not prevail.

Dennis sat in one of the arm-chairs, put his feet on the trolley
and settled himself to read. Life in the Air Force had converted him
from an amateur to a mere addict. There were certain trite passages of
poetry which from a diverse multitude of associations never failed to
yield the sensations he craved; he never experimented; these were the
branded drug, the sure specific, big magic. He opened the anthology as
a woman opens her familiar pack of cigarettes.

Outside the windows the cars swept past continuously, out of town,
into town, lights ablaze, radios at full throttle.

"*I wither slowly in thine arms,*" he read. "*Here at the quiet limit of
the world,*" and repeated to himself: "Here at the quiet limit of the
world. Here at the quiet limit of the world" . . . as a monk will repeat a
single pregnant text, over and over again in prayer.

Presently the telephone rang.

"The Happier Hunting Ground," he said.

A woman's voice came to him, hoarse, it seemed, with emotion; in
other circumstances he might have thought her drunk. "This is Theo-
dora Heinkel, Mrs. Walter Heinkel, of 207 Via Dolorosa, Bel Air. You
must come at once. I can't tell you over the phone. My little Arthur
— they've just brought him in. He went out first thing and never
came back. I didn't worry because he's sometimes been away like that
before. I said to Mr. Heinkel, 'But, Walter, I can't go out to dine
when I don't know where Arthur is' and Mr. Heinkel said, 'What
the heck? You can't walk out on Mrs. Leicester Scrunch at the last
minute,' so I went and there I was at the table on Mr. Leicester Scrunch's
right hand when they brought me the news . . . Hullo, hullo, are you
there?"

Dennis picked up the instrument which he had laid on the blotting
pad. "I will come at once, Mrs. Heinkel; 207 Via Dolorosa I think
you said."

"I said I was sitting at Mr. Leicester Scrunch's right hand when they brought me the news. He and Mr. Heinkel had to help me to the automobile."

"I am coming at once."

"I shall never forgive myself as long as I live. To think of his being brought home alone. The maid was out and the city wagon-driver had to telephone from the drug-store . . . Hullo, hullo. Are you there? I said the city wagon-driver had to telephone from the drug-store."

"I am on my way, Mrs. Heinkel."

Dennis locked the office and backed the car from the garage; not his own, but the plain black van which was used for official business. Half an hour later he was at the house of mourning. A corpulent man came down the garden path to greet him. He was formally dressed for the evening in the high fashion of the place — Donegal tweeds, sandals, a grass-green silk shirt, open at the neck with an embroidered monogram covering half his torso. "Am I pleased to see you?" he said.

"Mr. W. H., all happiness," said Dennis involuntarily.

"Pardon me?"

"I am the Happier Hunting Ground," said Dennis.

"Yes, come along in."

Dennis opened the back of the wagon and took out an aluminium container. "Will this be large enough?"

"Plenty."

They entered the house. A lady, also dressed for the evening in a long, low gown and a diamond tiara, sat in the hall with a glass in her hand.

"This has been a terrible experience for Mrs. Heinkel."

"I don't want to see him. I don't want to speak of it," said the lady.

"The Happier Hunting Ground assumes all responsibility," said Dennis.

"This way," said Mr. Heinkel. "In the pantry."

The Sealyham lay on the draining board beside the sink. Dennis lifted it into the container.

"Perhaps you wouldn't mind taking a hand?"

Together he and Mr. Heinkel carried their load to the wagon.

"Shall we discuss arrangements now, or would you prefer to call in the morning?"

"I'm a pretty busy man mornings," said Mr. Heinkel. "Come into the study."

There was a tray on the desk. They helped themselves to whisky.

"I have our brochure here setting out our service. Were you thinking of interment or incineration?"

"Pardon me?"

"Buried or burned?"

"Burned, I guess."

"I have some photographs here of various styles of urn."

"The best will be good enough."

"Would you require a niche in our columbarium or do you prefer to
keep the remains at home?"

"What you said first."

"And the religious rites? We have a pastor who is always pleased
to assist."

"Well, Mr. — ?"

"Barlow."

"Mr. Barlow, we're neither of us what you might call very church-
going people, but I think on an occasion like this Mrs. Heinkel would
want all the comfort you can offer."

"Our Grade A service includes several unique features. At the
moment of committal, a white dove, symbolizing the deceased's soul, is
liberated over the crematorium."

"Yes," said Mr. Heinkel, "I reckon Mrs. Heinkel would appreciate
the dove."

"And every anniversary a card of remembrance is mailed without
further charge. It reads: *Your little Arthur is thinking of you in
heaven to-day and wagging his tail.*"

"That's a very beautiful thought, Mr. Barlow."

"Then if you will just sign the order . . ."

Mrs. Heinkel bowed gravely to him as he passed through the hall.
Mr. Heinkel accompanied him to the door of his car. "It has been
a great pleasure to make your acquaintance, Mr. Barlow. You have
certainly relieved me of a great responsibility."

"That is what the Happier Hunting Ground aims to do," said Dennis,
and drove away.

At the administrative building, he carried the dog to the refrigerator.
It was a capacious chamber, already occupied by two or three other
small cadavers. Next to a Siamese cat stood a tin of fruit juice and a
plate of sandwiches. Dennis took his supper into the reception-room,
and, as he ate it, resumed his interrupted reading.

II

WEEKS passed, the rain came, invitations dwindled and ceased. Dennis Barlow was happy in his work. Artists are by nature versatile and precise; they only repine when involved with the monotonous and the makeshift. Dennis had observed this during the recent war; a poetic friend of his in the Grenadiers was an enthusiast to the end, while he himself fretted almost to death as a wingless officer in Transport Command.

He had been dealing with Air Priorities at an Italian port when his first, his only book came out. England was no nest of singing-birds in that decade; lamas scanned the snows in vain for a reincarnation of Rupert Brooke. Dennis's poems, appearing among the buzz-bombs and the jaunty, deeply depressing publications of His Majesty's Stationery Office, achieved undesignedly something of the effect of the resistance Press of occupied Europe. They were extravagantly praised and but for the paper restrictions would have sold like a novel. On the day the *Sunday Times* reached Caserta with a two-column review, Dennis was offered the post of personal assistant to an Air Marshal. He sulkily declined, remained in "Priorities" and was presented in his absence with half a dozen literary prizes. On his discharge he came to Hollywood to help write the life of Shelley for the films.

There in the Megalopolitan studios he found reproduced, and enhanced by the nervous agitation endemic to the place, all the gross futility of service life. He repined, despaired, fled.

And now he was content; adept in a worthy trade, giving satisfaction to Mr. Schultz, keeping Miss Poski guessing. For the first time he knew what it was to "explore an avenue"; his way was narrow but it was dignified and umbrageous and it led to limitless distances.

Not all his customers were as open-handed and tractable as the Heinkels. Some boggled at a ten-dollar burial, others had their pets embalmed and then went East and forgot them; one after filling half the ice-box for over a week with a dead she-bear changed her mind and called in the taxidermist. These were the dark days, to be set against the ritualistic, almost orgiastic cremation of a non-sectarian chimpanzee and the burial of a canary over whose tiny grave a squad of Marine buglers had sounded Taps. It is forbidden by Californian law to scatter human remains from an aeroplane, but the sky is free to the animal world and on one occasion it fell to Dennis to commit the ashes of a tabby-cat to the slip-stream over Sunset Boulevard. That day he was photographed for the local paper and his social ruin consummated. But he was complacent. His poem led a snakes-and-ladders existence of composition and excision but it continued just perceptibly to grow. Mr. Schultz raised his wages. The scars of adolescence healed. There at the quiet limit of the world he experienced a tranquil joy such as he had known only once before, one glorious early Eastertide when, honourably lamed in a house-match, he had lain in bed and heard below the sanatorium windows the school marching out for a field-day.

But while Dennis prospered, things were not well with Sir Francis. The old man was losing his equanimity. He fidgeted with his food and shuffled sleeplessly about the veranda in the silent hour of dawn. Juanita del Pablo was taking unkindly to her translation and, powerless to strike the great, was rending her old friend. Sir Francis confided his growing troubles to Dennis.

Juanita's agent was pressing the metaphysical point; did his client exist? Could you legally bind her to annihilate herself? Could you come to any agreement with her before she had acquired the ordinary marks of identity? Sir Francis was charged with the metamorphosis. How lightly, ten years before, he had brought her into existence — the dynamite-bearing Maenad of the Bilbao water-front! With what leaden effort did he now search the nomenclature of Celtic mythology and write the new life-story — a romance of the Mountains of Mourne, of the bare-foot child whom the peasants spoke of as a fairies' changeling, the confidante of leprechauns, the rough-and-tumble tomboy who pushed the moke out of the cabin and dodged the English tourists among rocks and waterfalls! He read it aloud to Dennis and knew it was no good.

He read it aloud in conference, before the now nameless actress, her agent and solicitor; there were also present the Megalopolitan Directors of Law, Publicity, Personality and International Relations. In all his career in Hollywood Sir Francis had never been in a single assembly with so many luminaries of the Grand Sanhedrin of the Corporation. They turned down his story without debate.

"Take a week at home, Frank," said the Director of Personality. "Try to work out a new slant. Or maybe you feel kind of allergic to the assignment?"

"No," said Sir Francis feebly. "No, not at all. This conference has been most helpful. I know what you gentlemen require. I'm sure I shall have no further difficulty."

"Always very pleased to look over anything you cook up," said the Director of International Relations. But when the door closed behind him, the great men looked at one another and shook their heads.

"Just another has-been," said the Director of Personality.

"There's a cousin of my wife's just arrived," said the Director of Publicity. "Maybe I'd better give him a try-out on the job."

"Yes, Sam," they all said, "have your wife's cousin look it over."

After that Sir Francis remained at home and for several days his secretary came out daily to take dictation. He footled with a new name for Juanita and a new life-story: Kathleen FitzBourke the toast of the Galway Blazers; the falling light among the banks and walls of that stiff country and Kathleen FitzBourke alone with hounds, far from the crumbling towers of FitzBourke Castle . . . Then there came a day when his secretary failed to arrive. He telephoned to the studio. The call was switched from one administrative office to another until eventually a voice said: "Yes, Sir Francis, that is quite in order. Miss Mavrocordato has been transferred to the Catering Department."

"Well, I must have somebody."

"I'm not sure we have anyone available right now, Sir Francis."

"I see. Well, it is very inconvenient but I'll have to come down and finish the work I am doing in the studio. Will you have a car sent for me?"

"I'll put you through to Mr. Van Gluck."

Again the call went to and fro like a shuttlecock until finally a voice said: "Transportation Captain. No, Sir Francis, I'm sorry, we don't have a studio automobile right here right now."

Already feeling the mantle of Lear about his shoulders Sir Francis took a taxi to the studio. He nodded to the girl at the desk with something less than his usual urbanity.

"Good morning, Sir Francis," she said. "Can I help you?"

"No, thank you."

"There isn't anyone particular you were looking for?"

"No one."

The elevator-girl looked enquiringly at him. "Going up?"

"Third floor, of course."

He walked down the familiar featureless corridor, opened the familiar door and stopped abruptly. A stranger sat at the desk.

"I'm so sorry," said Sir Francis. "Stupid of me. Never done that before." He backed out and shut the door. Then he studied it. It was his number. He had made no mistake. But in the slot which had borne his name for twelve years — ever since he came to this department from the script-writers' — there was now a card typewritten with the name "Lorenzo Medici." He opened the door again. "I say," he said. "There must be some mistake."

"Maybe there is too," said Mr. Medici, cheerfully. "Everything seems kinda screwy around here. I've spent half the morning clearing junk out of this room. Piles of stuff, just like someone had been living here — bottles of medicine, books, photographs, kids' games. Seems it belonged to some old Britisher who's just kicked off."

"I am that Britisher and I have not kicked off."

"Mighty glad to hear it. Hope there wasn't anything you valued in the junk. Maybe it's still around somewhere."

"I must go and see Otto Baumbein."

"He's screwy too but I don't figure he'll know anything about the junk. I just pushed it out in the passage. Maybe some janitor . . ."

Sir Francis went down the passage to the office of the assistant director. "Mr. Baumbein is in conference right now. Shall I have him call you?"

"I'll wait."

He sat in the outer office where two typists enjoyed long, intimately amorous telephone conversations. At last Mr. Baumbein came out. "Why, Frank," he said. "Mighty nice of you to look us up. I appreciate that. I do really. Come again. Come often, Frank."

"I wanted to talk to you, Otto."

"Well, I'm rather busy right now, Frank. How say I give you a ring next week sometime?"

"I've just found a Mr. Medici in my office."

"Why, yes, Frank. Only he says it 'Medissy,' like that; how you said it kinda sounds like a wop and Mr. Medici is a very fine young man with a very, very fine and wonderful record, Frank, who I'd be proud to have you meet."

"Then where do I work?"

"Well now see here, Frank, that's a thing I want very much to talk to you about but I haven't the time right now. I haven't the time, have I, dear?"

"No, Mr. Baumbein," said one of the secretaries. "You certainly haven't the time."

"You see. I just haven't the time. I know what, dear, try fix it for Sir Francis to see Mr. Erikson. I know Mr. Erikson would greatly appreciate it."

So Sir Francis saw Mr. Erikson, Mr. Baumbein's immediate superior, and from him learned in blunt Nordic terms what he had already in the last hour darkly surmised; that his long service with Megalopolitan Pictures Inc. had come to an end.

"It would have been civil to tell me," said Sir Francis.

"The letter is on its way. Things get hung up sometimes, as you know; so many different departments have to give their O.K. — the Legal Branch, Finance, Labour Disputes Section. But I don't anticipate any trouble in your case. Luckily you aren't a Union man. Now and then the Big Three make objections about waste of manpower — when we bring someone from Europe or China or somewhere and then fire him in a week. But that doesn't arise in your case. You've had a record run. Just on twenty-five years, isn't it? There's not even any provision in your contract for repatriation. Your Termination ought to whip right through."

Sir Francis left Mr. Erikson and made his way out of the great hive. It was called the Wilbur K. Lutit Memorial Block and had not been built when Sir Francis first came to Hollywood. Wilbur K. Lutit had been alive then; had, indeed, once pudgily shaken his hand. Sir Francis had watched the edifice rise and had had an honourable if not illustrious place at its dedication. He had seen the rooms filled and refilled, the name plates change on the doors. He had seen arrivals and departures, Mr. Erikson and Mr. Baumbein coming, others, whose names now escaped him, going. He remembered poor Leo who had fallen from great heights to die with his bill unpaid in the Tents of Kedar Hotel.

"Did you find who you were looking for?" asked the girl at the desk as he made his way out into the sunshine.

Turf does not prosper in Southern California and the Hollywood ground did not permit the larger refinements of cricket. The game indeed was fitfully played by some of the junior members, but for the majority it formed as small a part in their interests as do fishmongering or cordwaining to the Livery Companies of the City of London. For these the club was the symbol of their Englishry. Here they collected subscriptions for the Red Cross and talked at their ease, maliciously, out of the hearing of their alien employers and protectors. There on the day following Sir Francis Hinsley's unexpected death the expatriates repaired as though summoned by tocsin.

"Young Barlow found him."

"Barlow of Megalo?"

"He used to be at Megalo's. His contract wasn't renewed. Since then . . ."

"Yes, I heard. That was a shocking business."

"I never knew Sir Francis. He was rather before my time. Does anyone know why he did it?"

"*His* contract wasn't renewed."

They were words of ill-omen to all that assembled company, words never spoken without the furtive touching of wood or crossing of fingers; unholy words best left unsaid. To each of them was given a span of life between the signature of the contract and its expiration; beyond that lay the vast unknowable.

"Where is Sir Ambrose? He's sure to come this evening."

He came at length and it was noted that he already wore a band of crêpe on his Coldstream blazer. Late as it was he accepted a cup of tea, snuffed the air of suspense that filled the pavilion to stifling, and spoke:

"No doubt you've all heard of this ghastly business of old Frank?" A murmur.

"He fell on bad days at the end. I don't suppose there's anyone in Hollywood now except myself who remembers him in his prime. He did yeoman service."

"He was a scholar and a gentleman."

"Exactly. He was one of the first Englishmen of distinction to go into motion-pictures. You might say he laid the foundations on which I — on which we all have built. He was our first ambassador."

"I really think that Megalo might have kept him on. They wouldn't notice his salary. In the course of nature he couldn't have cost them much more."

"People live to a great age in this place."

"Oh, it wasn't that," said Sir Ambrose. "There were other reasons." He paused. Then the false and fruity tones continued: "I think I had better tell you because it is a thing which has a bearing on all our lives here. I don't think many of you visited old Frank in recent years. I did. I make a point of keeping up with all the English out here. Well, as you may know, he had taken in a young Englishman named Dennis Barlow." The cricketers looked at one another, some knowingly, others in surmise. "Now I don't want to say a word against Barlow. He came out here with a high reputation as a poet. He just hasn't made good, I'm afraid. That is nothing to condemn him for. This is a hard testing ground. Only the best survive. Barlow failed. As soon as I heard of it I went to see him. I advised him as bluntly as I could to clear out. I thought it my duty to you all. We don't want any poor Englishmen hanging around Hollywood. I told him as much, frankly and fairly, as one Englishman to another.

"Well, I think most of you know what his answer was. *He took a job at the pets' cemetery.*

"In Africa, if a white man is disgracing himself and letting down his people the authorities pack him off home. We haven't any such rights here, unfortunately. The trouble is we all suffer for the folly of one. Do you suppose Megalo would have sacked poor Frank in other circumstances? But when they saw him sharing a house with a fellow who worked in the pets' cemetery . . . Well, I ask you! You all know the form out here almost as well as I do. I've nothing to say against our American colleagues. They're as fine a set of chaps as you'll find anywhere and they've created the finest industry in the world. They have their standards — that's all. Who's to blame 'em? In a world of competition people are taken at their face value. Everything depends on reputation — 'face' as they say out East. Lose that and you lose everything. Frank lost face. I will say no more.

"Personally I'm sorry for young Barlow. I wouldn't stand in his shoes to-day. I've just come from seeing the lad. I thought it was the decent thing. I hope any of you who come across him will remember that his chief fault was inexperience. He wouldn't be guided. However . . .

"I've left all the preliminary arrangements in his hands. He's going up to Whispering Glades as soon as the police hand over the remains. Give him something to do, to take his mind off it, I thought.

"This is an occasion when we've all got to show the flag. We may have to put our hands in our pockets — I don't suppose old Frank has left much — but it will be money well spent if it puts the British colony right in the eyes of the industry. I called Washington and asked them to send the Ambassador to the funeral, but it doesn't seem they can manage it. I'll try again. It would make a lot of difference. In any case I don't think the studios will keep away if they know *we* are solid . . ."

As he spoke the sun sank below the busy western hillside. The sky was still bright but a deep shadow crept over the tough and ragged grass of the cricket field, bringing with it a sharp chill.

III

DENNIS was a young man of sensibility rather than of sentiment. He had lived his twenty-eight years at arm's length from violence, but he came of a generation which enjoys a vicarious intimacy with death. Never, it so happened, had he seen a human corpse until that morning when, returning tired from night duty, he found his host strung to the rafters. The spectacle had been rude and momentarily unnerving; perhaps it had left a scar somewhere out of sight in his subconscious mind. But his reason accepted the event as part of the established order. Others in gentler ages had had their lives changed by such a revelation; to Dennis it was the kind of thing to be expected in the world he knew and, as he drove to Whispering Glades, his conscious mind was pleasantly exhilarated and full of curiosity.

Times without number since he first came to Hollywood he had heard the name of that great necropolis on the lips of others; he had read it in the local news-sheets when some more than usually illustrious body was given more than usually splendid honours or some new acquisition was made to its collected masterpieces of contemporary art. Of recent weeks his interest had been livelier and more technical for it was in humble emulation of its great neighbour that the Happier Hunting Ground was planned. The language he daily spoke in his new trade was a *patois* derived from that high pure source. More than once Mr. Schultz had exultantly exclaimed after one of his performances: "It was worthy of Whispering Glades." As a missionary priest making his first pilgrimage to the Vatican, as a paramount chief of equatorial Africa mounting the Eiffel Tower, Dennis Barlow, poet and pets' mortician, drove through the Golden Gates.

They were vast, the largest in the world, and freshly regilt. A notice proclaimed the inferior dimensions of their Old World rivals. Beyond them lay a semi-circle of golden yew, a wide gravel roadway and an island of mown turf on which stood a singular and massive wall of marble sculptured in the form of an open book. Here, in letters a foot high, was incised:

The Dream

Behold I dreamed a dream and I saw a New Earth sacred to HAPPINESS. There amid all that Nature and Art could offer to elevate the Soul of Man I saw the Happy Resting Place of Countless Loved Ones. And I saw the Waiting Ones who still stood at the brink of that narrow stream that now separated them from those who had gone before. Young and old, they were happy too. Happy in Beauty, Happy in the certain knowledge that their Loved Ones were very near, in Beauty and Happiness such as the earth cannot give.

I heard a voice say: "Do this."

And behold I awoke and in the Light and Promise of my DREAM I made WHISPERING GLADES.

ENTER STRANGER and BE HAPPY.

And below, in vast cursive facsimile, the signature:

WILBUR KENWORTHY, THE DREAMER

A modest wooden signboard beside it read: *Prices on enquiry at Administrative Building. Drive straight on.*

Dennis drove on through green parkland and presently came in sight of what in England he would have taken for the country seat of an Edwardian financier. It was black and white, timbered and gabled, with twisting brick chimneys and wrought iron wind-vanes. He left his car among a dozen others and proceeded on foot through a box walk, past a sunken herb garden, a sun-dial, a bird-bath and fountain, a rustic seat and a pigeon-cote. Music rose softly all round him, the subdued notes of the "Hindu Love-song" relayed from an organ through count-less amplifiers concealed about the garden.

When as a newcomer to the Megalopolitan Studios he first toured the lots, it had taxed his imagination to realise that those solid-seeming streets and squares of every period and climate were in fact plaster façades whose backs revealed the structure of bill-boardings. Here the illusion was quite otherwise. Only with an effort could Dennis believe that the building before him was three-dimensional and permanent; but here, as everywhere in Whispering Glades, failing credulity was fortified by the painted word.

This perfect replica of an old English Manor, a notice said, *like all the buildings of Whispering Glades, is constructed throughout of Grade A steel and concrete with foundations extending into solid rock. It is certified proof against fire, earthquake and —— Their name liveth for evermore who record it in Whispering Glades.*

At the blank patch a signwriter was even then at work and Dennis, pausing to study it, discerned the ghost of the words "high explosive" freshly obliterated and the outlines of "nuclear fission" about to be filled in as substitute.

Followed by music he stepped as it were from garden to garden, for the approach to the offices lay through a florist's shop. Here one young lady was spraying scent over a stall of lilac while a second was talking on the telephone: ". . . Oh, Mrs. Bogolov, I'm really sorry but it's just one of the things that Whispering Glades does not do. The Dreamer does not approve of wreaths or crosses. We just arrange the flowers in their own natural beauty. It's one of the Dreamer's own ideas. I'm sure Mr. Bogolov would prefer it himself. Won't you just leave it to us, Mrs. Bogolov? You tell us what you want to spend and we will do the rest. I'm sure you will be more than satisfied. Thank you, Mrs. Bogolov, it's a pleasure . . ."

Dennis passed through and opening the door marked *Enquiries* found himself in a raftered banqueting hall. The "Hindu Love-song" was here also, gently discoursed from the dark oak panelling. A young lady rose from a group of her fellows to welcome him, one of that new race of exquisite, amiable, efficient young ladies whom he had met everywhere in the United States. She wore a white smock and over her sharply supported left breast was embroidered the words, *Mortuary Hostess.*

"Can I help you in any way?"

"I came to arrange about a funeral."

"Is it for yourself?"

"Certainly not. Do I look so moribund?"

"Pardon me?"

"Do I look as if I were about to die?"

"Why, no. Only many of our friends like to make Before Need Arrangements. Will you come this way?"

She led him from the hall into a soft passage. The décor here was

Georgian. The "Hindu Love-song" came to its end and was succeeded by the voice of a nightingale. In a little chintzy parlour he and his hostess sat down to make arrangements.

"I must first record the Essential Data."

He told her his name and Sir Francis's.

"Now, Mr. Barlow, what had you in mind? Embalmment of course, and after that incineration or not, according to taste. Our crematory is on scientific principles, the heat is so intense that all inessentials are volatilized. Some people did not like the thought that ashes of the casket and clothing were mixed with the Loved One's. Normal disposal is by inhumement, entombment, inurnment or immurement, but many people just lately prefer insarcophagusment. That is *very* individual. The casket is placed inside a sealed sarcophagus, marble or bronze, and rests permanently above ground in a niche in the mausoleum, with or without a personal stained-glass window above. That, of course, is for those with whom price is not a primary consideration."

"We want my friend buried."

"This is not your first visit to Whispering Glades?"

"Yes."

"Then let me explain the Dream. The Park is zoned. Each zone has its own name and appropriate Work of Art. Zones of course vary in price and within the zones the prices vary according to their proximity to the Work of Art. We have single sites as low as fifty dollars. That is in Pilgrims' Rest, a zone we are just developing behind the Crematory fuel dump. The most costly are those on Lake Isle. They range about a thousand dollars. Then there is Lovers' Nest, zoned about a very, very beautiful marble replica of Rodin's famous statue, the Kiss. We have double plots there at seven hundred and fifty dollars the pair. Was your Loved One married?"

"No."

"What was his business?"

"He was a writer."

"Ah, then Poets' Corner would be the place for him. We have many of our foremost literary names there, either in person or as Before Need reservations. You are no doubt acquainted with the works of Amelia Bergson?"

"I know of them."

"We sold Miss Bergson a Before Need reservation only yesterday, under the statue of the prominent Greek poet Homer. I could put your friend right next to her. But perhaps you would like to see the zone before deciding?"

"I want to see everything."

"There certainly is plenty to see. I'll have one of our guides take you round just as soon as we have all the Essential Data, Mr. Barlow. Was your Loved One of any special religion?"

"An Agnostic."

"We have two non-sectarian churches in the Park and a number of non-sectarian pastors. Jews and Catholics seem to prefer to make their own arrangements."

"I believe Sir Ambrose Abercrombie is planning a special service."

"Oh, was your Loved One in films, Mr. Barlow? In that case he ought to be in Shadowland."

"I think he would prefer to be with Homer and Miss Bergson."

"Then the University Church would be most convenient. We like to save the Waiting Ones a long procession. I presume the Loved One was Caucasian?"

"No, why did you think that? He was purely English."

"English are purely Caucasian, Mr. Barlow. This is a restricted park. The Dreamer has made that rule for the sake of the Waiting Ones. In their time of trial they prefer to be with their own people."

"I think I understand. Well, let me assure you Sir Francis was quite white."

As he said this there came vividly into Dennis's mind that image which lurked there, seldom out of sight for long; the sack or body suspended and the face above it with eyes red and horribly starting from their sockets, the cheeks mottled in indigo like the marbled end-papers of a ledger and the tongue swollen and protruding like an end of black sausage.

"Let us now decide on the casket."

They went to the show-rooms where stood coffins of every shape and material; the nightingale still sang in the cornice.

"The two-piece lid is most popular for gentlemen Loved Ones. Only the upper part is then exposed to view."

"Exposed to view?"

"Yes, when the Waiting Ones come to take leave."

"But, I say, I don't think that will quite do. I've seen him. He's terribly disfigured, you know."

"If there are any special little difficulties in the case you must mention them to our cosmeticians. You will be seeing one of them before you leave. They have never failed yet."

Dennis made no hasty choice. He studied all that was for sale; even the simplest of these coffins, he humbly recognised, outshone the most gorgeous product of the Happier Hunting Ground and when he approached the two thousand dollar level — and these were not the costliest — he felt himself in the Egypt of the Pharaohs. At length he decided on a massive chest of walnut with bronze enrichments and an interior of quilted satin. Its lid, as recommended, was in two parts.

"You are sure that they will be able to make him presentable?"

"We had a Loved One last month who was found drowned. He had been in the sea a month and they only identified him by his wrist-watch. They fixed that stiff," said the hostess disconcertingly lapsing from the high diction she had hitherto employed, "so he looked like it was his wedding day. The boys up there surely know their job. Why if he's sat on an atom bomb, they'd make him presentable."

"That's very comforting."

"I'll say it is." And then slipping on her professional manner again as though it were a pair of glasses, she resumed. "How will the Loved One be attired? We have our own tailoring section. Sometimes after a very long illness there are not suitable clothes available and sometimes the Waiting Ones think it a waste of a good suit. You see we can fit a Loved One out very reasonably as a casket-suit does not have to be designed for hard wear and in cases where only the upper part is exposed for leave-taking there is no need for more than jacket and vest. Something dark is best to set off the flowers."

Dennis was entirely fascinated. At length he said: "Sir Francis was not much of a dandy. I doubt of his having anything quite suitable for casket wear. But in Europe, I think, we usually employ a shroud."

"Oh, we have shrouds too. I'll show you some."

The hostess led him to a set of sliding shelves like a sacristy chest where vestments are stored, and drawing one out revealed a garment such as Dennis had never seen before. Observing his interest she held it up for his closer inspection. It was in appearance like a suit of clothes, buttoned in front but open down the back; the sleeves hung loose, open at the seam; half an inch of linen appeared at the cuff and the V of the waistcoat was similarly filled; a knotted bow-tie emerged from the opening of a collar which also lay as though slit from behind. It was the apotheosis of the "dickey."

"A specialty of our own," she said, "though it is now widely imitated. The idea came from the quick-change artists of vaudeville. It enables one to dress the Loved Ones without disturbing the pose."

"Most remarkable. I believe that is just the article we require."

"With or without trousers?"

"What precisely is the advantage of trousers?"

"For Slumber-Room wear. It depends whether you wish the leave-taking to be on the chaise-longue or in the casket."

"Perhaps I had better see the Slumber Room before deciding."

"You're welcome."

She led him out to the hall and up a staircase. The nightingale had now given place to the organ and strains of Handel followed them to the Slumber Floor. Here she asked a colleague, "Which room have we free?"

"Only Daffodil."

"This way, Mr. Barlow."

They passed many closed doors of pickled oak until at length she opened one and stood aside for him to enter. He found a little room, brightly furnished and papered. It might have been part of a luxurious modern country club in all its features save one. Bowls of flowers stood disposed about a chintz sofa and on the sofa lay what seemed to be the wax effigy of an elderly woman dressed as though for an evening party. Her white gloved hands held a bouquet and on her nose glittered a pair of rimless pince-nez.

"Oh," said his guide, "how foolish of me. We've come into Primrose by mistake. This," she added superfluously, "is occupied."

"Yes."

"The leave-taking is not till the afternoon but we had better go before one of the cosmeticians finds us. They like to make a few final adjustments before Waiting Ones are admitted. Still it gives you an idea of the chaise-longue arrangement. We usually recommend the casket half-exposure for gentlemen because the legs never look so well."

She led him out.

"Will there be many for the leave-taking?"

"Yes, I rather think so, a great many."

"Then you had better have a suite with an anteroom. The Orchid Room is the best. Shall I make a reservation for that?"

"Yes, do."

"And the half-exposure in the casket, not the chaise-longue?"

"Not the chaise-longue."

She led him back towards the reception-room.

"It may seem a little strange to you, Mr. Barlow, coming on a Loved One unexpectedly in that way."

"I confess it did a little."

"You will find it quite different on the day. The leave-taking is a very, very great source of consolation. Often the Waiting Ones last saw their Loved Ones on a bed of pain surrounded by all the gruesome concomitants of the sick-room or the hospital. Here they see them as they knew them in buoyant life, transfigured with peace and happiness. At the funeral they have time only for a last look as they file past. Here in the Slumber Room they can stand as long as they like photographing a last beautiful memory on the mind."

She spoke, he observed, partly by the book, in the words of the Dreamer, partly in her own brisk language. They were back in the reception-room now and she spoke briskly. "Well, I guess I've got all I want out of you, Mr. Barlow, except your signature to the order and a deposit."

Dennis had come prepared for this. It was part of the Happier Hunting Ground procedure. He paid her five hundred dollars and took her receipt.

"Now one of our cosmeticians is waiting to see you and get *her* Essential Data, but before we part, may I interest you in our Before Need Provision Arrangements?"

"Everything about Whispering Glades interests me profoundly, but that aspect, perhaps, less than others."

"The benefits of the plan are twofold" — she was speaking by the book now with a vengeance — "financial and psychological. You, Mr. Barlow, are now approaching your optimum earning phase. You are no doubt making provision of many kinds for your future — investments, insurance policies and so forth. You plan to spend your declining days in security but have you considered what burdens you may not be piling up for those you leave behind? Last month, Mr. Barlow, a husband and wife were here consulting us about Before Need Provision. They were prominent citizens in the prime of life with two daughters just budding into womanhood. They heard all the particulars, they were impressed and said they would return in a few days to complete arrangements. Only next day those two passed on, Mr. Barlow, in an automobile accident, and instead of them there came two distraught orphans to ask what arrangements their parents had made. We were obliged to inform them that *no* arrangements had been made. In the hour of their greatest need those children were left comfortless. How different it would have been had we been able to say to them: 'Welcome to all the Happiness of Whispering Glades.' "

"Yes, but you know I haven't any children. Besides I am a foreigner. I have no intention of dying here."

"Mr. Barlow, you are afraid of death."

"No, I assure you."

"It is a natural instinct, Mr. Barlow, to shrink from the unknown. But if you discuss it openly and frankly you remove morbid reflexions. That is one of the things the psycho-analysts have taught us. Bring your dark fears into the light of the common day of the common man, Mr. Barlow. Realise that death is not a private tragedy of your own but the general lot of man. As Hamlet so beautifully writes: 'Know that death is common; all that live must die.' Perhaps you think it morbid and even dangerous to give thought to this subject. Mr. Barlow, the contrary has been proved by scientific investigation. Many people let their vital energy lag prematurely and their earning capacity diminish simply through fear of death. By removing that fear they actually increase their expectation of life. Choose now, at leisure and in health, the form of final preparation you require, pay for it while you are best able to do so, shed all anxiety. Pass the buck, Mr. Barlow; Whispering Glades can take it."

"I will give the matter every consideration."

"I'll leave our brochure with you. And now I must hand you over to the cosmetician."

She left the room and Dennis at once forgot everything about her. He had seen her before everywhere. American mothers, Dennis reflected, presumably knew their daughters apart, as the Chinese were said subtly to distinguish one from another of their seemingly uniform race, but to the European eye the Mortuary Hostess was one with all her sisters of the air-liners and the reception-desks, one with Miss Poski at the Happier Hunting Ground. She was the standard product. A man could leave such a girl in a delicatessen shop in New York, fly three thousand miles and find her again in the cigar stall at San Francisco, just as he would find his favorite comic strip in the local paper; and she would croon the same words to him in moments of endearment and express the same views and preferences in moments of social discourse. She was convenient; but Dennis came of an earlier civilisation with sharper needs. He sought the intangible, the veiled face in the fog, the silhouette at the lighted doorway, the secret graces of a body which hid itself under formal velvet. He did not covet the spoils of this rich continent, the sprawling limbs of the swimming-pool, the wide-open painted eyes and mouths under the arc-lamps. But the girl who now entered was unique. Not indefinably; the appropriate distinguishing epithet leapt to Dennis's mind the moment he saw her: sole Eve in a bustling hygenic Eden, this girl was a decadent.

She wore the white livery of her calling; she entered the room, sat at the table and poised her fountain pen with the same professional assurance as her predecessor's, but she was what Dennis had vainly sought during a lonely year of exile.

Her hair was dark and straight, her brows wide, her skin transparent and untarnished by sun. Her lips were artifically tinctured, no doubt, but not coated like her sisters' and clogged in all their delicate pores with crimson grease; they seemed to promise instead an unmeasured range of sensual converse. Her full-face was oval, her profile pure and classical and light. Her eyes greenish and remote, with a rich glint of lunacy.

Dennis held his breath. When the girl spoke it was briskly and prosaically.

"What did your Loved One pass on from?" she asked.

"He hanged himself."

"Was the face much disfigured?"

"Hideously."

"That is quite usual. Mr. Joyboy will probably take him in hand personally. It is a question of touch, you see, massaging the blood from the congested areas. Mr. Joyboy has very wonderful hands."

"And what do you do?"

"Hair, skin and nails and I brief the embalmers for expression and pose. Have you brought any photographs of your Loved One? They are the greatest help in re-creating personality. Was he a very cheerful old gentleman?"

"No, rather the reverse."

"Shall I put him down as serene and philosophical or judicial and determined?"

"I think the former."

"It is the hardest of all expressions to fix, but Mr. Joyboy makes it his speciality — that and the joyful smile for children. Did the Loved One wear his own hair? And the normal complexion? We usually classify them as rural, athletic and scholarly — that is to say red, brown or white. Scholarly? And spectacles? A monocle. They are always a difficulty because Mr. Joyboy likes to incline the head slightly to give a more natural pose. Pince-nez and monocles are difficult to keep in place once the flesh has firmed. Also of course the monocle looks less natural when the eye is closed. Did you particularly wish to feature it?"

"No, let us eliminate the monocle."

"Just as you wish, Mr. Barlow. Of course, Mr. Joyboy *can* fix it."

"No. I think your point about the eye being closed is decisive."

"Very well. Did the Loved One pass over with a rope?"

"Braces. What you call suspenders."

"That should be quite easy to deal with. Sometimes there is a permanent line left. We had a Loved One last month who passed over with electric cord. Even Mr. Joyboy could do nothing with that. We had to wind a scarf right up to the chin. But suspenders should come out quite satisfactorily."

"You have a great regard for Mr. Joyboy, I notice."

"He is a true artist, Mr. Barlow. I can say no more."

"You enjoy your work?"

"I regard it as a very, very great privilege, Mr. Barlow."

"Have you been at it long?"

Normally, Dennis had found, the people of the United States were slow to resent curiosity about their commercial careers. This cosmetician, however, seemed to draw another thickness of veil between herself and her interlocutor.

"Eighteen months," she said briefly. "And now I have almost come to the end of my questions. Is there any individual trait you would like portrayed? Sometimes for instance the Waiting Ones like to see a pipe in the Loved One's mouth. Or anything special in his hands? In the case of children we usually give them a toy to hold. Is there anything specially characteristic of your Loved One? Many like a musical instrument. One lady made her leave-taking holding a telephone."

"No, I don't think that would be suitable."

"Just flowers? One further point — dentures. Was he wearing them when he passed on?"

"I really don't know."

"Will you try and find out? Often they disappear at the police mortuary and it causes great extra work for Mr. Joyboy. Loved Ones who pass over by their own hand *usually* wear their dentures."

"I'll look round his room and if I don't see them I'll mention it to the police."

"Thank you very much, Mr. Barlow. Well, that completes my Essential Data. It has been a pleasure to make your acquaintance."

"When shall I see you again?"

"The day after to-morrow. You had better come a little before the leave-taking to see that everything is as you wish."

"Who shall I ask for?"

"Just say the cosmetician of the Orchid Room."

"No name?"

"No name is necessary."

She left him and the forgotten hostess returned.

"Mr. Barlow, I have the Zone Guide ready to take you to the site."

Dennis awoke from a deep abstraction. "Oh, I'll take the site on trust," he said. "To tell you the truth I think I've seen enough for one day."

IV

DENNIS sought and obtained leave of absence from the Happier Hunting Ground for the funeral and its preliminaries. Mr. Schultz did not give it readily. He could ill spare Dennis; more motor cars were coming off the assembly-lines, more drivers appearing on the roads and more pets in the mortuary; there was an outbreak of food poisoning in Pasadena. The ice-box was packed and the crematorium fires blazed early and late.

"It is really very valuable experience for me, Mr. Schultz," Dennis said, seeking to extenuate the reproach of desertion. "I see a great deal of the methods of Whispering Glades and am picking up all kinds of ideas we might introduce here."

"What for you want new ideas?" asked Mr. Schultz. "Cheaper fuel, cheaper wages, harder work, that is all the new ideas I want. Look, Mr. Barlow, we got all of the trade of the coast. There's nothing in our class between San Francisco and the Mexican border. Do we get people to pay five thousand dollars for a pet's funeral? How many pay five hundred? Not two in a month. What do most of our clients say? 'Burn him up cheap, Mr. Schultz, just so the City don't have him and make me a shame.' Or else it's a fifty-dollar grave and head-stone inclusive of collection. There ain't the demand for fancy stuff since the war, Mr. Barlow. Folks pretend to love their pets, talk to them like they was children, along comes a citizen with a new auto, floods of tears, and then it's 'Is a headstone really socially essential, Mr. Schultz?' "

"Mr. Schultz, you're jealous of Whispering Glades."

"And why wouldn't I be, seeing all that dough going on relations they've hated all their lives, while the pets who've loved them and stood by them, never asked no questions, never complained, rich or poor, sickness or health, get buried anyhow like animals? Take your three days off, Mr. Barlow, only don't expect to be paid for them on account you're thinking up some fancy ideas."

The coroner caused no trouble. Dennis gave his evidence; the Whispering Glades van carried off the remains; Sir Ambrose blandly managed the press. Sir Ambrose, also, with the help of other prominent Englishmen composed the Order of the Service. Liturgy in Hollywood is the concern of the State rather than of the Clergy. Everyone at the Cricket Club wanted a part.

"There should be a reading from the Works," said Sir Ambrose. "I'm not sure I can lay my hand on a copy at the moment. These things disappear mysteriously when one moves house. Barlow, you are a literary chap. No doubt you can find a suitable passage. Something I'd suggest that gives one the essence of the man we knew — his love of nature, his fair-play, you know."

"Did Frank love nature or fair-play?"

"Why, he must have done. Great figure in letters and all that; honoured by the King."

"I don't ever remember seeing any of his works in the house."

"Find something, Barlow. Just some little personal scrap. Write it yourself if necessary. I expect you know his style. And, I say, come to think of it, you're a poet. Don't you think this is just the time to write something about old Frank? Something I can recite at the graveside you know. After all, damn it, you owe it to him — and to us. It isn't much to ask. We're doing all the donkey work."

"Donkey work" was the word, thought Dennis as he watched the cricketers compiling the list of invitations. There was a cleavage on this subject. A faction were in favour of keeping the party small and British, the majority headed by Sir Ambrose wished to include all the leaders of the film industry. It was no use "showing the flag" he explained if there was no one except poor old Frank to show it to. It was never in doubt who would win. Sir Ambrose had all the heavy weapons. Cards were accordingly printed in large numbers.

Dennis meanwhile searched for any traces of Sir Francis's "Works." There were few books in the bungalow and those few mostly Dennis's own. Sir Francis had given up writing before Dennis could read. He did not remember those charming books which had appeared while he lay in the cradle, books with patterned paper boards and paper labels, with often a little scribble by Lovat Fraser on the title page, fruits of a frivolous but active mind, biography, travel, criticism, poetry, drama — belles lettres in short. The most ambitious was A Free Man Greets the Dawn, half autobiographical, a quarter political, a quarter mystical, a work which went straight to the heart of every Boots subscriber in the early twenties, and earned Sir Francis his knighthood. A Free Man Greets the Dawn had been out of print for years now, all its pleasant phrases unhonoured and unremembered.

When Dennis met Sir Francis in Megalopolitan studios the name Hinsley was just not unknown. There was a sonnet by him in Poems of Today. If asked, Dennis would have guessed that he had been killed in the Dardanelles. It was not surprising that Dennis possessed none of the Works. Nor, to any who knew Sir Francis, was it surprising that he did not. To the end he was the least vain of literary men and in consequence the least remembered.

Dennis searched long in vain and was contemplating a desperate sortie to the public library when he found a stained old copy of the Apollo preserved, Heaven knew why, in Sir Francis's handkerchief drawer. The blue cover had faded to grey, the date was February 1920. It comprised chiefly poems by women, many of them, probably, grandmothers by now. Perhaps one of these warm lyrics explained the magazine's preservation after so many years in so remote an outpost. There was, however, at the end a book review signed F. H. It dealt, Dennis noticed, with a poetess whose sonnets appeared on an earlier page. The name was now forgotten, but perhaps here, Dennis reflected, was something "near the heart of the man," something which explained his long exile; something anyway which obviated a trip to the public library . . . "This slim volume redolent of a passionate and reflective

talent above the ordinary . . ." Dennis cut out the review and sent
it to Sir Ambrose. Then he turned to his task of composition.

The pickled oak, the chintz, the spongey carpet and the Georgian
staircase all ended sharply on the second floor. Above that lay a quarter
where no layman penetrated. It was approached by elevator, an open
functional cage eight feet square. On this top floor everything was
tile and porcelain, linoleum and chromium. Here there were the
embalming rooms with their rows of inclined china slabs, their taps and
tubes and pressure pumps, their deep gutters and the heavy smell of
formaldehyde. Beyond lay the cosmetic rooms with their smell of
shampoo and hot hair and acetone and lavender.

An orderly wheeled the stretcher into Aimée's cubicle. It bore a
figure under a sheet. Mr. Joyboy walked beside it.

"Good morning, Miss Thanatogenos."

"Good morning, Mr. Joyboy."

"Here is the strangulated Loved One for the Orchid Room."

Mr. Joyboy was the perfection of high professional manners. Before
he came there had been some decline of gentility in the ascent from
show-room to workshop. There had been talk of "bodies" and "cadavers";
one jaunty young embalmer from Texas had even spoken of "the meat."
That young man had gone within a week of Mr. Joyboy's appointment
as Senior Mortician. That event occurred a month after Aimée Thanatogenos came to Whispering Glades as junior cosmetician. She
remembered the bad old days before his arrival and gratefully recognised the serene hush which seemed by nature to surround him.

Mr. Joyboy was not a handsome man by the standards of motion-
picture studios. He was tall but unathletic. There was lack of shape
in his head and body, a lack of colour; he had scant eyebrows and
invisible eyelashes; the eyes behind his pince-nez were pinkish-grey;
his hair, though neat and scented, was sparse; his hands were fleshy,
his best feature was perhaps his teeth and they though white and
regular seemed rather too large for him; he was a trifle flat-footed and
more than a trifle paunchy. But these physical defects were nugatory
when set against his moral earnestness and the compelling charm
of his softly resonant voice. It was as though there were an amplifier
concealed somewhere within him and his speech came from some distant
and august studio; everything he said might have been for a peak-hour
listening period.

Dr. Kenworthy always bought the best and Mr. Joyboy came to Whispering Glades with a great reputation. He had taken his baccalaureate in embalming in the Middle West and for some years before his appointment to Whispering Glades had been one of the Undertaking Faculty at an historic Eastern University. He had served as Chief Social Executive at two National Morticians' Conventions. He had led a good-will mission to the morticians of Latin America. His photograph, albeit with a somewhat ribald caption, had appeared in *Time* magazine.

Before he came there had been murmurs in the embalming room that Mr. Joyboy was a mere theorist. These were dispelled on the first morning. He had only to be seen with a corpse to be respected. It was like the appearance of a stranger in the hunting field who from the moment he is seen in the saddle, before hounds move off, proclaims himself unmistakably a horseman.

Mr. Joyboy was unmarried and every girl in Whispering Glades gloated on him. Aimée knew that her voice assumed a peculiar tone when she spoke to him. "Was he a very difficult case, Mr. Joyboy?"

"Well, a wee bit, but I think everything has turned out satisfactorily."

He drew the sheet back and revealed the body of Sir Francis lying naked save for a new pair of white linen drawers. It was white and slightly translucent, like weathered marble.

"Oh, Mr. Joyboy, he's beautiful."

"Yes, I fancy he has come up nicely"; he gave a little poulterer's pinch to the thigh. "Supple," he raised an arm and gently bent the wrist. "I think we have two or three hours before he need take the pose. The head will have to incline slightly to put the carotid suture in the shadow."

"But, Mr. Joyboy, you've given him the Radiant Childhood smile."

"Yes, don't you like it?"

"Oh, *I* like it, of course, but his Waiting One did not ask for it."

"Miss Thanatogenos, for you the Loved Ones just naturally smile."

"Oh, Mr. Joyboy."

"It's true, Miss Thanatogenos. It seems I am just powerless to prevent it. When I am working for you there's something inside me says 'He's on his way to Miss Thanatogenos' and my fingers just seem to take control. Haven't you noticed it?"

"Well, Mr. Joyboy, I did remark it only last week. 'All the Loved Ones that come from Mr. Joyboy lately,' I said, 'have the most beautiful smiles.' "

"All for you, Miss Thanatogenos."

No music was relayed here. The busy floor echoed with the swirling and gurgling of taps in the embalming rooms, the hum of electric dryers in the cosmetic rooms. Aimée worked like a nun, intently, serenely, methodically; first the shampoo, then the shave, then the manicure. She parted the white hair, lathered the rubbery cheeks and plied the razor; she clipped the nails and probed the cuticle. Then she drew up the wheeled table on which stood her paints and brushes and creams and concentrated breathlessly on the crucial phase of her art.

Within two hours the main task was complete. Head, neck and hands were now in full colour; somewhat harsh in tone, somewhat gross in patina, it seemed, in the penetrating light of the cosmetic room, but the *oeuvre* was designed for the amber glow of the Slumber Room and the stained light of the chancel. She completed the blue stipple work round the eyelids and stood back complacently. On soft feet Mr. Joyboy had come to her side and was looking down on her work.

"Lovely, Miss Thanatogenos," he said. "I can always trust you to carry out my intention. Did you have difficulty with the right eyelid?"

"Just a little."

"A tendency to open in the inside corner?"

"Yes, but I worked a little cream under the lid and then firmed it with No. 6."

"Excellent. I never have to tell *you* anything. We work in unison. When I send a Loved One in to you, Miss Thanatogenos, I feel as though I were speaking to you through him. Do you ever feel that at all yourself?"

"I know I'm always special proud and careful when it is one of yours, Mr. Joyboy."

"I believe you are, Miss Thanatogenos. Bless you."

Mr. Joyboy sighed. A porter's voice said: "Two more Loved Ones just coming up, Mr. Joyboy. Who are they for?" Mr. Joyboy sighed again and went about his business.

"Mr. Vogel; are you free for the next?"

"Yes, Mr. Joyboy."

"One of them is an infant," said the porter. "Will you be taking her yourself?"

"Yes, as always. Is it a mother and child?"

The porter looked at the labels on the wrists. "No, Mr. Joyboy, no relation."

"Very well, Mr. Vogel, will you take the adult? Had they been mother and child I should have taken both, busy though I am. There is a something in individual technique — not everyone would notice it perhaps; but if I saw a pair that had been embalmed by different hands I should know at once and I should feel that the child did not properly belong to its mother; as though they had been estranged in death. Perhaps I seem whimsical?"

"You do love children, don't you, Mr. Joyboy?"

"Yes, Miss Thanatogenos. I try not to discriminate, but I am only human. There is something in the innocent appeal of a child that brings out a little more than the best in me. It's as if I was inspired, sometimes, from outside; something higher . . . but I mustn't start on my pet subject now. To work — "

Presently the outfitters came and dressed Sir Francis Hinsley in his shroud, deftly fitting it. Then they lifted him — he was getting rigid —and placed him in the casket.

Aimée went to the curtain which separated the embalming rooms from the cosmetic rooms and attracted the notice of an orderly.

"Will you tell Mr. Joyboy that my Loved One is ready for posing? I think he should come now. He is firming."

Mr. Joyboy turned off a tap and came to Sir Francis Hinsley. He raised the arms and set the hands together, not in a form of prayer, but folded one on the other in resignation. He raised the head, adjusted the pillow and twisted the neck so that a three-quarter face was exposed to view. He stood back, studied his work and then leaned forward again to give the chin a little tilt.

"Perfect," he said. "There are a few places where he's got a little rubbed putting him in the casket. Just go over them once with the brush quite lightly."

"Yes, Mr. Joyboy."

Mr. Joyboy lingered a moment, then turned away.

"Back to baby," he said.

V

THE funeral was fixed for Thursday; Wednesday afternoon was the time for leave-taking in the Slumber Room. That morning Dennis called at Whispering Glades to see that everything was in order.

He was shown straight to the Orchid Room. Flowers had arrived in great quantities, mainly from the shop below, mostly in their "natural beauty." (After consultation the Cricket Club's fine trophy in the shape of crossed bats and wickets had been admitted. Dr. Kenworthy had himself given judgement; the trophy was essentially a reminder of life not of death; that was the crux.) The ante-room was so full of flowers that there seemed no other furniture or decoration; double doors led to the Slumber Room proper.

Dennis hesitated with his fingers on the handle and was aware of communication with another hand beyond the panels. Thus in a hundred novels had lovers stood. The door opened and Aimée Thanatogenos stood quite close to him; behind her more, many more flowers and all about her a rich hot-house scent and the low voices of a choir discoursing sacred music from the cornice. At the moment of their meeting a treble voice broke out with poignant sweetness: "Oh for the Wings of a Dove."

No breath stirred the enchanted stillness of the two rooms. The leaded casements were screwed tight. The air came, like the boy's voice, from far away, sterilized and transmuted. The temperature was slightly cooler than is usual in American dwellings. The rooms seemed isolated and unnaturally quiet, like a railway coach that has stopped in the night far from any station.

"Come in, Mr. Barlow."

Aimée stood aside and now Dennis saw that the centre of the room was filled with a great cumulus of flowers. Dennis was too young ever to have seen an Edwardian conservatory in full ball rig but he knew the literature of the period and in his imagination had seen such a picture; it was all there, even the gilt chairs disposed in pairs as though for some starched and jewelled courtship.

There was no catafalque. The coffin stood a few inches from the carpet on a base that was hidden in floral enrichments. Half the lid was open. Sir Francis was visible from the waist up. Dennis thought of the wax-work of Marat in his bath.

The shroud had been made to fit admirably. There was a fresh gardenia in the buttonhole and another between the fingers. The hair was snow-white and parted in a straight line from brow to crown revealing the scalp below, colourless and smooth as though the skin had rolled away and the enduring skull already lay exposed.

The complete stillness was more startling than any violent action. The body looked altogether smaller than life-size now that it was, as it were, stripped of the thick pelt of mobility and intelligence. And the face which inclined its blind eyes towards him — the face was entirely horrible; as ageless as a tortoise and as inhuman; a painted and smirking obscene travesty by comparison with which the devil-mask Dennis had found in the noose was a festive adornment, a thing an uncle might don at a Christmas party.

Aimée stood beside her handiwork — the painter at the private view — and heard Dennis draw his breath in sudden emotion.

"Is it what you hoped?" she asked.

"More" — and then — "Is he quite hard?"

"Firm."

"May I touch him?"

"Please not. It leaves a mark."

"Very well."

Then in accordance with the etiquette of the place, she left him to his reflections.

There was brisk coming-and-going in the Orchid Slumber Room later that day; a girl from the Whispering Glades secretariat sat in the ante-room recording the names of the visitors. These were not the most illustrious. The stars, the producers, the heads of departments would come next day for the interment. That afternoon they were represented by underlings. It was like the party held on the eve of a wedding to view the presents, attended only by the intimate, the idle and the unimportant. The Yes-men were there in force. Man proposed. God disposed. These bland, plump gentlemen signalled their final, abiding assent to the arrangement, nodding into the blind mask of death.

Sir Ambrose made a cursory visit.

"Everything set for tomorrow, Barlow? Don't forget your ode. I should like it at least an hour before the time so that I can run over it in front of the mirror. How is it going?"

"I think it will be all right."

"I shall recite it at the graveside. In the church there will be merely the reading from the Works and a song by Juanita — 'The Wearing of the Green.' It's the only Irish song she's learned yet. Curious how flamenco she makes it sound. Have you arranged the seating in the church?"

"Not yet."

"The Cricket Club will be together of course. Megalopolitan will want the first four rows. Erikson is probably coming himself. Well, I can leave all that to you, can't I?" As he left the mortuary he said: "I am sorry for young Barlow. He must feel all this terribly. The great thing is to give him plenty to do."

Dennis presently drove to the University Church. It was a small, stone building whose square tower rose among immature holm-oaks on the summit of a knoll. The porch was equipped with an apparatus by which at will a lecture might be switched on to explain the peculiarities of the place. Dennis paused to listen.

The voice was a familiar one, that of the travel-film: "You are standing in the Church of St. Peter-without-the-walls, Oxford, one of England's oldest and most venerable places of worship. Here generations of students have come from all over the world to dream the dreams of youth. Here scientists and statesmen still unknown dreamed of their future triumphs. Here Shelley planned his great career in poetry. From here young men set out hopefully on the paths of success and happiness. It is a symbol of the soul of the Loved One who starts from here on the greatest success story of all time. The success that waits for all of us whatever the disappointments of our earthly lives.

"This is more than a replica, it is a reconstruction. A building-again of what those old craftsmen sought to do with their rude implements of by-gone ages. Time has worked its mischief on the beautiful original. Here you see it as the first builders dreamed of it long ago.

"You will observe that the side aisles are constructed solely of glass and grade A steel. There is a beautiful anecdote connected with this beautiful feature. In 1935 Dr. Kenworthy was in Europe seeking in that treasure house of Art something worthy of Whispering Glades. His tour led him to Oxford and the famous Norman Church of St. Peter. He found it dark. He found it full of conventional and depressing memorials. 'Why,' asked Dr. Kenworthy, 'do you call it St. Peter-without-the-walls?' and they told him it was because in the old days the city wall had stood between it and the business centre. 'My church,' said Dr. Kenworthy, 'shall have no walls.' And so you see it today full of God's sunshine and fresh air, birdsong and flowers . . .'"

Dennis listened intently to the tones so often parodied yet never rendered more absurd or more hypnotic than the original. His interest was no longer purely technical nor purely satiric. Whispering Glades held him in thrall. In a zone of insecurity in the mind where none but the artist dare trespass, the tribes were mustering. Dennis, the frontier-man, could read the signs.

The voice ceased and after a pause began again: "You are standing in the Church of St. Peter-without-the-walls . . ." Dennis switched off the apparatus, re-entered the settled area and set about his prosaic task.

The secretariat had provided him with typewritten name-cards. It was a simple matter to deal them out on the benches. Under the organ was a private pew, separated from the nave by an iron grill and a gauze curtain. Here, where there was a need of it, the bereaved families sat in purdah, hidden from curious glances. This space Dennis devoted to the local gossip-writers.

In half an hour his work was done and he stepped out into the gardens which were no brighter or more flowery or fuller of birdsong than the Norman church.

The unwritten verses lay heavy on him. Not a word was yet written and the languorous, odorous afternoon did not conduce to work. There was also another voice speaking faintly and persistently, calling him to a more strenuous task than Frank Hinsley's obsequies. He left his car at the lychgate and followed a gravel walk which led downhill. The graves were barely visible, marked only by little bronze plaques, many of them as green as the surrounding turf. Water played everywhere from a buried network of pipes, making a glittering rain-belt waist-high, out of which rose a host of bronze and Carrara statuary, allegorical, infantile or erotic. Here a bearded magician sought the future in the obscure depths of what seemed to be a plaster football. There a toddler clutched to its stony bosom a marble Mickey Mouse. A turn in the pathe disclosed Andromeda, naked and fettered in ribbons, gazing down her polished arm at a marble butterfly which had settled there. And all the while his literary sense was alert, like a hunting hound. There was something in Whispering Glades that was necessary to him, that only he could find.

At length he found himself on the margin of a lake, full of lilies and water-fowl. A notice said: "Tickets here for the Lake Island of Innisfree" and three couples of young people stood at the foot of a rustic landing stage. He took a ticket.

"Just the one?" asked the lady at the *guichet*.

The young people were as abstracted as he, each pair lapped in an almost visible miasma of adolescent love. Dennis stood unregarded until at length an electric launch drew out of the opposing shore and came silently to its mooring. They embarked together and after a brief passage the couples slipped away into the gardens. Dennis stood irresolutely on the bank.

The coxswain said: "Expecting someone to meet you here, kid?"

"No."

"There've been no single dames all afternoon. I'd have noticed if there had been. Mostly folk comes in couples. Once in a while a guy has a date here and then more often than not the dame never shows up. Better get the dame before you get the ticket I guess."

"No," said Dennis. "I have merely come to write a poem. Would this be a good place?"

"I wouldn't know, kid. I never wrote a poem. But they've certainly got it fixed up poetic. It's named after a very fancy poem. They got bee-hives. Once they had bees, too, but folks was always getting stung so now it's done mechanical and scientific; no sore fannies and plenty of poetry.

"It certainly is a poetic place to be planted in. Costs round about a thousand bucks. The poeticest place in the whole darn park. I was here when they made it. They figured the Irish would come but it seems the Irish are just naturally poetic and won't pay that much for for plantings. Besides, they've got a cemetery of their own down town, being Catholic. It's mostly the good-style Jews we get here. They appreciate the privacy. It's the water you see keeps out the animals. Animals are a headache in cemeteries. Dr. Kenworthy made a crack about that one Annual. Most cemeteries, he says, provide a dog's toilet and a cat's motel. Pretty smart, huh? Dr. Kenworthy is a regular guy when it comes to the Annual.

"No trouble with dogs and cats on the island. Dames is our headache, dames and guys in very considerable numbers come here to neck. I reckon they appreciate the privacy, too, same as cats."

While he spoke some young people had emerged from the bosky and stood waiting his summons to embark; Paolos and Francescas emerging from their nether world in an incandescent envelope of oblivious love. One girl blew bubbles of gum like a rutting camel but her eyes were wide and soft with remembered pleasure.

In contrast to the ample sweep of surrounding parkland, the Lake Island was cosy. An almost continuous fringe of shrub screened its shores from observation. Paths of mown grass wandered between leafy clumps, opened out into enclosed funerary glades, and converged on a central space, where stood a wattle cabin, nine rows of haricots (which by a system of judicious transplantation were kept in perpetual scarlet flower) and some wicker hives. Here the sound of bees was like a dynamo, but elsewhere in the island it came as a gentle murmur hardly distinguishable from the genuine article.

The graves nearest to the apiary were the most costly of all but no more conspicuous than those elsewhere in the park; simple bronze plaques, flush with the turf, bore the most august names in the commercial life of Los Angeles. Dennis looked into the hut and withdrew apologizing to the disturbed occupants. He looked into the hives and saw in the depths of each a tiny red eye which told that the sound-apparatus was working in good order.

It was a warm afternoon; no breeze stirred the evergreens; peace came dropping slow, too slow for Dennis.

He followed a divergent path and presently came to a little green cul-de-sac, the family burial plot, a plaque informed him, of a great fruiterer. Kaiser's Stoneless Peaches raised their rosy flock cheeks from every greengrocer's window in the land. Kaiser's Radio Half-hour brought Wagner into every kitchen. Here already lay two Kaisers, wife and aunt. Here in the fulness of time would lie Kaiser himself. A gunnera spread a wide lowly shelter over the place. Dennis lay down in its dense shade. The apiary, at this distance, came near to verisimilitude. Peace came dropping rather more quickly.

He had brought pencil and note book with him. It was not thus that he wrote the poems which brought him fame and his present peculiar fortune. They had taken their shapes in frigid war-time railway journeys — the racks piled high with equipment, the dimmed lights falling on a dozen laps, the faces above invisible, cigarette-smoke mixing with frosty breath; the unexplained stops, the stations dark as the empty footways. He had written them in Nissen huts and in spring evenings, on a bare heath, a mile from the airfield, and on the metal benches of transport planes. It was not thus that one day he would write what had to be written; not here that the spirit would be appeased which now more faintly pressed its mysterious claim. This high hot afternoon was given for reminiscence rather than for composition. Rhythms from the anthologies moved softly through his mind.

He wrote:

> Bury the great Knight
> With the studio's valediction
> Let us bury the great Knight
> Who was once the arbiter of popular fiction.

And:

> They told me, Francis Hinsley, they told me you were hung
> With red protruding eye-balls and black protruding tongue
> I wept as I remembered how often you and I
> Had laughed about Los Angeles and now 'tis here you'll lie;
> Here pickled in formaldehyde and painted like a whore,
> Shrimp-pink incorruptible, not lost nor gone before.

He gazed up into the rhubarb roof. A peach without a stone. That was the metaphor for Frank Hinsley. Dennis recalled that he had once tried to eat one of Mr. Kaiser's much-advertised products and had discovered a ball of damp, sweet cotton-wool. Poor Frank Hinsley, it was very like him.

This was no time for writing. The voice of inspiration was silent; the voice of duty muffled. The night would come when all men could work. Now was the time to watch the flamingoes and meditate on the life of Mr. Kaiser. Dennis turned on his face and studied the counterfeit handwriting of the women of the house. Not forceful characters it seemed. Kaiser owed nothing to women. The stoneless peach was his alone.

Presently he heard steps approach and, without moving, could see that they were a woman's. Feet, ankles, calves came progressively into view. Like every pair in the country they were slim and neatly covered. Which came first in this strange civilisation, he wondered, the foot or the shoe, the leg or the nylon stocking? Or were these uniform elegant limbs, from the stocking-top down, marketed in one cellophane envelope at the neighbourhood-store? Did they clip by some labour-saving device to the sterilized rubber privacies above? Did they come from the same department as the light irrefragable plastic head? Did the entire article come off the assembly-lines ready for immediate home-service?

Dennis lay quite still and the girl came within a yard, knelt down in the same shade and prepared to recline beside him before she said, "Oh."

Dennis sat up and turning saw the girl from the mortuary. She was wearing very large, elliptical violet sun-glasses which she now removed to stare the closer and recognise him.

"Oh," she said, "pardon me. Aren't you the friend of the strangulated Loved One in the Orchid Room? My memory's very bad for live faces. You did startle me. I didn't expect to find anyone here."

"Have I taken your place?"

"Not really. I mean it's Mr. Kaiser's place, not mine or yours. But it's usually deserted at this time so I've taken to coming here after work and I suppose I began to think of it as mine. I'll go some other place."

"Certainly not. I'll go. I only came here to write a poem."

"A *poem*."

He had said something. Until then she had treated him with that impersonal insensitive friendliness which takes the place of ceremony in that land of waifs and strays. Now her eyes widened. "Did you say a *poem?*"

"Yes. I am a poet, you see."

"Why, but I think that's wonderful. I've never seen a live poet before. Did you know Sophie Dalmeyer Krump?"

"No."

"She's in Poets' Corner now. She came during my first month when I was only a novice-cosmetician, so of course I wasn't allowed to work on her. Besides she passed on in a street car accident and needed special treatment. But I took the chance to study her. She had very marked Soul. You might say I learned Soul from studying Sophie Dalmeyer Krump. Now whenever we have a treatment needing special Soul, Mr. Joyboy gives it to me."

"Would you have me, if I passed on?"

"You'd be difficult," she said, examining him with a professional eye. "You're the wrong age for Soul. It seems to come more naturally in the very young or the very old. But I'll certainly do my best. I think it's a very, very wonderful thing to be a poet."

"But you have a very poetic occupation here."

He spoke lightly, teasing, but she answered with great gravity. "Yes, I know. I know I have really. Only sometimes at the end of a day when I'm tired I feel as if it was all rather ephemeral. I mean you and Sophie Dalmeyer Krump write a poem and it's printed and maybe read on the radio and millions of people hear it and maybe they'll still be reading it in hundreds of years' time. While my work is burnt sometimes within a few hours. At the best it's put in the mausoleum and even there it deteriorates, you know. I've seen painting there not ten years old that's completely lost tonality. Do you think anything can be a great art which is so impermanent?"

"You should regard it as being like acting or singing or playing an instrument."

"Yes, I do. But nowadays they can make a permanent record of them, too, can't they?"

"Is that what you brood about when you come here alone?"

"Only lately. At first I used just to lie and think how lucky I was to be here."

"Don't you think that any more?"

"Yes, of course I do really. Every morning and all day while I am at work. It's just in the evenings that something comes over me. A lot of artists are like that. I expect poets are, too, sometimes, aren't they?"

"I wish you'd tell me about your work," said Dennis.

"But you've seen it yesterday."

"I mean about yourself and your work. What made you take it up? Where did you learn? Were you interested in that sort of thing as a child? I'd really be awfully interested to know."

"I've always been Artistic," she said. "I took Art at College as my second subject one semester. I'd have taken it as my first subject only Dad lost his money in religion so I had to learn a trade."

"He lost his money in religion?"

"Yes, the Four Square Gospel. That's why I'm called Aimée, after Aimée McPherson. Dad wanted to change the name after he lost his money. I wanted to change it too but it rather stuck. Mother always kept forgetting what we'd changed it to and then she'd find a new one. Once you start changing a name, you see, there's no reason ever to stop. One always hears one that sounds better. Besides you see poor Mother was an alcoholic. But we always come back to Aimée between fancy names and in the end it was Aimée won through."

"And what else did you take at College?"

"Just Psychology and Chinese. I didn't get on so well with Chinese. But, of course, they were secondary subjects, too; for Cultural background."

"Yes. And what was your main subject?"

"Beauticraft."

"Oh."

"You know — permanents, facials, wax — everything you get in a Beauty Parlour. Only, of course, we went in for history and theory too. I wrote my thesis on 'Hairstyling in the Orient.' That was why I took Chinese. I thought it would help, but it didn't. But I got my diploma with special mention for Psychology and Art."

"And all this time between psychology and art and Chinese, you had the mortuary in view?"

"Not at all. Do you really want to hear? I'll tell you because it's really rather a poetic story. You see I graduated in '43 and lots of the girls of my class went to war-work but I was never at all interested in that. It's not that I'm unpatriotic. Wars simply don't interest me. Everyone's like that now. Well, I was like that in '43. So I went to the Beverly-Waldorf and worked in the Beauty Parlour, but you couldn't really get away from the war even there. The ladies didn't seem to have a mind for anything higher than pattern bombing. There was one lady who was worse than any of them, called Mrs. Komstock. She came every Saturday morning for a blue rinse and set, and I seemed to take her fancy; she always asked for me; no one else would do, but she never tipped me more than a quarter. Mrs. Komstock had one son in Washington and one in Delhi, a grand-daughter in Italy and a nephew who was high in indoctrination and I had to hear everything about them all until it got so I dreaded Saturday mornings more than any day in the week. Then after a time Mrs. Komstock took sick but that wasn't the end of her. She used to send for me to come up to her apartment every week and she still only gave me a quarter and she still talked about the war just as much only not so sensibly. Then imagine my surprise when one day Mr. Jebb, who was the manager, called me over and said: 'Miss Thanatogenos, there's a thing I hardly like to ask you. I don't know exactly how you'll feel about it, but it's Mrs. Komstock who's dead and her son from Washington is here and he's very anxious to have you fix Mrs. Komstock's hair just as it used to be. It seems there aren't any recent photographs and no one at Whispering Glades knows the style and Colonel Komstock can't exactly describe it. So, Miss Thanatogenos, I was wondering, would you mind very much to oblige Colonel Komstock going over to Whispering Glades and fix Mrs. Komstock like Colonel Komstock remembers?'

"Well, I didn't know quite what to think. I'd never seen a dead person before because Dad left Mother before he died, if he is dead, and Mother went East to look for him when I life College and died there. And I had never been inside Whispering Glades as after we lost our money Mother took to New Thought and wouldn't have it that there was such a thing as death. So I felt quite nervous coming here the first time. And then everything was so different from what I expected. Well you've seen it and you know. Colonel Komstock shook hands and said: 'Young lady, you are doing a truly fine and beautiful action' and gave me fifty dollars.

"Then they took me to the embalming rooms and there was Mrs. Komstock lying on the table in her wedding dress. I shall never forget the sight of her. She was transfigured. That's the only word for it. Since then I've had the pleasure of showing their Loved Ones to more people than I can count and more than half of them say: 'Why, they're quite transfigured.' Of course there was no colour in her yet and her hair was kinda wispy; she was pure white like wax, and so cool and silent. I hardly dared touch her at first. Then I gave her a shampoo and her blue rinse and a set just as she always had it, curly all over and kinda fluffed up where it was thin. Then while she was drying the cosmetician put the colour on. She let me watch and I got talking with her and she told me how there was a vacancy for a novice-cosmetician right at the moment so I went straight back and gave Mr. Jebb my notice. That was nearly two years ago and I've been here ever since."

"And you don't regret it?"

"Ah, never, never for a moment. What I said just now about being ephemeral every artist thinks sometimes of his work, doesn't he? Don't you yourself?"

"And they pay you more than in the Beauty Parlour, I hope?"

"Yes, a little. But then you see Loved Ones can't tip so that it works out nearly the same. But it isn't for the money I work. I'd gladly come for nothing only one has to eat and the Dreamer insists on our being turned out nicely. It's only in the last year that I've come really to love the work. Before that I was just glad to serve people that couldn't talk. Then I began to realise what a work of consolation it was. It's a wonderful thing to start every day knowing that you are going to bring back joy into one aching heart. Of course mine is only a tiny part of it. I'm just a handmaid to the morticians but I have the satisfaction of showing the final result and seeing the reaction. I saw it with you, yesterday. You're British and sort of inexpressive but I knew just what you were feeling."

"Sir Francis was transfigured certainly."

"It was when Mr. Joyboy came he sort of made me realize what an institution Whispering Glades really is. Mr. Joyboy's kinda holy. From the day he came the whole tone of the mortuary became greatly elevated. I shall never forget how one morning Mr. Joyboy said to one of the younger morticians: 'Mr. Parks, I must ask you to remember you are not at the Happier Hunting Ground.'"

Dennis betrayed no recognition of that name but he felt a hypodermic stab of thankfulness that he had kept silence when, earlier in their acquaintaince, he had considered forming a bond between them by lightly mentioning his trade. It would not have gone down. He merely looked blank and Aimée said: "I don't suppose you'd ever have heard of that. It's a dreadful place here where they bury animals."

"Not poetic?"

"I was never there myself but I've heard about it. They try and do everything the same as us. It seems kinda blasphemous."

"And what do you think about when you come here alone in the evenings?"

"Just Death and Art," said Aimée Thanatogenos simply.

"Half in love with easeful death."

"What was that you said?"

"I was quoting a poem.

> ". . . For many a time
> I have been half in love with easeful death.
> Call'd him soft names in many a mused rhyme,
> To take into the air my quiet breath;
> Now more than ever seems it rich to die,
> To cease upon the midnight with no pain . . ."

"Did you write that?"

Dennis hesitated. "You like it?"

"Why it's beautiful. It's just what I've thought so often and haven't been able to express. To make it 'rich to die' and 'to cease upon the midnight with no pain.' That's exactly what Whispering Glades exists for, isn't it. I think it's wonderful to be able to write like that. Did you write it after you came here first?"

"It was written long before."

"Well it couldn't be more lovely if you'd written it in Whispering Glades — on the Lake Island itself. Was it something like that you were writing when I came along?"

"Not exactly."

Across the water the carillon in the Belfry Beautiful musically announced the hour.

"That's six o'clock. I have to go early to-day."

"And I have a poem to finish."

"Will you stay and do it here?"

"No. At home. I'll come with you."

"I'd love to see the poem when it's done."

"I'll send it to you."

"Aimée Thanatogenos is my name. I live quite close but send it here, to Whispering Glades. This is my true home."

When they reached the ferry the water-man looked at Dennis with complicity. "So she turned up all right, kid," he said.

VI

MR. JOYBOY was debonnaire in all his professional actions. He peeled off his rubber gloves like a hero of Ouida returning from stables, tossed them into a kidney bowl and assumed the clean pair which his assistant held ready for him. Next he took a visiting card — one of a box of blanks supplied to the florist below — and a pair of surgical scissors. In one continuous movement he cut an ellipse, then snicked half an inch at either end along the greater axis. He bent over the corpse, tested the jaw and found it firm set; he drew back the lips and laid his card along the teeth and gums. Now was the moment; his assistant watched with never-failing admiration the deft flick of the thumbs with which he turned the upper corners of the card, the caress of the rubber finger-tips with which he drew the dry and colourless lips into place. And, behold, where before had been a grim line of endurance, there was now a smile! It was masterly. It needed no other touch. Mr. Joyboy stood back from his work, removed the gloves and said: "For Miss Thanatogenos."

Of recent weeks the expressions that greeted Aimée from the trolley had waxed from serenity to jubilation. Other girls had to work on faces that were stern or resigned or plumb vacant; there was always a nice bright smile for Aimée.

These attentions were noted sourly in the cosmetic rooms where love of Mr. Joyboy illumined the working hours of all the staff. In the evenings each had her consort or suitor; none seriously aspired to be Mr. Joyboy's mate. As he passed among them, like an art-master among his students, with a word of correction here or commendation there, sometimes laying his gentle hand on a living shoulder or a dead haunch, he was a figure of romance, a cult shared by all in common, not a prize to be appropriated by any one of them.

Nor was Aimée entirely at ease in her unique position. That morning in particular she met the corpse's greeting with impaired frankness for she had taken a step which she knew Mr. Joyboy could not possibly approve.

There was a spiritual director, an oracle, in these parts who daily filled a famous column in one of the local newspapers. Once, in days of family piety, it bore the title "Aunt Lydia's Post Bag"; now it was "The Wisdom of the Guru Brahmin," adorned with the photograph of a bearded and almost naked sage. To this exotic source resorted all who were in doubt or distress.

It might be thought that at this extremity of the New World un-ceremonious manners and frank speech occasioned no doubt; the uni-versal good humour no distress. But it was not so — etiquette, child-psychology, aesthetics and sex reared their questioning heads in this Eden too, and to all readers the Guru Brahmin offered solace and solution.

To him Aimée had applied some time ago when the smiles had first become unequivocal. Her problem was not about Mr. Joyboy's intentions but about her own. The answer had not been quite satisfactory: *No, A. T., I do not consider that you are in love — yet. Esteem for a man's character and admiration of his business ability may form the basis of an improving friendship but they are not Love. What you describe of your feelings in his presence does not incline us to believe that there is a physical affinity between you — yet. But remember love comes late to many. We know cases who have only experienced real love after several years of marriage and the arrival of Junior. See plenty of your friend. Love may come.*

That had been before Dennis Barlow brought a further perplexity to her conscience. It was now six weeks since she met him on the Lake Island, and that morning on the way to work she had posted a letter which had occupied half her night in writing. It was indeed the longest letter she had ever written:

Dear Guru Brahmin,

You may remember that I wrote to you in May last for your advice. This time I am enclosing a stamped and addressed envelope for a private answer as I am going to say things I should not like to have referred to in print. Please reply by return or anyway as soon as convenient as I am very worried and must soon do something about it.

In case you do not remember I will remind you that I work in the same business with a man who is head of the department and in every way the most wonderful character I can imagine. It is a great privilege to be associated with one who is so successful and refined, a natural leader, artist and model of breeding. In all sorts of little ways he has made it plain that he prefers me to the other girls and though he has not said so yet because he is not the sort to do so lightly I am sure he loves me honourably. But I do not have the same feelings when I am with him as the girls say they have when they are with their boys and what one sees in the movies.

But I think I do have such feelings about another but he is not at all such an admirable character. First he is British and therefore in many ways quite Un-American. I do not mean just his accent and the way he eats but he is cynical at things which should be Sacred. I do not think he has any religion. Neither have I because I was progressive at College and had an unhappy upbringing as far as religion went and other things too, but I am ethical. (As this is confidential I may as well say my mother was alcoholic which perhaps makes me more sensitive and reserved than other girls.) He also has no idea of Citizenship or Social Conscience. He is a poet and has had a book printed in England and very well criticised by the critics there. I have seen the book and some of the criticisms so I know this is true but he is very mysterious about what he is doing here. Sometimes he talks as if he was in the movies and sometimes as though he did nothing at all except write poetry. I have seen his house. He lives alone as the friend (male) he lived with passed on six weeks ago. I do not think he goes out with any other girl or is married. He has not very much money. He is very distinguished looking in an Un-American way and very amusing when he is not being irreverent. Take the Works of Art in Whispering Glades Memorial Park, he is often quite irreverent about them which I think an epitome of all that is finest in the American Way of Life. So what hope is there of true happiness?

Also he is not at all cultured. At first I thought he must be being a poet and he has been to Europe and seen the Art there but many of our greatest authors seem to mean nothing to him.

Sometimes he is very sweet and loving and then he suddenly becomes unethical and makes me feel unethical too. So I should value your advice very highly. Hoping that this long letter has not been too much,

Cordially yours,

Aimée Thanatogenos.

He has written a lot of poems to me some of them very beautiful and quite ethical others not so much.

The knowledge that this letter was in the mail burdened Aimée's conscience and she was grateful when the morning passed without any other sign from Mr. Joyboy than the usual smile of welcome on the trolley. She painted away diligently while at the Happier Hunting Ground Dennis Barlow was also busy.

They had both ovens going and six dogs, a cat and a barbary goat to dispose of. None of the owners was present. He and Mr. Schultz were able to work briskly. The cat and the dogs were twenty-minute jobs. Dennis raked the ashes out while they were still glowing and put them in labelled buckets to cool. The goat took nearly an hour. Dennis looked at it from time to time through the fire-glass pane and finally crushed the horned skull with a poker. Then he turned out the gas, left the oven doors open and prepared the containers. Only one owner had been induced to buy an urn.

"I'm going along now," said Mr. Schultz. "Will you please to wait till they're cold enough to pack up? They're all for home-delivery except the cat. She's for the columbarium."

"O.K., Mr. Schultz. How about the goat's card? We can't very well say he's wagging his tail in heaven. Goats don't wag their tails."

"They do when they go to the can."

"Yes, but it wouldn't look right on the greeting card. They don't purr like cats. They don't sing an orison like birds."

"I suppose they just remember."

Dennis wrote: *Your Billy is remembering you in heaven to-night.*

He stirred the little smoking grey heaps in the bottom of the buckets. Then he returned to the office and resumed his search of the *Oxford Book of English Verse* for a poem for Aimée. He possessed few books and was beginning to run short of material. At first he had tried writing poems for her himself, but she showed a preference for the earlier masters. Moreover, the Muse nagged him. He had abandoned the poem he was writing, long ago it seemed, in the days of Frank Hinsley. That was not what the Muse wanted. There was a very long, complicated and important message she was trying to convey to him. It was about Whispering Glades, but it was not, except quite indirectly, about Aimée. Sooner or later the Muse would have to be placated. She came first. Meanwhile Aimée must draw from the bran-tub of the anthologies. Once he came near to exposure when she remarked that "Shall I compare thee to a summer's day" reminded her of something she had learned at school, and once near to disgrace when she condemned "On thy midnight pallet lying" as unethical. "Now sleeps the crimson petal, now the white," had struck bang in the centre of the bull, but he knew few poems so high and rich and voluptuous. The English poets were proving uncertain guides in the labyrinth of Californian courtship — nearly all were too casual, too despondent, too ceremonious, or too exacting; they scolded, they pleaded, they extolled. Dennis required salesmanship; he sought to present Aimée with an irresistible picture not so much of her own merits or even of his, as of the enormous gratification he was offering. The films did it; the crooners did it; but not, it seemed, the English poets.

After half an hour he abandoned the search. The first two dogs were ready to be packed. He shook up the goat, which still glowed under its white and grey surface. There would be no poem for Aimée that day. He would take her instead to the Planetarium.

The embalmers had the same meals as the rest of the mortuary staff, but they ate apart at a central table where by recent, but hallowed, tradition they daily spun a wire cage of dice and the loser paid the bill for them all. Mr. Joyboy spun, lost, and cheerfully paid. They always broke about even on the month. The attraction of the gamble was to show that they were men to whom ten or twenty dollars less or more at the end of the week was not a matter of great concern.

At the door of the canteen Mr. Joyboy lingered sucking a digestive lozenge. The girls came out in ones or twos lighting their cigarettes; among them, alone, Aimée who did not smoke. Mr. Joyboy drew her apart into the formal garden. They stood under an allegorical group representing "the Enigma of Existence."

"Miss Thanatogenos," said Mr. Joyboy, "I want to tell you how much I appreciate your work."

"Thank you, Mr. Joyboy."

"I mentioned it yesterday to the Dreamer."

"Oh, thank you, Mr. Joyboy."

"Miss Thanatogenos, for some time the Dreamer has been looking forward. You know how he looks forward. He is a man of boundless imagination. He considers that the time has come when women should take their proper place in Whispering Glades. They have proved themselves in the lowlier tasks to be worthy of the higher. He believes moreover that there are many people of delicate sensibility who are held back from doing their duty to their Loved Ones by what I can only call prudery, but which Dr. Kenworthy considers a natural reluctance to expose their Loved Ones to anything savouring in the least degree of immodesty. To be brief, Miss Thanatogenos, the Dreamer intends to train a female embalmer and his choice, his very wise choice, has fallen on you."

"Oh, Mr. Joyboy!"

"Say nothing. I know how you feel. May I tell him you accept?"

"Oh, Mr. Joyboy!"

"And now, if I may intrude a personal note, don't you think this calls for a little celebration? Would you do me the honour of taking supper with me this evening?"

"Oh, Mr. Joyboy, I don't know what to say. I did make a sort of date."

"But that was before you heard the news. That puts rather a different complexion on matters, I guess. Besides, Miss Thanatogenos, it was not my intention that we should be alone. I wish you to come to my home. Miss Thanatogenos, I claim as my right the very great privilege and pleasure of presenting the first lady-embalmer of Whispering Glades to my Mom."

It was a day of high emotion. All that afternoon Aimée was unable to keep her attention on her work. Fortunately, there was little of importance on hand. She helped the girl in the next cubicle to glue a toupee to a more than usually slippery scalp; she hastily brushed over a male baby with flesh tint; but all the time her mind was in the em-

balmers' room, attentive to the swish and hiss of the taps, to the coming
and going of orderlies with covered kidney bowls, to the low demands
for suture or ligature. She had never set foot beyond the oilcloth
curtains which screened the embalming-rooms; soon she would have
the freedom of them all.

At four o'clock the head cosmetician told her to pack up. She arranged her paints and bottles with habitual care, washed her brushes,
and went to the cloakroom to change.

She was meeting Dennis on the lake shore. He kept her waiting,
and when he came accepted the news that she was going out to supper
with annoying composure. "With the Joyboy?" he said. "That ought
to be funny." But she was so full of her news that she could not forbear
to tell him. "I say," he said, "that *is* something. How much is it worth?"

"I don't know. I didn't go into the question."

"It's bound to be something handsome. Do you suppose it's a hundred
a week?"

"Oh, I don't suppose anyone except Mr. Joyboy gets that."

"Well, fifty, anyway. Fifty is pretty good. We could get married
on that."

Aimée stopped in her tracks and stared at him. "What did you say?"

"We can get married, don't you see? It can't be less than fifty, can it?"

"And what, pray, makes you think I should marry you?"

"Why, my dear girl, it's only money that has been holding me back.
Now you can keep me, there's nothing to stop us."

"An American man would despise himself for living on his wife."

"Yes, but you see I'm European. We have none of these prejudices
in the older civilisations. I don't say fifty is much, but I don't mind
roughing it a little."

"I think you're entirely contemptible."

"Don't be an ass. I say, you aren't really in a rage, are you?"

Aimée was really in a rage. She left him abruptly and that evening,
before she set out for supper, scrawled a hasty note to the Guru
Brahmin: *Please don't bother to answer my letter of this morning.
I know my own mind now*, and despatched it to the newspaper-office by
special delivery.

With a steady hand Aimée fulfilled the prescribed rites of an
American girl preparing to meet her lover — dabbed herself under the
arms with a preparation designed to seal the sweatglands, gargled another
to sweeten the breath, and brushed into her hair some odorous drops

from a bottle labelled: "Jungle Venom" — *"From the depth of the fever-ridden swamp,"* the advertisement had stated, *"where juju drums throb for the human sacrifice, Jeannette's latest exclusive creation* Jungle Venom *comes to you with the remorseless stealth of the hunting cannibal."*

Thus fully equipped for a domestic evening, her mind at ease, Aimée waited for Mr. Joyboy's musical "Hallo, there!" from the front door. She was all set to accept her manifest destiny.

But the evening did not turn out quite as she hoped. Its whole style fell greatly below her expectation. She went out rarely, scarcely at all indeed, and perhaps for this reason had exaggerated notions. She knew Mr. Joyboy as a very glorious professional personage, a regular contributor to *The Casket,* an intimate of Dr. Kenworthy's, the sole sun of the mortuary. She had breathlessly traced with her vermilion brush the inimitable curves of his handiwork. She knew of him as a Rotarian and a Knight of Pythias; his clothes and his car were irreproachably new, and she supposed that when he drove sprucely off into his private life he frequented a world altogether loftier than anything in her own experience. But it was not so.

They travelled a long way down Santa Monica Boulevard before finally turning into a building estate. It was not a prepossessing quarter; it seemed to have suffered a reverse. Many of the lots were vacant, but those which were occupied had already lost their first freshness and the timber bungalow at which they finally stopped was in no way more remarkable than its fellows. The truth is that morticians, however eminent, are not paid like film stars. Moreover, Mr. Joyboy was careful. He saved and he paid insurance. He sought to make a good impression in the world. One day he would have a house and children. Meanwhile anything spent inconspicuously, anything spent on Mom, was money down the drain.

"I never seem to get round to doing anything about the garden," Mr. Joyboy said, as though dimly aware of some unexpressed criticism in Aimée's survey. "This is just a little place I got in a hurry to settle Mom in when we came West."

He opened the front door, stepped back to allow Aimée to pass, and then yodelled loudly behind her: "Yoohoo, Mom! Here we come!"

Hectoring male tones filled the little house. Mr. Joyboy opened a door and ushered Aimée into the source of the nuisance, a radio on the central table of a nondescript living-room. Mrs. Joyboy sat very near it.

"Sit down quietly," she said, "until this is over."

Mr. Joyboy winked at Aimée. "The old lady hates to miss the political commentaries," he said.

"Quietly," repeated Mrs. Joyboy, fiercely.

They sat silent for ten minutes until the raucous stream of misinformation gave place to a gentler voice advocating a brand of toilet paper.

"Turn it off," said Mrs. Joyboy. "Well, he says there'll be war again this year."

"Mom, this is Aimée Thanatogenos."

"Very well. Supper's in the kitchen. You can get it when you like."

"Hungry, Aimée?"

"No, yes! I suppose a little."

"Let's go see what surprise the little lady has been cooking up for us."

"Just what you always have," said Mrs. Joyboy; "I ain't got the time for surprises."

Mrs. Joyboy turned in her chair towards a strangely veiled object which stood at her other elbow. She drew the fringe of a shawl, revealed a wire cage, and in it an almost naked parrot. "Sambo," she said winningly, "Sambo." The bird put its head on one side and blinked. "Sambo," she said. "Won't you speak to me?"

"Why, Mom, you know that bird hasn't spoken in years."

"He speaks plenty when you're away, don't you, my Sambo?"

The bird put its head on the other side, blinked, and suddenly ruffled his few feathers and whistled like a train. "There," said Mrs. Joyboy. "If I hadn't Sambo to love me I might as well be dead."

There was tinned noodle soup, a bowl of salad with tinned crab compounded in it, there was ice-cream and coffee. Aimée helped carry the trays. Aimée and Mr. Joyboy removed the radio and laid the table. Mrs. Joyboy watched them malevolently from her chair. The mothers of great men often disconcert their sons' admirers. Mrs. Joyboy had small angry eyes, frizzy hair, pince-nez on a very thick nose, a shapeless body and positively insulting clothes.

"It isn't how we're used to living nor where we're used to living," she said. "We come from the East and if anyone had listened to me that's where we'd be today. We had a coloured girl in Vermont came in regular — fifteen bucks a week and glad of it. You can't find that here. You can't find anything here. Look at that lettuce. There's more things and cheaper things and better things where we come from. Not that we ever had much of anything seeing all I get to keep house on."

"Mom loves a joke," said Mr. Joyboy.

"Joke! Call it a joke to keep house on what I get *and* visitors coming in." Then, fixing Aimée, she added, "And the girls *work* in Vermont."

"Aimée works very hard, Mom; I told you."

"Nice work, too. I wouldn't let a daughter of mine do it. Where's your mother?"

"She went East. I think she died."

"Better dead there than alive here. *Think?* That's all children care nowadays."

"Now, Mom, you've no call to say things like that. You know I care. . . ."

Later, at last, the time came when Aimée could decently depart; Mr. Joyboy saw her to the gate.

"I'd drive you home," he said, "only I don't like to leave Mom. The street car passes the corner. You'll be all right."

"Oh, I'll be all right," said Aimée.

"Mom just loved you."

"Did she?"

"Why, yes. I always know. When Mom takes a fancy to people she treats them natural same as she treats me."

"She certainly treated me natural."

"I'll say she did. Yes, she treated you natural and no mistake. You certainly made a great impression on Mom."

That evening before she went to bed Aimée wrote yet another letter to the Guru Brahmin.

VII

THE GURU BRAHMIN was two gloomy men and a bright young secretary. One gloomy man wrote the column, the other, a Mr. Slump, dealt with the letters which required private answers. By the time they came to work the secretary had sorted the letters on their respective desks. Mr. Slump, who was a survival from the days of Aunt Lydia and retained her style, usually had the smaller pile, for most of the Guru Brahmin's correspondents liked to have their difficulties exposed to the public. It gave them a sense of greater importance and also, on occasions, led to correspondence with other readers.

The scent of "Jungle Venom" still clung to Aimée's writing paper.

"Dear Aimée," Mr. Slump dictated, adding a link to his endless chain of cigarettes, "I am the tiniest bit worried by the tone of your last letter."

The cigarettes Mr. Slump smoked were prepared by doctors, so the advertisements declared, with the sole purpose of protecting his respiratory system. Yet Mr. Slump suffered and the young secretary suffered with him, hideously. For the first hours of every day he was possessed by a cough which arose from tartarean depths and was relieved only by whisky. On bad mornings it seemed to the suffering secretary that Mr. Slump would vomit. This was one of the bad mornings. He retched, shivered, and wiped his face with his handkerchief.

"A home-loving, home-making American girl should find nothing to complain of in the treatment you describe. Your friend was doing you the highest honour in his power by inviting you to meet his mother and she would not be a mother in the true sense if she had not wished to see you. A time will come, Aimée, when your son will bring a stranger home. Nor do I think it a reflection on him that he helps his mother in the house. You say he looked undignified in his apron. Surely it is the height of true dignity to help others regardless of convention. The only explanaton of your changed attitude is that you do not love him as he has the right to expect, in which case you should tell him so frankly at the first opportunity.

"You are well aware of the defects of the other friend you mention and I am sure I can leave it to your good sense to distinguish between glamour and worth. Poems are very nice things but — in my opinion — a man who will cheerfully take his part in the humble chores of the home is worth ten glib poets."

"Is that too strong?"

"It is strong, Mr. Slump."

"Hell, I feel awful this morning. The girl sounds like a prize bitch anyway."

"We're used to that."

"Yes. Well, tone it down a bit. Here's another one from the woman who bites her nails. What did we advise last time?"

"Meditation on the Beautiful."

"Tell her to go on meditating."

Five miles away in the cosmetic room Aimée paused in her work to re-read the poem she had received that morning from Dennis.

God set her brave eyes wide apart, [she read]
And painted them with fire;
They stir the ashes of my heart
To embers of desire . . .

Her body is a flower, her hair
About her neck doth play;
I find her colours everywhere,
They are the pride of day.

Her little hands are soft and when
I see her fingers move,
I know in very truth that men
Have died for less than love.
Ah, dear, live lovely thing! My eyes
Have sought her like a prayer. . . .

A single tear ran down Aimée's cheek and fell on the smiling waxy mask below her. She put the manuscript into the pocket of her linen smock and her little soft hands began to move over the dead face.

At the Happier Hunting Ground Dennis said: "Mr. Schultz, I want to improve my position."

"It can't be done, not at present. The money just isn't here in the business. You know that as well as I do. You're getting five bucks more than the man before you. I don't say you aren't worth it, Dennis. If business looks up you're the first for a raise."

"I'm thinking of getting married. My girl doesn't know I work here. She's romantic. I don't know she'd think well of this business."

"Have you anything better to go to?"

"No."

"Well, you tell her to lay off being romantic. Forty bucks a week regular is forty bucks."

"Through no wish of my own I have become the protagonist of a Jamesian problem. Do you ever read any Henry James, Mr. Schultz?"

"You know I don't have the time for reading."

"You don't have to read much of him. All his stories are about the same thing — American innocence and European experience."

"Thinks he can outsmart us, does he?"

"James was the innocent American."

"Well, I've no time for guys running down their own folks."

"Oh, he doesn't run them down. The stories are all tragedies one way or another."

"Well, I ain't got the time for tragedies neither. Take an end of this casket. We've only half-an-hour before the pastor arrives."

There was a funeral with full honours that morning, the first for a month. In the presence of a dozen mourners the coffin of an Alsatian was lowered into the flower-lined tomb. The Reverend Errol Bartholomew read the service.

"Dog that is born of bitch hath but a short time to live, and is full of misery. He cometh up, and is cut down like a flower; he fleeth as it were a shadow, and never continueth in one stay. . . ."

Later in the office, as he gave Mr. Bartholomew his cheque, Dennis said: "Tell me, how does one become a non-sectarian clergyman?"

"One has the Call."

"Yes, of course; but after the Call, what is the process? I mean is there a non-sectarian bishop who ordains you?"

"Certainly not. Anyone who has received the Call has no need for human intervention."

"You just say one day 'I am a non-sectarian clergyman' and set up shop?"

"There is considerable outlay. You need buildings. But the banks are usually ready to help. Then, of course, what one aims at is a radio congregation."

"A friend of mine has the Call, Mr. Bartholomew."

"Well, I should advise him to think twice about answering it. The competition gets hotter every year, especially in Los Angeles. Some of the recent non-sectarians stop at nothing — not even at psychiatry and table-turning."

"That's bad."

"It is entirely without scriptural authority."

"My friend was thinking of making a specialty of funeral work. He has connections."

"Chicken feed, Mr. Barlow. There is more to be made in weddings and christenings."

"My friend doesn't feel quite the same about weddings and christenings. What he needs is Class. You would say, would you not, that a non-sectarian clergyman was the social equal of an embalmer?"

"I certainly would, Mr. Barlow. There is a very deep respect in the American heart for ministers of religion."

The Wee Kirk o' Auld Lang Syne lies on an extremity of the park out of sight from the University Church and the Mausoleum. It is a lowly building without belfry or ornament, designed to charm rather than to impress, dedicated to Robert Burns and Harry Lauder, souvenirs of whom are exhibited in an annex. The tartan carpet alone gives colour to the interior. The heather which was originally planted round the walls flourished too grossly in the Californian sun, outgrew Dr. Kenworthy's dream so that at length he uprooted it and had the immediate area walled, levelled and paved, giving it the air of a schoolyard well in keeping with the high educational traditions of the race it served. But unadorned simplicity and blind fidelity to tradition were alike foreign to the Dreamer's taste. He innovated; two years before Aimée came to Whispering Glades, he introduced into this austere spot a Lovers' Nook; not a lush place comparable to the Lake Isle which invited to poetic dalliance, but something, as it seemed to him, perfectly Scottish; a place where a bargain could be driven and a contract sealed. It consisted of a dais and a double throne of rough-hewn granite. Between the two seats thus formed stood a slab pierced by a heart-shaped aperture. Behind was the inscription:

THE LOVERS' SEAT
THIS SEAT IS MADE OF AUTHENTIC OLD SCOTCH STONE FROM THE HIGH-
LANDS OF ABERDEEN. IN IT IS INCORPORATED THE ANCIENT SYMBOL OF
THE HEART OF THE BRUCE. ACCORDING TO THE TRADITION OF THE GLENS
LOVERS WHO PLIGHT THEIR TROTH ON THIS SEAT AND JOIN THEIR LIPS
THROUGH THE HEART OF THE BRUCE SHALL HAVE MANY A CANTY DAY
WITH ANE ANITHER AND MAUN TOTTER DOWN HAND IN HAND LIKE THE
IMMORTAL ANDERSON COUPLE.

The words of the prescribed oath were cut on the step so that a seated couple could conveniently recite them:

TILL A THE SEAS GANG DRY MY DEAR
AND THE ROCKS MELT WI THE SUN;
I WILL LUVE THEE STILL MY DEAR,
WHILE THE SANDS O LIFE SHALL RUN.

The fancy caught the popular taste and the spot is much frequented. Little there tempts the lounger. The ceremony is over in less than a minute, and on most evenings couples may be seen waiting their turn while strange accents struggle with a text which acquires something of the sanctity of mumbo-jumbo on the unpractised lips of Balts and Jews and Slavs. They kiss through the hole and yield place to the next couple, struck silent as often as not with awe at the mystery they have enacted. There is no birdsong here. Instead the skirl of the pipes haunts the pines and the surviving forest-growth of heather.

Here, a few days after her supper with Mr. Joyboy, a newly resolute Aimée led Dennis and, as he surveyed the incised quotations which, in the manner of Whispering Glades, abounded in the spot, he was thankful that a natural abhorrence of dialect had prevented him from borrowing any of the texts of his courtship from Robert Burns.

They waited their turn and presently sat side by side on the double throne. "Till a' the seas gang dry, my dear," whispered Aimée. Her face appeared deliciously at the little window. They kissed, then gravely descended and passed through waiting couples without a glance.

"What is a 'canty day,' Dennis?"

"I've never troubled to ask. Something like hogmanay, I expect."

"What is that?"

"People being sick on the pavement in Glasgow."

"Oh!"

"Do you know how the poem ends? 'Now we maun totter down, John, But hand in hand we'll go, And *sleep together* at the foot, John Anderson my jo.' "

"Dennis, why is all the poetry you know so coarse? And you talking of being a pastor."

"Non-sectarian; but I incline to the Anabaptists in these matters. Anyway, everything is ethical to engaged couples."

After a pause Aimée said: "I shall have to write and tell Mr. Joyboy and the — and someone else."

She wrote that night. Her letters were delivered by the morning post.

Mr. Slump said: "Send her our usual letter of congratulation and advice."

"But, Mr. Slump, she's marrying the wrong one."

"Don't mention that side of it."

Five miles away Aimée uncovered the first corpse of the morning. It came from Mr. Joyboy bearing an expression of such bottomless woe that her heart was wrung.

VIII

Mr. Slump was late and crapulous.

"Another letter from la belle Thanatogenos," said Mr. Slump. "I thought we'd had the last of that dame."

Dear Guru Brahmin,

Three weeks ago I wrote you that everything was all right and I had made up my mind and felt happy but I am still unhappy, unhappier in a way than I was before. Sometimes my British friend is sweet to me and writes poetry but often he wants unethical things and is so cynical when I say no we must wait. I begin to doubt we shall ever make a real American home. He says he is going to be a pastor. Well as I told you I am progressive and therefore have no religion but I do not think religion is a thing to be cynical about because it makes some people very happy and all cannot be progressive at this stage of Evolution. He has not become a pastor yet he says he has something to do first which he had promised a man but he doesn't say what it is and sometimes I wonder is it something wrong he is so secretive.

Then there is my own career. I was offered a Big Chance to improve my position and now no more is said of that. The head of the department is the gentleman I told you of who helps his mother in the housework, and since I plighted my troth with my British friend and wrote to tell him he never speaks to me even as much as he speaks professionally to the other girls of the department. And the place where we work is meant to be Happy that is one of the first rules and everyone looks to this gentleman for an Example and he is very unhappy, unlike what the place stands for. Sometimes he even looks mean and that was the last thing he ever looked before. All my fiancé does is to make unkind jokes about his name. I am worried too about the interest he shows in my work. I mean I think it quite right a man should show interest in a girl's work but he shows too much. I mean there are certain technical matters in any business I suppose which people do not like to have talked about outside the office and it is just those matters he is always asking about. . . .

"That's how women always are," said Mr. Slump. "It just breaks their hearts to let any man go."

There was often a missive waiting for Aimée on her work-table. When they had parted sourly the night before, Dennis transcribed a poem before going to bed and delivered it at the mortuary on his way to work. These missives in his fine script had to fill the place of the missing smiles; the Loved Ones on their trolleys were now as woebegone and reproachful as the master.

That morning Aimée arrived still sore from the bickering of the preceding evening and found a copy of verses waiting for her. She read them and once more her heart opened to her lover.

> Aimée, thy beauty is to me
> Like those Nicean barks of yore. . . .

Mr. Joyboy passed the cosmetic rooms on his way out, dressed for the street. His face was cast in pitiful gloom. Aimée smiled shyly, deprecating; he nodded heavily and passed by, and then on an impulse she wrote on the top of the lyric: "Try and understand, Aimée," slipped into the embalming room and reverently laid the sheet of paper on the heart of a corpse who was there waiting Mr. Joyboy's attention.

After an hour Mr. Joyboy returned. She heard him enter his room; she heard the taps turned on. It was not until lunch-time that they met.

"That poem," he said, "was a very beautiful thought."

"My fiancé wrote it."

"The Britisher you were with Tuesday?"

"Yes, he's a very prominent poet in England."

"Is that so? I don't ever recall meeting a British poet before. Is that all he does?"

"He's studying to be a pastor."

"Is that so? See here, Aimée, if you have any more of his poems I should greatly appreciate to see them."

"Why, Mr. Joyboy, I didn't know you were one for poems."

"Sorrow and disappointment kinda makes a man poetic I guess."

"I've lots of them. I keep them here."

"I would certainly like to study them. I was at the Knife and Fork Club Dinner last night and I became acquainted with a literary gentleman from Pasadena. I'd like to show them to him. Maybe he'd be able to help your friend some way."

"Why, Mr. Joyboy, that's real chivalrous of you." She paused. They had not spoken so many words to one another since the day of her engagement. The nobility of the man again overwhelmed her. "I hope," she said shyly, "that Mrs. Joyboy is well."

"Mom isn't so good to-day. She's had a tragedy. You remember Sambo, her parrot?"

"Of course."

"He passed on. He was kinda old, of course, something over a hun' dred, but the end was sudden. Mrs. Joyboy certainly feels it."

"Oh, I am sorry."

"Yes, she certainly feels it. I've never known her so cast down. I've been arranging for the disposal this morning. That's why I went out. I had to be at the Happier Hunting Ground. The funeral's Wednesday. I was wondering, Miss Thanatogenos: Mom doesn't know so many people in this State. She certainly would appreciate a friend at the funeral. He was a sociable bird when he was a bit younger. Enjoyed parties back East more than anyone. It seems kinda bitter there shouldn't be anyone at the last rites."

"Why, Mr. Joyboy, of course I'd be glad to come."

"Would you, Miss Thanatogenos? Well, I call that real nice of you."

Thus at long last Aimée came to the Happier Hunting Ground.

IX

AIMÉE THANATOGENOS spoke the tongue of Los Angeles; the sparse furniture of her mind — the objects which barked the intruder's shins — had been acquired at the local High School and University; she presented herself to the world dressed and scented in obedience to the advertisements; brain and body were scarcely distinguishable from the standard product, but the spirit — ah, the spirit was something apart; it had to be sought afar; not here in the musky orchards of the Hesperides, but in the mountain air of the dawn, in the eagle-haunted passes of Hellas. An umbilical cord of cafés and fruit shops, of ancestral shady businesses (fencing and pimping) united Aimée, all unconscious, to the high places of her race. As she grew up the only language she knew expressed fewer and fewer of her ripening needs; the facts which littered her memory grew less substantial; the figure she saw in the looking-glass seemed less recognisably herself. Aimée withdrew herself into a lofty and hieratic habitation.

Thus it was that the exposure as a liar and a cheat of the man she loved, and to whom she was bound by the tenderest vows, affected only a part of her. Her heart was broken perhaps, but it was a small inexpensive organ of local manufacture. In a wider and grander way she felt that things had been simplified. She held in her person a valuable concession to bestow; she had been scrupulous in choosing justly between rival claimants. There was no room now for further hesitation. The voluptuous tempting tones of "Jungle Venom" were silenced.

It was, however, in the language of her upbringing that she addressed her final letter to the Guru Brahmin.

Mr. Slump was ill-shaven; Mr. Slump was scarcely sober; "Slump is slipping," said the managing editor. "Have him pull himself up or else fire him." Unconscious of impending doom, Mr. Slump said: "For Christ's sake, Thanatogenos again. What does she say, lovely? I don't seem able to read this morning."

"She has had a terrible awakening, Mr. Slump. The man she thought she loved proves to be a liar and cheat."

"Aw, tell her go marry the other guy."

"That seems to be what she intends doing."

The engagement of Dennis and Aimée had never been announced in any paper and needed no public denial. The engagement of Mr. Joyboy and Aimée had a column-and-a-half in the *Morticians Journal* and a photograph in *The Casket*, while the house-journal *Whispers from the Glades* devoted nearly an entire issue to the romance. A date was fixed for the wedding at the University Church. Mr. Joyboy had been reared a Baptist and the minister who buried the Baptist dead gladly offered his services. The wardrobe-mistress found a white slumber-robe for the bride. Dr. Kenworthy intimated his intention of being there in person. The corpses who came to Aimée for her ministrations now grinned with triumph.

And all this time there was no meeting between Dennis and Aimée. She had last seen him at the parrot's grave when, quite unabashed, it seemed, he had winked at her over the gorgeous little casket. In his heart, however, he had been abashed and thought it well to lie low for a day or two. Then he saw the announcement of the engagement.

It was not an easy matter for Aimée to refuse communication with anyone. She did not live in circumstances where she could say "I am not at home to Mr. Barlow" and order her servants to refuse him admission. She had no servant; if the telephone rang, she answered it. She had to eat. She had to shop. In either case she stood open to those friendly casual-seeming encounters in which American social life abounds. One evening shortly before the wedding-day Dennis lay in wait for her, followed her to a Nutburger counter and took the next stool.

"Hullo, Aimée. I want to talk to you."

"There's nothing you can say means anything now."

"But, my dear girl, you seem to have forgotten that we're engaged to be married. My theological studies are prospering. The day when I shall claim you is at hand."

"I'd rather die."

"Yes, I confess I overlooked that alternative. D'you know, this is the first time I've ever eaten a nutburger? I've often wondered what they were. It is not so much their nastiness as their total absence of taste that shocks one. But let us get this clear. Do you deny that you solemnly swore to marry me?"

"A girl can change her mind, can't she?"

"Well, you know, I don't honestly think she can. You made a very solemn promise."

"Under false pretenses. All those poems you sent and pretended you'd written for me, that I thought so cultivated I even learned bits of them by heart — all by other people, some by people who passed on hundreds of years ago. I never felt so mortified as when I found out."

"So that's the trouble, is it? Well, I deny it absolutely."

"You deny sending me poems by people who'd passed on?"

"I deny saying they were by me."

"I'm going now. I don't want to eat anything."

"Well, you chose the place. When I took you out I never gave you nutburgers, did I?"

"As often as not it was I took you out."

"Well, whoever paid, we always had something better than nutburgers. You can't walk down the street crying like that. I've my car parked across the way. Let me drop you home."

They stepped out into the neon-lighted boulevard. "Now, Aimée," said Dennis, "let us not have a tiff."

"Tiff? I loathe everything about you."

"When we last met we were engaged to be married. I think I am entitled to some explanation. So far, all you have complained of is that I am not the author of some of the best-known poems in the English language. Well, I ask you, is Popjoy?"

"You meant me to think you wrote them."

"There, Aimée, you misjudge me. I am appalled to learn that you thought anything of the kind. It is I who should be disillusioned when I think that I have been squandering my affections on a girl ignorant of the commonest treasures of literature. But I realise that you have different educational standards from those I am used to. No doubt you know more than I about science and citizenship. But in the dying world I come from quotation is a national vice. No one would think of making an after-dinner speech without the help of poetry. It used to be the classics, now it's lyric verse. Liberal Members of our House of Commons constantly quote Shelley; Tories and Socialists don't get up and complain of being disillusioned when they learn that their ornaments are not original. They keep quiet and pretend they knew all the time."

"I shall never believe anything you say again."

"Well, damn it, what don't you believe?"

"I don't believe in you."

"Ah, that's another point. There's all the difference between believing someone and believing in them."

"Oh, do stop being reasonable."

"Very well." Dennis drew into the side of the road and attempted to take her in his arms. She resisted with fiery agility. He desisted and lit a cigar. Aimée sobbed in the corner and presently said: "That awful funeral."

"The Joyboy parrot? Yes, I think I can explain that. Mr. Joyboy would have an open casket. I advised against it and, after all, I know. I've studied the business. An open casket is all right for dogs and cats who lie down and curl up naturally. But parrots don't. They look absurd with a head on a pillow. But I came up against a blank wall of snobbery. What was done in Whispering Glades must be done at the Happier Hunting Ground. Or do you think that the whole thing was a frame-up? I believe that sanctimonious pest *wanted* the poor parrot to look absurd so as to lower me in your eyes. I believe that's it. Who asked you to the funeral, anyway? Were you acquainted with the late parrot?"

"To think that all the time you were going out with me you were secretly going to *that place*. . . ."

"My dear, you as an American should be the last to despise a man from starting at the bottom of the ladder. I can't claim to be as high in the mortuary world as your Mr. Joyboy, but I am younger, very

much better looking, and I wear my own teeth. I have a future in the
Non-sectarian Church. I expect to be head chaplain at Whispering
Glades when Mr. Joyboy is still swilling out corpses. I have the mak-
ings of a great preacher — something in the metaphysical seventeenth-
century manner, appealing to the intellect rather than to crude emotion.
Something Laudian — ceremonious, verbose, ingenious and doctrinally
quite free of prejudice. I have been thinking a good deal about my
costume, full sleeves, I think . . ."

"Oh, do be quiet; You bore me so."

"Aimée, as your future husband and spiritual director, I must tell
you that that is no way to speak of the man you love."

"I don't love you."

" 'Till a' the seas gang dry, my dear.' "

"I haven't the least idea what that means."

" 'And the rocks melt wi' the sun.' That's plain enough, anyway. 'I
will luve.' You can't fail to understand those words, surely? It's just
the way the crooners pronounce them. 'I will luve thee still, my dear,
While the sands o' life shall run.' The last words I admit are a little
obscure, but the general sense is obvious to the most embittered. Have
you forgotten the Heart of the Bruce?"

The sobs ceased, and the ensuing silence told Dennis that intellectual processes were at work in the exquisite dim head in the corner.
"Was it Bruce wrote that poem?" she asked at length.

"No; but the names are so similar that the difference is immaterial."

Another pause. "Didn't this Bruce, or whatever he's called, make
some way round his oath?"

Dennis had not counted greatly on the ceremony at the Kirk o' Auld
Lang Syne. He had introduced it whimsically. Now, however, he
poured on the advantage. "Listen, you delicious, hopeless creature. You
are on the horns of a dilemma — which is European for being in
a jam."

"Drive me home."

"Very well, I can explain as we go. You think Whispering Glades
the most wonderful thing outside heaven. I see your point. In my
rough British way I share your enthusiasm. I have been planning an
opus on the subject, but I am afraid I can't say with Dowson 'If you
ever come to read it, you will understand.' You won't, my dear, not
a word of it. All this is by the way. Now, your Mr. Joyboy is the
incarnate spirit of Whispering Glades — the one mediating logos be-

tween Dr. Kenworthy and common humanity. Well, we're obsessed by Whispering Glades, both of us — 'half in love with easeful death,' as I once told you — and to save further complications let me explain that I did not write that poem either — you're the nautch girl and vestal virgin of the place, and naturally I attach myself to you and you attach yourself to Joyboy. Psychologists will tell you that kind of thing happens every day.

"It may be that by the Dreamer's standards there are defects in my character. The parrot looked terrible in his casket. So what? You loved me and swore to love me eternally with the most sacred oath in the religion of Whispering Glades. So you see the dilemma, jam or *impasse*. Sanctity is indivisible. If it isn't sacred to kiss me through the heart of Burns or Bruce, it isn't sacred to go to bed with old Joyboy."

There was silence still. Dennis had made an impression far beyond his expectation.

"Here you are," he said at length, stopping at Aimée's apartment house. This was not the moment he realised for soft advances. "Jump out."

Aimée said nothing and for a moment did not move. Then in a whisper she said: "You could release me."

"Ah, but I won't!"

"Not when you know I've quite forgotten you?"

"But you haven't."

"Yes. When I turn away I can't even remember what you look like. When you are not there I don't think of you at all."

Left to herself in the concrete cell which she called her apartment, Aimée fell victim to all the devils of doubt. She switched on her radio; a mindless storm of Teutonic passion possessed her and drove her to the cliff-edge of frenzy; then abruptly stopped. "This rendition comes to you by courtesy of Kaiser's Stoneless Peaches. Remember, no other peach now marketed is perfect and completely stoneless. When you buy a Kaiser's Stoneless Peach you are buying full weight of succulent peach flesh and nothing else. . . ."

She turned to the telephone and dialled Mr. Joyboy's number.

"Please, please come over. I'm so worried."

From the ear-piece came a babel, human and inhuman, and in the midst of it a still small voice saying, "Speak up, honey-baby. I can't quite get you."

"I'm so miserable."

"It isn't just easy hearing you, honey-baby. Mom's got a new bird and she's trying to make him talk. Maybe we better leave whatever it is and talk about it to-morrow."

"Please, dear, come right over now; couldn't you?"

"Why, honey-baby, I couldn't leave Mom the very evening her new bird arrived, could I? How would she feel? It's a big evening for Mom, honey-baby. I have to be here with her."

"It's about our marriage."

"Yes, honey-baby, I kinda guessed it was. Plenty of little problems come up. They all look easier in the morning. Take a good sleep, honey-baby."

"I must see you."

"Now, honey-baby, I'm going to be firm with you. Just you do what Poppa says this minute or Poppa will be real mad at you."

She rang off and once more resorted to grand opera; she was swept up and stupefied in the gust of sound. It was too much. In the silence that followed, her brain came to life a little. Again the telephone. The local newspaper.

"I want to speak to the Guru Brahmin."

"Why, he doesn't work evenings. I'm sorry."

"It's very important. Couldn't you please give me his home number?"

"There's two of them. Which d'you want?"

"Two? I didn't know. I want the one who answers letters."

"That will be Mr. Slump, but he doesn't work here after to-morrow, and he wouldn't be home at this time anyway. You could try Mooney's Saloon. That's where the editorials mostly go evenings."

"And his real name is Slump?"

"That's what he tells me, sister."

Mr. Slump had that day been discharged from his paper. Everyone in the office had long expected the event except Mr. Slump himself, who had taken the story of his betrayal to several unsympathetic drinking-places.

The barman said: "There's a call for you, Mr. Slump. Are you here?"

It seemed likely to Mr. Slump in his present state of mind that this would be his editor, repentant; he reached across the bar for the instrument.

"Mr. Slump?"

"Yes."

"I've found you at last. I'm Aimée Thanatogenos. . . . You remember me?"

It was a memorable name. "Sure," said Mr. Slump at length.

"Mr. Slump, I am in great distress. I need your advice. You remember the Britisher I told you about. . . ."

Mr. Slump held the telephone to the ear of the man next to him, grinned, shrugged, finally laid it on the bar, lit a cigarette, took a drink, ordered another. Tiny anxious utterances rose from the stained wood. It took Aimée some time to make her predicament clear. Then the regular flow of sound ceased and gave place to little, spasmodic whispers. Mr. Slump listened again. "Hullo . . . Mr. Slump . . . Are you listening? . . . Did you hear me? . . . hullo!"

"Well, sister, what is it?"

"You heard what I said?"

"Sure, I heard fine."

"Well . . . what am I to do?"

"Do! I'll tell you what to do. Just take the elevator to the top floor. Find a nice window and jump out. That's what you can do." There was a little sobbing gasp and then a quiet "Thank you."

"I told her to go take a high jump."

"We heard."

"Wasn't I right?"

"You know best, brother."

"Well, for Christ's sake, with a name like that!"

In Aimée's bathroom cupboard, among the instruments and chemicals which are the staples of feminine well-being, lay the brown tube of barbiturates which is the staple of feminine repose. Aimée swallowed her dose, lay down and awaited sleep. It came at length brusquely, perfunctorily, without salutation or caress. There was no delicious influx, touching, shifting, lifting, setting free and afloat the grounded mind. At 9:40 P.M. she was awake and distraught, with a painful dry sense of contraction and tension about the temples; her eyes watered, she yawned; suddenly it was 5:25 A.M. and she was awake once more.

It was still night; the sky was starless and below it the empty streets flamed with light. Aimée rose and dressed and went out under the arc lamps. She met no one during the brief walk from her apartment to Whispering Glades. The Golden Gates were locked from midnight until morning, but there was a side door always open for the use of

the night-staff. Aimée entered and followed the familiar road upwards
to the terrace of the Kirk o' Auld Lang Syne. Here she sat and waited
for dawn.

Her mind was quite free from anxiety. Somehow, somewhere in the
blank black hours she had found counsel; she had communed perhaps
with the spirits of her ancestors, the impious and haunted race who had
deserted the altars of the old Gods, had taken ship and wandered, driven
by what pursuing furies through what mean streets and among what
barbarous tongues! Her father had frequented the Four Square Gospel
Temple: her mother drank. Attic voices prompted Aimée to a higher
destiny; voices which far away and in another age had sung of the
Minotaur, stamping far underground at the end of the passage; which
spoke to her more sweetly of the still Boeotian water-front, the armed
men all silent in the windless morning, the fleet motionless at anchor,
and Agamemnon turning away his eyes; spoke of Alcestis and proud
Antigone.

The East lightened. In all the diurnal revolution these first fresh
hours alone are untainted by man. They lie late abed in that region.
In exaltation Aimée watched the countless statues glimmer, whiten and
take shape while the lawns changed from silver and grey to green.
She was touched by warmth. Then suddenly all round her as far as
eye could see the slopes became a dancing surface of light, of millions
of minute rainbows and spots of fire; in the control house the man on
duty had turned the irrigation cock and water was flooding through the
net-work of pierced and buried pipes. At the same time parties of
gardeners with barrows and tools emerged and tramped to their various
duties. It was full day.

Aimée walked swiftly down the gravelled drive to the mortuary
entrance. In the reception-room the night staff were drinking coffee.
They glanced at her incuriously as she passed silently through them,
for urgent work was done at all hours. She took the lift to the top
story where everything was silent and empty save for the sheeted dead.
She knew what she wanted and where to find them; a wide-mouthed
blue bottle and a hypodermic syringe. She indited no letter of farewell
or apology. She was far removed from social custom and human ob-
ligations. The protagonists, Dennis and Mr. Joyboy, were quite forgotten. The matter was between herself and the deity she served.

It was quite without design that she chose Mr. Joyboy's work-room
for the injection.

X

Mr. Schultz had found a young man to take Dennis's place and Dennis was spending his last week at the Happier Hunting Ground in showing him the ropes. He was an apt young man much interested in the prices of things.

"He hasn't your personality," said Mr. Schultz. "He won't have the same human touch but I figure he'll earn his keep other ways."

On the morning of Aimée's death Dennis set his pupil to work cleaning the generating-plant of the crematorium and was busy with the correspondence-lessons in preaching to which he now subscribed, when the door of the office opened and he recognised with great surprise his bare acquaintance and rival in love, Mr. Joyboy.

"Mr. Joyboy," he said. "Not another parrot so soon?"

Mr. Joyboy sat down. He looked ghastly. Finding himself alone with Dennis he began to blubber. "It's Aimée," he said.

Dennis answered with high irony: "You have not come to arrange *her* funeral?" upon which Mr. Joyboy cried with sudden passion. "You knew it. I believe you killed her. You killed my honey-baby."

"Joyboy, these are wild words."

"She's dead."

"My fiancée?"

"*My* fiancée."

"Joyboy, this is no time to wrangle. What makes you think she is dead? She was perfectly well at suppertime last night."

"She's there, in my workshop, under a sheet."

"That, certainly, is what your newspapers would call 'factual.' You're sure it's her?"

"Of course I'm sure. She was poisoned."

"Ah! The nutburger?"

"Cyanide. Self-administered."

"This needs thinking about, Joyboy." He paused. "I loved that girl."

"I loved her."

"*Please.*"

"She was my honey-baby."

"I must beg you not to intrude these private and rather peculiar terms of endearment into what should be a serious discussion. What have you done?"

"I examined her, then I covered her up. We have some deep re-
frigerators we sometimes use for half-finished work. I put her in
there." He began to weep tempestuously.

"What have you come to me for?"

Mr. Joyboy snorted.

"I can't hear you."

"Help," said Mr. Joyboy. "It's your fault. You've gotta do something."

"This is no time for recrimination, Joyboy. Let me merely point out
that you are the man publicly engaged to her. In the circumstances
some emotion is natural — but do not go to extremes. Of course I never
thought her wholly sane, did you?"

"She was my — "

"Don't say it, Joyboy. Don't say it or I shall turn you out."

Mr. Joyboy fell to more abandoned weeping. The apprentice opened
the door and stood momentarily embarrassed at the spectacle.

"Come in," said Dennis. "We have here a client who has just lost
a little pet. You will have to accustom yourself to exhibitions of distress
in your new rôle. What did you want?"

"Just to say the gas furnace is working fine again."

"Excellent. Well now go and clear the collecting-van. Joyboy,"
he continued when they were again alone, "I beg you to control yourself
and tell me plainly what is in your mind. All I can discern at the
moment is a kind of family litany of mommas and poppas and babies."

Mr. Joyboy made other noises.

"That sounded like 'Dr. Kenworthy.' Is that what you are trying
to say?"

Mr. Joyboy gulped.

"Dr. Kenworthy knows?"

Mr. Joyboy groaned.

"He does not know?"

Mr. Joyboy gulped.

"You want me to break the news to him?"

Groan.

"You want me to help keep him in ignorance?"

Gulp.

"You know, this is just like table-turning."

"Ruin," said Mr. Joyboy. "Mom."

"You think that your career will suffer if Dr. Kenworthy learns you
have the poisoned corpse of our fiancée in the ice-box? For your

mother's sake this is to be avoided? You are proposing that I help dispose of the body?"

Gulp, and then a rush of words. "You've gotta help me . . . through you it happened . . . simple American kid . . . phoney poems . . . love . . . Mom . . . baby . . . gotta help . . . gotta . . . gotta."

"I don't like this repetition of 'gotta,' Joyboy. Do you know what Queen Elizabeth said to her Archbishop — an essentially non-sectarian character incidentally? 'Little man, little man, "must" is not a word to be used to princes.' If I help you it will be freely and from the highest motives. Tell me has anyone besides yourself access to this ice-box?" Groan. "Well then go away, Joyboy. Go back to your work. I will give the matter my attention. Come and see me again after luncheon."

Mr. Joyboy went. Dennis heard the car start. Then he went out alone into the pets' cemetery with his own thoughts which were not a thing to be shared with Mr. Joyboy.

Thus musing he was disturbed by a once familiar visitor.

It was a chilly day and Sir Ambrose Abercrombie wore tweeds, cape and deerstalker-cap, the costume in which he had portrayed many travesties of English rural life. He carried a shepherd's crook.

"Ah, Barlow," he said, "still hard at it?"

"One of our easier mornings. I hope it is not a bereavement which brings you here?"

"No, nothing like that. Never kept an animal out here. Miss 'em, I can tell you. Brought up among dogs and horses. Daresay you were, too, so you won't misunderstand me when I say this is no place for them. Wonderful country of course, splendid lot of people, but no one who was really fond of dogs would bring one here." He paused and gazed curiously about him at the modest monuments. "Attractive place you've got here. Sorry to see you're moving."

"You received one of my cards?"

"Yes, got it here. Thought at first it must be someone playing rather a poor kind of joke. It's genuine, is it?"

From the depths of his plaid he produced a printed card and handed it to Dennis. It read:

Squadron Leader the Rev. Dennis Barlow
begs to announce that he is shortly starting business at 1154 Arbuckle
Avenue, Los Angeles. All non-sectarian services expeditiously con-

ducted at competitive prices. Funerals a specialty. Panegyrics in prose or poetry. Confessions heard in strict confidence.

"Yes, quite genuine," said Dennis.

"Ah. I was afraid it might be."

Another pause. Dennis said, "The cards were sent out by an agency, you know. I didn't suppose you would be particularly interested."

"But I am particularly interested. Is there somewhere we could go and talk?"

Wondering whether Sir Ambrose was to be his first penitent, Dennis led him indoors. The two Englishmen sat down in the office. The apprentice popped his head in, to report well of the collecting-van. At length Sir Ambrose said: "It won't do, Barlow. You must allow me an old man's privilege of speaking frankly. It won't do. After all you're an Englishman. They're a splendid bunch of fellows out here, but you know how it is. Even among the best you find a few rotters. You know the international situation as well as I do. There are always a few politicians and journalists simply waiting for the chance to take a knock at the Old Country. A thing like this is playing into their hands. I didn't like it when you started work here. Told you so frankly at the time. But at least this is a more or less private concern. But religion's quite another matter. I expect you're thinking of some pleasant country rectory at home. Religion's not like that here. Take it from me, I know the place."

"It's odd you should say that, Sir Ambrose. One of my chief aims was to raise my status."

"Then chuck it, my dear boy, before it's too late." Sir Ambrose spoke at length of the industrial crisis in England, the need for young men and dollars, the uphill work of the film community in keeping the flag flying. "Go home, my dear boy. That is your proper place."

"As a matter of fact," said Dennis, "things have rather changed with me since that announcement was written. The Call I heard has grown fainter."

"Capital," said Sir Ambrose.

"But there are certain practical difficulties. I have invested all my small savings in my theological studies."

"I expected something of the kind. That is where the Cricket Club comes in. I hope the time will never come when we are not ready to help a fellow countryman in difficulties. We had a committee meet-

ing last night and your name was mentioned. There was complete agreement. To put it in a nutshell, my boy, we will send you
home."

"First class?"

"Tourist. I'm told it's jolly comfortable. How about it?"

"No drawing-room in the train?"

"No drawing-room."

"Well," said Dennis, "I suppose that as a clergyman I should have
had to practise certain austerities."

"Spoken like a man," said Sir Ambrose. "I have the cheque with me.
We signed it last night."

Some hours later the mortician returned.

"You have regained command of yourself? Sit down and listen attentively. You have two problems, Joyboy, and let me emphasise that
they are *yours*. I am in no way implicated. I resign all rights in the girl.
You are in possession of the corpse of *your* fiancée and *your* career is
threatened. You are a well-known man in your profession and you
would never live down the scandal. You have then two problems —
to dispose of the body and to explain the disappearance. You have
come to me for help and it so happens that in both these things I and
only I can help you.

"I have here at my disposal an excellent crematorium. We are happy-
go-lucky people at the Happier Hunting Ground. There are no
formalities. If I arrive here with a casket and say 'Mr. Schultz, I've a
sheep here to incinerate,' he says, 'Go ahead.' Once you seemed inclined to look down on us for our easy manners. Now perhaps you feel
differently. All we have to do is to collect our Loved One, if you will
forgive the expression, and bring her here. To-night after working
hours will be the time.

"Secondly, to explain the disappearance. Miss Thanatogenos had few
acquaintances and no relations. She disappears on the eve of her wedding. It is known that I once favoured her with my attentions. What
could be more plausible than that her natural good taste should have
triumphed at the last moment and she should have eloped with her
earlier lover? All that is necessary is for me to disappear at the same
time. No one in Southern California, as you know, ever enquires what
goes on beyond the mountains. She and I perhaps may incur momentary
condemnation as unethical. You may receive some slightly unwelcome
commiseration. There the matter will end.

"For some time I have felt oppressed by the unpoetic air of Los Angeles. I have work to do and this is not the place to do it. It was only our young friend who kept me here — she and penury. And talking of penury, Joyboy, I take it you have substantial savings?"

"I've some insurance."

"What can you borrow on that? Five thousand dollars?"

"No, no, nothing like that."

"Two?"

"No."

"How much then?"

"A thousand maybe."

"Draw it out, Joyboy. We shall need it all. And cash this cheque at the same time. Together it will be enough. It may seem to you sentimental but I wish to leave the United States in the same style as I came. Whispering Glades must not fall below Megalopolitan Studios in hospitality. From your bank go to the travel agency and take me a ticket to England — a drawing-room to New York, Cunarder single stateroom with bath from there on. I shall need ready cash for incidental expenses. So bring the rest in a lump sum with the tickets. All understood? Very well. I will be at your mortuary with the collecting-van soon after dinner."

Mr. Joyboy was waiting for Dennis at the side entrance of the mortuary. Whispering Glades was ideally equipped for the smooth movement of bodies. On a swift and silent trolley they set Dennis's largest collecting-box, first empty, later full. They drove to the Happier Hunting Ground where things were more makeshift but between them without great difficulty they man-handled their load to the crematorium, and stowed it in the oven. Dennis turned on the gas and lit it. Flame shot from all sides of the brick oven. He closed the iron door.

"I reckon she'll take an hour and a half," he said. "Do you want to stay?"

"I can't bear to think of her going out like this — she loved to see things done right."

"I rather thought of conducting a service. My first and last non-sectarian office."

"I couldn't bear that," said Mr. Joyboy.

"Very well. I will recite instead a little poem I have written for the occasion.

"Aimée, thy beauty was to me,
Like those Nicean barks of yore."

"Hey, you can't say that. That's the phoney poem."
"Joyboy, please remember where you are.

"That gently, o'er a perfumed sea,
The weary way-worn wanderer bore
To his own native shore.

"It's really remarkably apposite, is it not?"
But Mr. Joyboy had left the building.
The fire roared in the brick oven. Dennis must wait until all was consumed. Meanwhile he entered the office and made a note in the book kept there for that purpose.

To-morrow and on every anniversary as long as the Happier Hunting Ground existed a postcard would go to Mr. Joyboy: *Your little Aimée is wagging her tail in heaven to-night, thinking of you.*

"Like those Nicean barks of yore," he repeated:

"That gently, o'er a perfumed sea,
The weary way-worn wanderer bore
To his own native shore."

On this last evening in Los Angeles Dennis knew that he was singularly privileged. The strand was littered with bones and wreckage. He was adding his bit; something that had long irked him, his young heart. He was carrying back instead a great, shapeless chunk of experience, the artist's load; bearing it home to his ancient and comfortless shore; to work on it hard and long, for God knew how long — it was the moment of vision for which a lifetime is often too short.

He picked up the novel which Miss Poski had left on his desk and settled down to await his loved one's final combustion.

From Officers and Gentlemen

MAKING OF A HERO

The episode drawn from Officers and Gentlemen *satirizes the wartime propaganda efforts to glorify "the common man." Its trumpery hero, Trimmer, was in peacetime a hairdresser on the* Aquitania; *he has assumed the name McTavish, and has managed to get a commission in a Scottish regiment. Earlier in the story, Trimmer, while on leave in Glasgow, had an affair with a former client of his, the beautiful Virginia Troy. Unfortunately, the Second-in-Command of his battalion spotted him masquerading as a major, and Trimmer has had no choice but to convert his pretense of having joined the Commandos into actual reality. Now he is about to receive the shattering news that he has been assigned to lead a Commando raid.*

No. 6 Transit Camp, London District, was a camp in name only. It had been a large, unfashionable, entirely respectable hotel. The more valuable pieces of furniture had been sent to store, but the air was one of easy well-being. No bomb had yet broken a window-pane. Here Movement Control sent lost detachments. Here occasionally was brought a chaplain under close arrest. In this green pasture Trimmer and his section for a time lay down. Here Kerstie Kilbannock elected to do her war-work.

Kerstie was a good wife to Ian, personable, faithful, even-tempered and economical. All the pretty objects in their house had been bargains. Her clothes were cleverly contrived. She was sometimes suspected of fabricating the luncheon *vin rosé* by mixing the red and white wines left over from dinner; no more damaging charge was ever brought against her. There were nuances in her way with men which suggested she had once worked with them and competed on equal terms. Point by point she was the antithesis of her friend Virginia Troy.

On his going into uniform Ian's income fell by £1,500. Kerstie did not complain. She packed her sons off to their grandmother in Ayrshire and took two friends named Brenda and Zita into her house as paying guests. She took them also, unpaid, into her canteen at No. 6 Transit Camp, London District. Kerstie was paid, not much but enough. The remuneration was negative; wearing overalls, eating free, working all day, weary at night, she spent nothing. When Virginia Troy, casually met during an air-raid at the Dorchester Hotel, confided that she was hard up and homeless — though still trailing clouds of former wealth and male subservience — Kerstie took her into Eaton Terrace — "Darling, don't breathe to Brenda and Zita that you aren't paying" — and into her canteen — "Not a word, darling, that you're being paid."

Working as waitresses these ladies, so well brought up, giggled and gossiped about their customers like real waitresses. Before she began work Virginia was initiated into some of their many jokes. Chief of these, by reason of his long stay, was the officer they called "Scottie." Scottie's diverse forms of utter awfulness filled them with delight.

"Wait till you see him, darling. Just wait."

Virginia waited a week. All the ladies preferred the "other ranks" canteen by reason of the superior manners which prevailed there. It was Easter Monday, after Virginia had been there a week, that she took her turn beside Kerstie at the officers' bar.

"Here comes our Scottie," said Kerstie and, nosy and knowing, Trimmer sauntered across the room towards them. He was aware that his approach always created tension and barely suppressed risibility and took this as a tribute to his charm.

"Good evening, beautiful," he said in his fine, free manner. "How about a packet of Players from under the counter?" and then, seeing Virginia, he fell suddenly silent, out of it, not up to it, on this evening of all evenings.

Fine and free, nosy and knowing, Trimmer had seemed, but it was all a brave show, for that afternoon the tortoise of total war had at last overtaken him. A telephone message bade him report next day at H.O.O.HQ. at a certain time, to a certain room. It boded only ill. He had come to the bar for stimulus, for a spot of pleasantry with "les girls" and here, at his grand climacteric, in this most improbable of places, stood a portent, something beyond daily calculation. For in his empty days he had given much thought to his escapade with Virginia in Glasgow. So far as such a conception was feasible to Trimmer, she was a hallowed memory. He wished now Virginia were alone. He wished he were wearing his kilt. This was not the lovers' meeting he had sometimes adumbrated at his journey's end.

On this moment of silence and uncertainty Virginia struck swiftly with a long, cool and cautionary glance.

"Good evening, Trimmer," she said.

"You two know each other?" asked Kerstie.

"Oh, yes. Well. Since before the war," said Virginia.

"How very odd."

"Not really, is it, Trimmer?"

Virginia, as near as is humanly possible, was incapable of shame, but she had a firm residual sense of the appropriate. Alone, far away, curtained in fog — certain things had been natural in Glasgow in November which had no existence in London, in spring, amongst Kerstie and Brenda and Zita.

Trimmer recovered his self-possession and sharply followed the line.

"I used to do Mrs. Troy's hair," he said, "on the *Aquitania.*"

"Really? I crossed in her once. I don't remember you."

"I was rather particular in those days what customers I took."

"That puts you in your place, Kerstie," said Virginia. "He was always an angel to me. He used to call himself Gustave then. His real name's Trimmer."

"I think that's rather sweet. Here are your cigarettes, Trimmer."

"Ta. Have one?"

"Not on duty."

"Well, I'll be seeing you."

Without another glance he sauntered off, disconcerted, perplexed but carrying himself with an air. He wished he had been wearing his kilt.

"You know," said Kerstie, "I think that rather spoils our joke. I mean there's nothing very funny about his being what he is when one knows what he is — is there? — if you see what I mean."

"I see what you mean," said Virginia.

"In fact, it's all rather sweet of him."

"Yes."

"I must tell Brenda and Zita. He won't mind, will he? I mean he won't disappear from our lives now we know his secret?"

"Not Trimmer," said Virginia.

Next morning at 1000 hours General Whale looked sadly at Trimmer and asked:

"McTavish, what is your state of readiness?"

"How d'you mean, sir?"

"Is your section all present and prepared to move immediately?"

"Yes, sir, I suppose so."

"Suppose so?" said G.S.O. II (Planning). "When did you last inspect them?"

"Well, we haven't exactly had any actual inspection."

"All right, Charles," interposed General Whale, "I don't think we need go into that. McTavish, I've some good news for you. Keep it under your hat. I'm sending you on a little operation."

"Now, sir? To-day?"

"Just as soon as it takes the navy to lay on a submarine. They won't keep you hanging about long, I hope. Move to Portsmouth to-night. Make out your own list of demolition stores and check it with Ordnance there. Tell your men it's routine training. All right?"

"Yes, sir. I suppose so, sir."

"Good. Well, go with Major Albright to the planning-room and he'll put you in the picture. Kilbannock will be with you, but purely as an observer, you understand. You are in command of the operation. Right?"

"Yes, I think so, sir, thank you."

"Well, in case I don't see you again, good luck."

When Trimmer had followed G.S.O. II (Planning) and Ian Kilbannock from the room, General Whale said to his ADC, "Well, he took that quite quietly."

"I gather there's not much prospect of opposition."

"No. But McTavish didn't know that, you know."

Trimmer remained quiet while he was "put in the picture." It was significant, Ian Kilbannock reflected while he listened to the exposition of G.S.O. II (Planning) that this metaphoric use of "picture" had come into vogue at the time when all the painters of the world had finally abandoned lucidity. G.S.O. II (Planning) had a little plastic model of the objective of "Popgun." He had air photographs and transcripts of pilots' instruction. He spoke of tides, currents, the phases of the moon, charges of gun-cotton, fuses and detonators. He drafted a move order. He designated with his correct initials the naval authority to whom Popgun Force should report. He gave the time of the train to Portsmouth and the place of accommodation there. He delivered a stern warning about the need for "security." Trimmer listened agape but not aghast, in dreamland. It was as though he were being invited to sing in Grand Opera or to ride the favourite in the Derby. Any change from No. 6 Transit Camp, London District, was a change for the worse, but he had come that morning with the certainty that those paradisal days were over. He had expected, at the best, to be sent out to rejoin Hookforce in the Middle East, at the worst to rejoin his regiment in Iceland. Popgun sounded rather a lark.

When the conference was over Ian said: "The Press will want to know something of your background when this story is released. Can you think up anything colourful?"

"I don't know. I might."

"Well, let's get together this evening. Come to my house for a drink before the train. I expect you've got a lot to do now."

"Yes, I suppose I have."

"You haven't by any chance lost that section of yours, have you?"

"Not exactly. I mean, they must be somewhere around."

"Well, you'd better spend the day finding them, hadn't you?"

"Yes, I suppose I ought," said Trimmer gloomily.

This was the day when the ladies in Eaton Terrace kept their weekly holiday. Kerstie had arranged substitutes so that all four could be at liberty together. They slept late, lunched in hotels, did their shopping, went out with men in the evenings. At half-past six all were at home. The black-out was up; the fire lighted. The first sirens had not yet sounded. Brenda and Zita were in dressing-gowns. Zita's hair was in curling-pins and a towel. Brenda was painting Kerstie's toe-nails. Virginia was still in her room. Ian intruded on the scene.

"Have we anything to eat?" he asked. "I've brought a chap I've got to talk to and he's catching a train at half-past eight."

"Well, well, well," said Trimmer, entering behind him. "This *is* a surprise for all concerned."

"Captain McTavish," said Ian, "of No. X Commando."

"Oh, we know him."

"Do you? Do they?"

"Behold a hero," said Trimmer. "Just off to death or glory. Do I understand one of you lovelies is married to this peer of the realm?"

"Yes," said Kerstie, "I am."

"What is all this?" asked Ian, puzzled.

"Just old friends meeting."

"There's nothing to eat," said Kerstie, "except some particularly nasty-looking fish. Brenda and Zita are going out and Virginia says she doesn't want anything. There's some gin."

"Does Mrs. Troy live here too, then?" asked Trimmer.

"Oh yes. All of us. I'll call her." Kerstie went to the door and shouted: "Virginia, look what's turned up."

"There's something here I don't understand," said Ian.

"Never mind, darling. Give Trimmer some gin."

"Trimmer?"

"That's what we call him."

"I think perhaps I won't stay," said Trimmer, all the bounce in him punctured suddenly at the thought of Virginia's proximity.

"Oh rot," said Ian. "There's a lot I want to ask you. We may not have time at Portsmouth."

"What on earth are you and Trimmer going to do at Portsmouth?"

"Oh, nothing much."

"Really, how odd they are being."

Then Virginia joined them, modestly wrapped in a large bath-towel. "What's this?" she said. "Guests? Oh, you again? You do get around, don't you?"

"I'm just going," said Trimmer.

"Virginia, you must be nicer to him. He's off to death or glory, he says."

"That was just a joke," said Trimmer.

"Obviously," said Virginia.

"*Virginia*," said Kerstie.

"I can get something to eat at the canteen," said Trimmer. "I ought to go and make sure that none of my fellows has given me the slip, anyway."

Ian concluded that he was in the presence of a mystery which like so many others, come war, come peace, was beyond his comprehension.

"All right," he said. "If you must. We'll meet at the seaside to-morrow. I'm afraid you'll never get a taxi here."

"It isn't far."

So Trimmer went out into the darkness and the sirens began to wail.

"Well, I must say," said Ian, returning to them. "That was all very awkward. What was the matter with you all?"

"He's a friend of ours. We somehow didn't expect him here, that's all."

"You weren't awfully welcoming."

"He's used to our little ways."

"I give it up," said Ian. "How about this horrible fish?"

But later when he and Kerstie were alone in their room, she came clean.

". . . and what's more," she concluded, "if you ask me, there's something rum between him and Virginia."

"How do you mean rum?"

"Darling, how is anything ever rum between Virginia and anyone?"

"Oh, but that's impossible."

"If you say so, darling."

"Virginia and McTavish?"

"Well, didn't they seem rum to you?"

"Something was rum. You all were, it seemed to me."

After a pause Kerstie said: "Weren't those bombs rather near?"

"No, I don't think so."

"Shall we go down?"

"If you think that you'd sleep better."

They carried their sheets and blankets into the area kitchen where iron bedsteads stood along the walls. Brenda and Zita and Virginia were already there, asleep.

"It's important about his having been a hairdresser. A first-class story."

"Darling, you surely aren't going to write about our Trimmer?"

"I might," said Ian. "You never know. I might."

Trimmer and his section lay long at Portsmouth. The navy were hospitable, incurious, not to be hurried. Ian travelled up and down to London as the whim took him. The ladies in his house were full of questions. Trimmer had become a leading topic among them.

"You'll hear in good time," said Ian, further inflaming their interest.

Trimmer's Sergeant knew something about demolition. He made a successful, trial explosion in an enclosed fold of the hills. The experiment was repeated a day or two later in the presence of G.S.O. II (Planning) H.O.O.HQ. and one of the men was incapacitated. One day Popgun Force was embarked in a submarine and Trimmer explained the projected operation. An hour later they were put ashore again, on a report of new minelaying in the channel. From that time they were placed virtually under close arrest in the naval barracks. Trimmer's bat-man, a man long manifestly mutinous, took the occasion to desert. This information was badly received at H.O.O.HQ.

"Strictly speaking of course, sir," said G.S.O. II (Planning), "Popgun should be cancelled. Security has been compromised."

"This is no time for strict speaking," said DLFHOO, " — security."

"Quite, sir. I only meant McTavish will look pretty silly if he finds the enemy waiting for him."

"He looks pretty silly to me now."

"Yes, sir. Quite."

So eventually Popgun Force re-embarked, comprising Trimmer, his Sergeant, five men, and Ian. Even thus depleted they seemed too many.

They sailed at midday. The ship submerged and immediately all sense of motion, all sense of being at sea, utterly ceased. It was like being in a tube train, Ian thought, stuck in the tunnel.

He and Trimmer were invited to make themselves comfortable in the comfortless little cell that was called the ward-room. The Sergeant was in the Petty Officers' mess. The men disposed among the torpedoes.

"We shan't be able to surface until after dark," said the Captain. "You may find it a bit close by then."

After luncheon the Third Hand distributed a specific against carbon dioxide poisoning.

"I should try and get some sleep," he said.

Ian and Trimmer lay on the hard padded seats and presently slept. Both awoke with headaches when the ship's officers came in for dinner.

"We ought to be at your island in about four hours," said the Captain.

After dinner the sailors went back to the control-room and the engines. Ian drank. Trimmer composed a letter.

Writing did not come easily to him and this was not an easy letter to write.

I am leaving this to be sent to you in case I do not come back. When I said death or glory it wasn't just a joke you see. I want you to know that I thought of you at the last. Ever since we met I've known I had found the real thing. It was good while it lasted.

He filled three pages of his message pad. He signed it, after cogitation, "Gustave." He read it through. As he did so he conjured up the image of Virginia, as he had seen her on the afternoon of his flight from Glasgow, as he had met her again in London; of Virginia not so much as he had seen her, but rather as she had seemed to see him. He re-read the letter under the imagined wide stare of those contemptuous eyes and that infinitesimal particle of wisdom that lay in Trimmer's depths asserted itself. It just would not do, not for Virginia. He folded it small, tore it across and let the pieces fall to the steel deck.

"I think I could do with a spot." he said to Ian.

"No, no. Later. You have responsibilities ahead."

Time passed slowly. At last there came a sudden exhilaration. "What's this?"

"Fresh air."

Presently the Captain came in and said: "Well, this is the time we ought to be coming in."

"Shall I go and stir my chaps up?"

"No, leave them. I doubt if you'll be able to land to-night."

"Why on earth not?" asked Ian.

"I seem to have lost your bloody island."

He left them.

"What the hell's he up to?" said Trimmer. "We can't go back now. They'll all desert if they try and lock us up in those barracks again."

The Third Hand came into the ward-room.

"What's happening?" asked Ian.

"Fog."

"Surely with all the gadgets you can find an island?"

"You might think so. We may yet. We can't be far off."

The ship was on the surface and the trap open. The night had been chosen with the best meteorological advice. The little empty island should have shone out under a gibbous moon. But there was no moon visible that night, no stars, only mist curling into the flats.

Half an hour passed. The ship seemed to be nosing about very slowly in the calm waters. The Captain returned to the ward-room.

"Sorry. It looks as though we've got to pack it up. Can't see anything. It may lift of course as quick as it came down. We've got some time in hand."

Ian filled his glass. Soon he began to yawn. Then to doze. The next thing he knew the Captain was with them again.

"O.K.," he said. "We're in luck. Everything is clear as day and here's your island straight ahead. I reckon you've an hour and a half for the job."

Trimmer and Ian awoke.

Sailors dragged four rubber dinghies into the open night and inflated them on deck from cylinders of compressed air. The demolition stores were lowered. Popgun Force sat two and two, bobbing gently at the ship's side. Low cliffs were clear before them, a hundred yards distant. Popgun Force paddled inshore.

Orders were detailed and lucid, drafted at H.O.O.HQ. Two men, the beach-party, were to remain with the boats. The Sergeant was to land the explosives and wait while Trimmer and Ian reconnoitred for the tower which, in the model, stood on the summit of the island half a mile inland. They would all be in sight of one another's signalling-lamps all the time.

As Ian climbed awkwardly over the rubber gunwale and stood knee deep in the water, which gently lapped the deep fringe of bladder-wrack, he felt the whisky benevolently stirring within him. He was not a man of strong affections. Hitherto he had not greatly liked Trimmer. He had been annoyed at the factitious importance which seemed to surround him in Eaton Terrace. But now he felt a comradeship in arms.

"Hold up, old boy," he said loudly and genially, for Trimmer had fallen flat.

He gave a heave. Hand in hand he and Trimmer landed on enemy territory. Popgun Force stood on the beach.

"All right to carry on smoking, sir?" asked the Sergeant.

"I suppose so," said Trimmer. "I don't see why not. I could do with a fag myself."

Little flames spurted on the beach.

"Well, carry on according to plan, Sergeant."

The cliffs presented no problem. They had fallen in half a dozen places and grassy slopes led up between them. Trimmer and Ian walked briskly forward and up.

"We ought to be able to see the place on the skyline," said Trimmer rather plaintively. "It all seems much flatter than the model."

" 'Very flat Norfolk,' " said Ian in an assumed voice.

"What on earth do you mean?"

"Sorry. I was quoting Noel Coward."

"What's he got to do with it?"

"Nothing really, I suppose."

"It's all very well to be funny. This is serious."

"Not to me, Trimmer."

"You're drunk."

"Not yet. I daresay I shall be before the evening's out. I thought it a wise precaution to bring a bottle ashore."

"Well, give me a go."

"Not yet, old boy. I have only your best interests at heart. Not yet."

He stood in the delusive moonlight and swigged. Trimmer stared anxiously about him. The gentle sound-effects of operation Popgun, the susurrus of the beach, the low mutter of the demolition party, the heavy breathing of the two officers as they resumed their ascent, were suddenly horrifically interrupted by an alien voice, piercing and not far distant. The two officers stopped dead.

"For Christ's sake," said Trimmer. "What's that? It sounds like a dog."

"A fox perhaps."

"Do foxes bark like that?"

"I don't think so."

"It can't be a dog."

"A wolf?"

"Oh, do try not to be funny."

"You're allergic to dogs? I had an aunt . . ."

"You don't find dogs without people."

"Ah. I see what you mean. Come to think of it I believe I read somewhere that the Gestapo use bloodhounds."

"I don't like this at all," said Trimmer. "What the hell are we going to do?"

"You're in command, old boy. In your place I'd just push on."

"Would you?

"Certainly."

"But you're drunk."

"Exactly. If I was in your place I'd be drunk too."

"Oh God. I wish I knew what to do."

"Push on, old boy. All quiet now. The whole thing may have been a hallucination."

"D'you think so?"

"Let's assume it was. Push on."

Trimmer drew his pistol and continued the advance. They reached the top of a grassy ridge, and saw half a mile to their flank a dark feature that stood out black against the silver landscape.

"There's your tower," said Ian.

"It doesn't look like a tower."

" 'Moonlight can be cruelly deceptive, Amanda,' " said Ian in his Noel Coward voice. "Push on."

They moved forward cautiously. Suddenly the dog barked again and Trimmer as suddenly fired his pistol. The bullet struck the turf a few yards ahead but the sound was appalling. Both officers fell on their faces.

"What on earth did you do that for?" asked Ian.

"D'you suppose I meant to?"

A light appeared in the building ahead. Ian and Trimmer lay flat. A light appeared downstairs. A door opened and a broad woman stood there, clearly visible, holding a lamp in one hand, a shotgun under her arm. The dog barked with frenzy. A chain rattled.

"God. She's going to let it loose," said Trimmer. "I'm off."

He rose and bolted, Ian close behind.

They came to a wire fence, tumbled over it and ran on down a steep bank.

"*Sales Boches!*" roared the woman and fired both barrels in their direction. Trimmer dropped.

"What's happened?" asked Ian, coming up with him where he lay groaning. "She can't have hit you."

"I tripped over something."

Ian stood and panted. The dog seemed not to be in pursuit. He looked about him.

"I can tell you what you tripped over. A railway line."

"A railway line?" Trimmer sat up. "By God, it is."

"Shall I tell you something else? There aren't any railways where we ought to be."

"Oh God," said Trimmer, "where are we?"

"I rather think we're on the mainland of France. Somewhere in the Cherbourg area, I daresay."

"Have you still got that bottle?"

"Of course."

"Give it to me."

"Steady on, old boy. One of us ought to be sober and it's not going to be me."

"I believe I've broken something."

"Well, I shouldn't sit there too long. A train's coming."

The rhythm of approaching wheels swelled along the line. Ian gave Trimmer a hand. He groaned, hobbled and sank to the ground. Very soon the glow and spark of the engine came into view and presently a goods-train rolled slowly past. Ian and Trimmer buried their faces in the sooty verge. Not until it was out of sight and almost out of hearing did either speak. Then Ian said: "D'you know it's only sixteen minutes since we landed?"

"Sixteen bloody minutes too long."

"We've got plenty of time to get back to the beach. Take it easy. I think we ought to make a slight detour. I didn't like the look of that old girl with the gun."

Trimmer stood up, resting on Ian's shoulder.

"I don't believe anything is broken."

"Of course it isn't."

"Why 'of course'? It might easily have been. I came the hell of a cropper."

"Listen, Trimmer, this is no time for argument. I am greatly relieved to hear that you are uninjured. Now step out and perhaps we shall get home."

"I ache all over like the devil."

"Yes, I'm sure you do. Step out. Soon over. Damn it, one might think it was you that was drunk, instead of me."

It took them twenty-five minutes to reach the boats. Trimmer's shaken body seemed to heal with use. Towards the end of the march he was moving fast and strongly but he suffered from cold. His teeth chattered and only a stern sense of duty prevented Ian from offering him whisky. They passed the place where they had left the demolition party but found it deserted.

"I suppose they did a bunk when they heard that shot," said Trimmer. "Can't blame them really."

But when they came to the beach all four dinghies were there with their guards. There was no sign of the rest of the force.

"They went inland, sir, after the train passed."

"*Inland?*"

"Yes, sir."

"What do we do now?"

"Sit and wait for them, I suppose."

"Oh?" Trimmer drew Ian aside and asked anxiously:

"You don't think we can go back to the ship and leave them to follow?"

"No."

"No. I suppose not. Damn. It's bloody cold here."

Every two minutes Trimmer looked at his watch, shivering and sneezing.

"Orders are to re-embark at zero plus sixty."

"Plenty of time to go yet."

"Damn."

The moon set. Dawn was still far distant.

At length Trimmer said: "Zero plus fifty-two. I'm frozen. What the hell does the Sergeant mean by going off on his own like this? His orders were to wait for orders. It's his own look-out if he's left behind."

"Give him till zero plus sixty," said Ian.

"I bet that woman's given the alarm. They've probably been captured. There's probably a howling mob of Gestapo looking for us at the moment — with bloodhounds . . . zero plus fifty-nine."

He sneezed. Ian took a final swig.

"Here, my dear Watson," he said, "if I am not mistaken, come our clients — one side or the other."

Footsteps softly approached. A dimmed torch winked the signal.

"Off we go then," said Trimmer, not pausing to greet his returning men.

There was a flash and a loud explosion inland behind them.

"Oh God," said Trimmer. "We're too late."

He scrambled for the boat.

"What was that?" Ian asked the Sergeant.

"Gun-cotton, sir. When we saw the train go by, not having heard anything from the Captain, I went up myself and laid a charge. Hop in quiet, lads."

"Splendid," said Ian. "Heroic."

"Oh, I wouldn't say that, sir. I just thought we might as well show the Jerries we'd been here."

"In a day or two's time," said Ian, "you and Captain McTavish and your men are going to wake up and find yourselves heroes. Can you do with some whisky?"

"Much obliged, sir."

"For God's sake, come on," said Trimmer from the boat.

"I'm coming. Be of good comfort, Master Trimmer, and play the man. We shall this day light such a candle by God's grace in England as I trust shall never be put out."

A signal was made just before dawn briefly announcing the success of the expedition. The submarine dived and the Captain in his cabin began to draft his account of the naval operation. In the ward-room Ian coached Trimmer in the military version. High spirits do not come easily under water. All were content.

Major Albright, G.S.O. II (Planning), H.O.O.HQ., was at Portsmouth to meet them when they came ashore that afternoon. He was effusive, almost deferential.

"What can we do for you? Just say."

"Well," said Trimmer, "how about a spot of leave? The chaps are pretty browned off with Portsmouth."

"You'll have to come to London."

"Don't mind if I do."

"General Whale wants to see you. He'll want to hear your own story, of course."

"Well, it's more Kilbannock's story really."

"Yes," said Ian. "You'd better leave all that side of it to me."

And later that night he told the DLFHOO all that he had decided the General should know.

"Jolly good show. Just what was needed. Jolly good," said the General. "We must get an M.C. for the Sergeant. McTavish ought to have something. Not quite a D.S.O. perhaps but certainly an M.C."

"You don't think of putting me in for anything, sir?"

"No. All I want from you is a citation for McTavish. Go and write it now. To-morrow you can see about a release to the Press."

In his life in Fleet Street Ian had undertaken many hard tasks for harder masters. This was jam. He returned to General Whale in ten minutes with a typewritten sheet.

"I've pitched it pretty low, sir, for the official citation. Confined myself strictly to the facts."

"Of course."

"When we give it to the Press, we might add a little colour, I thought."

"Certainly."

General Whale read:

Captain McTavish trained and led a small raiding force which landed on the coast of occupied France. On landing he showed a complete disregard of personal safety which communicated itself to his men. While carrying out his personal reconnaissance he came under small-arms fire. Fire was returned and the enemy post silenced. Captain McTavish pushed farther inland and identified the line of the railway.

Observation was kept and heavy traffic in strategic materials was noted. A section of the permanent way was successfully demolished, thereby gravely impeding the enemy's war effort. Captain McTavish, in spite of having sustained injuries in the course of the action, successfully re-embarked his whole force, without casualties, in accordance with the time-table. Throughout the latter phases of the operation he showed exemplary coolness.

"Yes," said General Whale. "That ought to do it."

The ladies of Eaton Terrace said:
"What about our Scottie now?"
"What indeed?"
"Were we beastly to him?"
"Not really."
"Not often."
"I always had a soft spot."
"Shall we ask him round?"
"D'you think he'd come?"
"We can try."
"It would jolly well serve us right if he despised us."
"I despise myself rather."
"Virginia. You haven't said anything. Shall we try and get hold of Scottie?"
"Trimmer? Do what you like, my dears, only count me out."
"Virginia, don't you *want* to make amends?"
"I don't," said Virginia and left them.

Ty. Lt. A/g Capt. McTAVISH, H. MC. Future employment of.
"Really," said the chairman, "I don't understand why this is a matter for our committee."
"Minute from the War Cabinet, sir."
"Extraordinary. I should have thought they had more important things on their minds. What's it all about?"
"Well, sir, you remember McTavish?"
"Yes, yes, of course. Nice bit of work. Excellent young officer."
"You haven't seen the *Daily Beast?*"
"Of course not."
"Exactly, sir. You know that Lord Copper has always had it in for the regular army — old school tie, and that sort of rot."

"I did not," said the General, filling his pipe. "I never see the rag."

"Anyway, they've dug up the story that McTavish began the war as an officer on probation in the Halberdiers and got turned down. They say it was because he'd been a barber."

"Nothing wrong with that."

"No, sir. But all the Halberdiers who had anything to do with him are in the Middle East. We've asked for a report, but it will take some time and if, as I presume it is, it's an adverse one, we can't very well use it."

"What a lot of fuss about nothing."

"Exactly, sir. The *Daily Beast* are making McTavish an example. Saying the army is losing its best potential leaders through snobbery. You know the kind of thing."

"I do not," said the General.

"One of the Labour members has put down a question about him."

"Oh Lord, has he? That's bad."

"The Minister wants an assurance that McTavish has been found employment suitable to his merits."

"Well, that oughtn't to be difficult. It was decided last week to raise three more commandos. Can't he be given one of those?"

"I don't think he's quite up to it."

"Really, Sprat, I should have thought he was just the kind of young officer you're always trying to poach. *You* don't object to his having been a barber, do you?"

"Of course not, sir."

"You were full of his praises last week. Make a note that he is to be found suitable employment in your outfit."

"Very good, sir."

"And by suitable I don't mean your ADC."

"God forbid," Sprat breathed.

"I mean something that will satisfy those Labour fellows in the House of Commons that we know how to use good men when we find them."

"Very good, sir."

DLFHOO returned to his headquarters, as he usually returned from attendance at the War Office, in black despair. He sent for Ian Kilbannock.

"You overdid it," he said.

Ian knew what he meant.

"Trimmer?"

"Trimmer. McTavish. Whatever he's called. You've gone and got the politicians interested. We're stuck with him now for the rest of the war."

"I've been giving some thought to the matter."

"Decent of you."

"You know," said Ian, who, since he and his general had become, as it were, accomplices in fraud, had adopted an increasingly familiar tone in the office, "you'll never get the best out of your subordinates by being sarcastic. I've been thinking about Trimmer and I've learned something. He's got sex appeal."

"Nonsense."

"I've seen evidence of it in my own immediate circle — particularly since his outing to France. I've had the Ministries of Information, Supply, Aircraft Production and the Foreign Office after him. They want a hero of just Trimmer's specifications to boost civilian morale and Anglo-American friendship. You can give him any rank you please and second him indefinitely."

Major-General Whale was silent.

"It's an idea," he said at length.

"It's particularly important to get him out of London. He's always hanging round my house these days."

From The Ordeal of Gilbert Pinfold*

PORTRAIT OF THE ARTIST IN MIDDLE AGE

IT may happen in the next hundred years that the English novelists of the present day will come to be valued as we now value the artists and craftsmen of the late eighteenth century. The originators, the exuberant men, are extinct and in their place subsists and modestly flourishes a generation notable for elegance and variety of contrivance. It may well happen that there are lean years ahead in which our posterity will look back hungrily to this period, when there was so much will and so much ability to please.

Among these novelists Mr. Gilbert Pinfold stood quite high. At the time of his adventure, at the age of fifty, he had written a dozen books all of which were still bought and read. They were translated into most languages and in the United States of America enjoyed intermittent but lucrative seasons of favour. Foreign students often chose them as the subject for theses, but those who sought to detect cosmic significance in Mr. Pinfold's work, to relate it to fashions in philosophy, social predicaments or psychological tensions, were baffled by his frank, curt replies to their questionnaires; their fellows in the English Literature School who chose more egotistical writers often found their theses more than half composed for them. Mr. Pinfold gave nothing away. Not that he was secretive or grudging by nature; he had nothing to give these students. He regarded his books as objects which he had made, things quite external to himself to be used and judged by others. He thought them well made, better than many reputed works of genius, but he was not vain of his accomplishment, still less of his reputation. He had no wish to obliterate anything he had written, but he would dearly have liked to revise it, envying painters, who are allowed to return to

---

*A prefatory note to *The Ordeal of Gilbert Pinfold* says: "Mr. Waugh does not deny that 'Mr. Pinfold' is largely based on himself."

the same theme time and time again, clarifying and enriching until they have done all they can with it. A novelist is condemned to produce a succession of novelties, new names for characters, new incidents for his plots, new scenery; but, Mr. Pinfold maintained, most men harbour the germs of one or two books only; all else is professional trickery of which the most daemonic of the masters — Dickens and Balzac even — were flagrantly guilty.

At the beginning of this fifty-first year of his life Mr. Pinfold presented to the world most of the attributes of well-being. Affectionate, high-spirited and busy in childhood; dissipated and often despairing in youth; sturdy and prosperous in early manhood; he had in middle age degenerated less than many of his contemporaries. He attributed this superiority to his long, lonely, tranquil days at Lychpole, a secluded village some hundred miles from London.

He was devoted to a wife many years younger than himself, who actively farmed the small property. Their children were numerous, healthy, good-looking and good-mannered, and his income just sufficed for their education. Once he had travelled widely; now he spent most of the year in the shabby old house which, over the years, he had filled with pictures and books and furniture of the kind he relished. As a soldier he had sustained in good heart much discomfort and some danger. Since the end of the war his life had been strictly private. In his own village he took very lightly the duties which he might have thought incumbent on him. He contributed adequate sums to local causes but had no interest in sport or in local government, no ambition to lead or to command. He had never voted in a parliamentary election, maintaining an idiosyncratic toryism which was quite unrepresented in the political parties of his time, and was regarded by his neighbours as being almost as sinister as socialism.

These neighbours were typical of the English countryside of the period. A few rich men farmed commercially on a large scale; a few had business elsewhere and came home merely to hunt; the majority were elderly and in reduced circumstances; people who, when the Pinfolds settled at Lychpole, lived comfortably with servants and horses, and now lived in much smaller houses and met at the fishmonger's. Many of these were related to one another and formed a compact little clan. Colonel and Mrs. Bagnold, Mr. and Mrs. Graves, Mrs. and Miss Fawdle, Colonel and Miss Garbett, Lady Fawdle-Upton and Miss Clarissa Bagnold all lived in a radius of ten miles from Lychpole. All were in some way related. In the first years of their marriage Mr. and Mrs. Pinfold had dined in all these households and had them to dine in return. But after the war the decline of fortune, less sharp in the Pinfolds' case than their neighbours', made their meetings less frequent. The Pinfolds were addicted to nicknames and each of these surrounding families had its own private, unsuspected appellation at Lychpole, not malicious but mildly derisive, taking its origin in most cases from some half-forgotten incident in the past. The nearest neighbour, whom they saw most often, was Reginald Graves-Upton, an uncle of the Graves-Uptons ten miles distant at Upper Mewling; a gentle, bee-keeping old bachelor who inhabited a thatched cottage up the lane less than a mile from the Manor. It was his habit on Sunday mornings to walk to church across the Pinfolds' fields and leave his Cairn terrier in the Pinfolds' stables while he attended Matins. He called for a quarter of an hour when he came to fetch his dog, drank a small glass of sherry and described the wireless programmes he had heard during the preceding week. This refined, fastidious old gentleman went by the recondite name of "the Bruiser," sometimes varied to "Pug," "Basher" and "Old Fisticuffs," all of which sobriquets derived from "Boxer"; for in recent years he had added to his few interests an object which he reverently referred to as "The Box."

This Box was one of many operating in various parts of the country. It was installed under the sceptical noses of Reginald Graves-Upton's nephew and niece at Upper Mewling. Mrs. Pinfold, who had been taken to see it, said it looked like a makeshift wireless set. According to the Bruiser and other devotees The Box exercised diagnostic and therapeutic powers. Some part of a sick man or animal — a hair, a drop of blood preferably — was brought to The Box, whose guardian would then "tune in" to the "Life-Waves" of the patient, discern the origin of the malady and prescribe treatment.

Mr. Pinfold was as sceptical as the younger Graves-Uptons. Mrs. Pinfold thought there must be something in it, because it had been tried, without her knowledge, on Lady Fawdle-Upton's nettle-rash and immediate relief followed.

"It's all suggestion," said young Mrs. Graves-Upton.

"It can't be suggestion, if she didn't know it was being done," said Mr. Pinfold.

"No. It's simply a matter of measuring the Life-Waves," said Mrs. Pinfold.

"An extremely dangerous device in the wrong hands," said Mr. Pinfold.

"No, no. That is the beauty of it. It can't do any harm. You see it only transmits *Life* Forces. Fanny Graves tried it on her spaniel for worms, but they simply grew enormous with all the Life Force going into them. Like serpents, Fanny said."

"I should have thought this Box counted as sorcery," Mr. Pinfold said to his wife when they were alone. "You ought to confess it."

"D'you really think so?"

"No, not really. It's just a lot of harmless nonsense."

The Pinfolds' religion made a slight but perceptible barrier between them and these neighbours, a large part of whose activities centered round their parish churches. The Pinfolds were Roman Catholic, Mrs. Pinfold by upbringing, Mr. Pinfold by a later development. He had been received into the Church — "conversion" suggests an event more sudden and emotional than his calm acceptance of the propositions of his faith — in early manhood, at the time when many Englishmen of humane education were falling into communism. Unlike them Mr. Pinfold remained steadfast. But he was reputed bigoted rather than pious. His trade by its nature is liable to the condemnation of the clergy as, at the best, frivolous; at the worst, corrupting. Moreover by the narrow standards of the age his habits of life were self-indulgent and his utterances lacked prudence. And at the very time when the leaders of his Church were exhorting their people to emerge from the catacombs into the forum, to make their influence felt in democratic politics and to regard worship as a corporate rather than a private act, Mr. Pinfold burrowed ever deeper into the rock. Away from his parish he sought the least frequented Mass; at home he held aloof from the multifarious organisations which have sprung into being at the summons of the hierarchy to redeem the times. He was sometimes referred to as a leading Catholic but his leadership was not conspicuous.

But Mr. Pinfold was far from friendless and he set great store by his friends. They were the men and women who were growing old with him, whom in the 1920s and '30s he had seen constantly; who in the diaspora of the '40s and '50s kept more tenuous touch with one another, the men at Bellamy's Club, the women at the half-dozen poky, pretty houses of Westminster and Belgravia to which had descended the larger hospitality of a happier age.

He had made no new friends in late years. Sometimes he thought he detected a slight coldness among his old cronies. It was always he, it seemed to him, who proposed a meeting. It was always they who first rose to leave. In particular there was one, Roger Stillingfleet, who had once been an intimate but now seemed to avoid him. Roger Stillingfleet was a writer, one of the few Mr. Pinfold really liked. He knew of no reason for their estrangement and, enquiring, was told that Roger had grown very odd lately. He never came in Bellamy's now, it was said, except to collect his letters or to entertain a visiting American.

It sometimes occurred to Mr. Pinfold that he must be growing into a bore. His opinions certainly were easily predictable.

His strongest tastes were negative. He abhorred plastics, Picasso, sun-bathing and jazz — everything in fact that had happened in his own lifetime. The tiny kindling of charity which came to him through his religion sufficed only to temper his disgust and change it to boredom. There was a phrase in the 'thirties: "It is later than you think," which was designed to cause uneasiness. It was never later than Mr. Pinfold thought. At intervals during the day and night he would look at his watch and learn always with disappointment how little of his life was past, how much there was still ahead of him. He wished no one ill, but he looked at the world *sub specie aeternitatis* and he found it flat as a map; except when, rather often, personal annoyance intruded. Then he would come tumbling from his exalted point of observation. Shocked by a bad bottle of wine, an impertinent stranger, or a fault in syntax, his mind like a cinema camera trucked furiously forward to confront the offending object close up with glaring lens; with the eyes of a drill sergeant inspecting an awkward squad, bulging with wrath that was half facetious, and with half-simulated incredulity; like a drill sergeant he was absurd to many but to some rather formidable.

Once upon a time all this had been thought diverting. People quoted his pungent judgments and invented anecdotes of his audacity, which were recounted as "typical Pinfolds." Now, he realised, his singularity had lost some of its attraction for others, but he was too old a dog to learn new tricks.

As a boy, at the age of puberty when most of his school fellows coarsened, he had been as fastidious as the Bruiser and in his early years of success diffidence had lent him charm. Prolonged prosperity had wrought the change. He had seen sensitive men make themselves a protective disguise against the rebuffs and injustices of manhood. Mr.

Pinfold had suffered little in these ways; he had been tenderly reared and, as a writer, welcomed and over-rewarded early. It was his modesty which needed protection and for this purpose, but without design, he gradually assumed this character of burlesque. He was neither a scholar nor a regular soldier; the part for which he cast himself was a combination of eccentric don and testy colonel and he acted it strenuously, before his children at Lychpole and his cronies in London, until it came to dominate his whole outward personality. When he ceased to be alone, when he swung into his club or stumped up the nursery stairs, he left half of himself behind and the other half swelled to fill its place. He offered the world a front of pomposity mitigated by indiscretion that was as hard, bright and antiquated as a cuirass.

Mr. Pinfold's nanny used to say: "Don't care went to the gallows"; also "Sticks and stones can break my bones, but words can never hurt me." Mr. Pinfold did not care what the village or his neighbours said of him. As a little boy he had been acutely sensitive to ridicule. His adult shell seemed impervious. He had long held himself inaccessible to interviewers and the young men and women who were employed to write "profiles" collected material where they could. Every week his press-cutting agents brought to his breakfast-table two or three rather offensive allusions. He accepted without much resentment the world's estimate of himself. It was part of the price he paid for privacy. There were also letters from strangers, some abusive, some adulatory. Mr. Pinfold was unable to discover any particular superiority of taste or expression in the writers of either sort. To both he sent printed acknowledgments.

His days passed in writing, reading and managing his own small affairs. He had never employed a secretary and for the last two years he had been without a manservant. But Mr. Pinfold did not repine. He was perfectly competent to answer his own letters, pay his bills, tie his parcels and fold his clothes. At night his most frequent recurring dream was of doing the *Times* crossword puzzle; his most disagreeable that he was reading a tedious book aloud to his family.

Physically, in his late forties, he had become lazy. Time was, he rode to hounds, went for long walks, dug his garden, felled small trees. Now he spent most of the day in an armchair. He ate less, drank more, and grew corpulent. He was very seldom so ill as to spend a day in bed. He suffered intermittently from various twinges and brief bouts of pain in his joints and muscles— arthritis, gout, rheumatism, fibrositis;

they were not dignified by any scientific name. Mr. Pinfold seldom consulted his doctor. When he did so it was as a "private patient." His children availed themselves of the National Health Act but Mr. Pinfold was reluctant to disturb a relationship which had been formed in his first years at Lychpole. Dr. Drake, Mr. Pinfold's medical attendant, had inherited the practice from his father and had been here before the Pinfolds came to Lychpole. Lean, horsy and weatherbeaten in appearance, he had deep roots and wide ramifications in the countryside, being brother of the local auctioneer, brother-in-law of the solicitor, and cousin of three neighbouring rectors. His recreations were sporting. He was not a man of high technical pretensions but he suited Mr. Pinfold well. He too suffered, more sharply, from Mr. Pinfold's troubles and when consulted remarked that Mr. Pinfold must expect these things at his age, that the whole district was troubled in this way and that Lychpole was notoriously the worst spot in it.

Mr. Pinfold also slept badly. It was a trouble of long standing. For twenty-five years he had used various sedatives, for the last ten years a single specific, chloral and bromide which, unknown to Dr. Drake, he bought on an old prescription in London. There were periods of literary composition when he would find the sentences he had written during the day running in his head, the words shifting and changing colour kaleidoscopically, so that he would again and again climb out of bed, pad down to the library, make a minute correction, return to his room, lie in the dark dazzled by the pattern of vocables until obliged once more to descend to the manuscript. But those days and nights of obsession, of what might without vainglory be called "creative" work, were a small part of his year. On most nights he was neither fretful nor apprehensive. He was merely bored. After even the idlest day he demanded six or seven hours of insensibility. With them behind him, with them to look forward to, he could face another idle day with something approaching jauntiness; and these his doses unfailingly provided.

Despite his age and dangerous trade Mr. Pinfold seemed to himself and to others unusually free of the fashionable agonies of *angst*.